D1243530

Perturbation Methods in Applied Mathematics

A BLAISDELL BOOK IN PURE AND APPLIED MATHEMATICS

CONSULTING EDITOR

George F. Carrier, Harvard University

Perturbation Methods in Applied Mathematics

JULIAN D. COLE
California Institute of Technology

Blaisdell Publishing Company
A DIVISION OF GINN AND COMPANY
Waltham, Massachusetts ▪ *Toronto* ▪ *London*

COPYRIGHT © 1968 BY BLAISDELL PUBLISHING COMPANY,
A DIVISION OF GINN AND COMPANY.
ALL RIGHTS RESERVED.
NO PART OF THE MATERIAL COVERED BY THIS COPYRIGHT MAY BE PRODUCED IN ANY FORM OR BY ANY MEANS OF REPRODUCTION.
LIBRARY OF CONGRESS CATALOG CARD NUMBER: 68-10229
PRINTED IN THE UNITED STATES OF AMERICA.

Preface

The applied mathematician, attempting to understand or solve some physical problems, is very often forced to adopt a perturbation procedure. In doing this, he usually calls on a backlog of experience gained from numerous examples rather than on some general theory of perturbations.

The aim of this book is to survey these perturbation methods, especially in connection with differential equations, in order to illustrate the general features common to various examples. The general ideas, however, are also applicable to integral equations, integrodifferential equations, and even difference equations.

In general, we are speaking of the dependence of a solution or class of solutions on a parameter ε (or parameters) and we are seeking an expression for the deviation (ε small) from a (possibly known) limiting solution corresponding to a limiting value of the parameter ($\varepsilon = 0$). Since the parameter enters the differential equations and boundary conditions in an analytic way and since the solutions arise by analytic processes, it is natural to expect the solution to exhibit an analytic dependence on the parameters of the problem. However, the perturbations are not necessarily small and, in fact, they are not for a wide class of interesting problems.

This text is written very much from the point of view of the applied mathematician; much less attention is paid to mathematical rigor than to rooting out the underlying ideas, using all means at our disposal. In particular, physical reasoning is often used as an aid to understanding various problems. The proper questions to ask and approximations to make often come from physical arguments.

The main mathematical tool used is *asymptotic* expansion in terms of a parameter (the approximation of a solution by an expansion of a finite number of terms), the error being small for sufficiently small values of the parameter. The applied mathematician would like the few terms of the asymptotic expansion he can calculate to illustrate all the essential features of the problem he is studying and to provide a close numerical approximation to the exact result. Surprisingly perhaps, this is often the case. It is desirable to base all these expansions on suitable limiting processes since this method provides a clear meaning to all stages of the approximation process. However, this has not proved possible in all cases for various reasons (occurrence of functions without limits), so that examples of various more general expansions are included.

In the first Section, some background about asymptotic expansion is provided. (For further details, the reader can consult *Asymptotic Expansions*, A. Erdelyi, Department of Mathematics, California Institute of Technology, 1955, Dover Press.) In the second and third Section, simple examples of ordinary differential equations are studied as illustrations of the various techniques. The fourth Section treats the wide variety of possibilities for partial differential equations, presenting numerous physical examples. Finally, the last Section deals with a typical use of asymptotic expansion, the construction of approximate equations; simplified models such as shallow-water theory, and linearized and transonic aerodynamics are derived from more exact equations by means of asymptotic expansions. In this way, the full meaning of *laws of similitude* becomes evident.

The basic ideas used in this book are, as is usual in scientific work, the ideas of many people. In writing the text, no particular attempt has been made to cite the original authors or to have a complete list of references and bibliography. The important basic idea of regarding perturbation problems systematically in terms of limits has been emphasized and applied by P. A. Lagerstrom. The idea of matching expansions valid in different regions is an old one, employed for special cases by A. A. Dorodnitsyn and K. O. Friedrichs, among others. However, the late Saul Kaplun, a student of Lagerstrom's, made deep contributions to the theory of matching asymptotic expansions, and these form the basis of the work in Sections 2 and 4. The special role of the subcharacteristics and the notion of a composite expansion appears in the California Institute of Technology Ph.D. thesis (1951) of Gordon Latta, another student of Lagerstrom. The idea of the two time variables appears in Russian work, but the special uses of it in Section 3 were worked out mostly by J. Kevorkian. The only book available at present in which some of the ideas used here are systematically presented is *Perturbation Methods in Fluid Mechanics*, M. D. Van Dyke, Academic

Press, 1964. The attempt has been made to make the context of this book a little more comprehensive, but, unfortunately perhaps, many of the problems studied are still fluid-mechanical. This is to a certain extent inevitable, partly because of the author's background. But fluid mechanics is advantageous in providing, rather easily, complex mathematical problems with a wide variety of phenomena. Of course, the mathematical structure is general, and our aim has been to exhibit this structure with convenient examples.

The author is indebted to many people for active assistance in the production of this work: particularly G. F. Carrier of Harvard University for initial encouragement and discussion; P. A. Lagerstrom, especially for the model examples of Sections 2.5, 2.7.2; E. Sternberg and J. K. Knowles for discussion of Section 4.5.4; and to W. Lick for some of the basic ideas and discussion of Section 5.2. Thanks are also due to the John Simon Guggenheim Memorial Foundation for a fellowship in 1963–1964, when the initial work was done, and to Harvard University for additional assistance during that time.

J. D. C.

Contents

3

4

5

Perturbation Methods in Applied Mathematics

CHAPTER **1**

Introduction

1.1 Ordering

The conventional order symbols are used as a mathematical measure of the order of magnitude of various quantities that appear. Some definitions follow. All are concerned with real variables unless otherwise noted.

Large O: $\phi(\mu) = O(\psi(\mu))$ for μ in some range if a constant k exists such that $|\phi| \leq k|\psi|$; $\phi(\mu) = O(\psi(\mu))$ as $\mu \to \mu_0$ if a neighborhood of μ_0 exists and a constant k exists such that $|\phi| \leq k|\psi|$; thus, $\phi = O(\psi)$ as $\mu \to \mu_0$ if ϕ/ψ is bounded.

Small o: $\phi(\mu) = o(\psi(\mu))$ as $\mu \to \mu_0$ if, given any $\delta > 0$, there exists a neighborhood N_δ of μ_0 such that $|\phi| \leq \delta|\psi|$ for μ in the neighborhood; thus, $\phi(\mu) = o(\psi(\mu))$ if $\phi/\psi \to 0$ as $\mu \to \mu_0$.

Sometimes it is desirable to extend these definitions to define equivalence classes of order of magnitude. Any two functions ϕ, ψ of μ belong to the same equivalence class in a neighborhood of μ_0 (ord ϕ or ord ψ) if

$$0 < \lim_{\mu \to \mu_0} \frac{\phi(\mu)}{\psi(\mu)} < \infty.$$

A partial ordering of equivalence classes is given by

$$\text{ord } \phi(\mu) < \text{ord } \psi(\mu) \qquad \text{if} \quad \lim_{\mu \to \mu_0} \frac{\phi}{\psi} \to 0.$$

Some more details of this ordering are given later where we discuss matching of asymptotic expansions.

If the functions involved in the order ϕ, ψ, and so forth, depend on other variables, for example, $\phi = \phi(\mu; x)$, uniformity of the ordering with respect to x can be defined. The order relations are uniform if the constant k and the neighborhoods N, N_δ can be chosen independent of the value of x.

Various operations such as addition of finite or even infinite sums, multiplication, and integration can be performed with the order relations. In general, differentiation of the order relations with respect to μ is not permissible.

1.2 Asymptotic sequences and expansions

A measure of decreasing orders of magnitude is provided by an asymptotic sequence of functions. A sequence $\phi_n(\mu)$, $n = 1, 2 \ldots$ (finite or infinite) is an asymptotic sequence if

$$\phi_{n+1}(\mu) = o(\phi_n(\mu)) \qquad \text{as} \quad \mu \to \mu_0 .$$

Uniformity can be defined both with respect to n or another variable x for $\phi_n(\mu; x)$. Some examples of asymptotic sequences are

$$\phi_n(\mu) = (\mu - \mu_0)^n, \qquad \mu \to \mu_0,$$

$$\phi_n(\mu) = e^{\mu}\mu^{-\lambda_n}, \qquad \mu \to \infty, \qquad \lambda_{n+1} > \lambda_n;$$

$$\phi_1 = \log \mu, \qquad \phi_2 = \mu \log \mu, \qquad \phi_3 = \mu, \qquad \phi_4 = \mu^2 \log^2 \mu,$$

$$\phi_5 = \mu^2 \log \mu, \qquad \phi_6 = \mu^2, \ldots, \qquad \mu \to 0.$$

Various operations, such as multiplication of two sequences $\{\phi_n \psi_n\}$ and integration, can be used to generate new sequences. Differentiation with respect to μ may not lead to a new asymptotic sequence.

Asymptotic expansion • A sum of the terms in an asymptotic sequence $\sum a_n \phi_n(\mu)$ is an asymptotic expansion of a function $F(\mu)$ to N terms as $\mu \to \mu_0$ if

$$F(\mu) = \sum_{n=1}^{N} a_n \phi_n(\mu) + o(\phi_N(\mu)). \tag{1.2.1}$$

Note that this implies

$$F(\mu) = \sum_{n=1}^{N-1} a_n \phi_n(\mu) + O(\phi_N(\mu)). \tag{1.2.2}$$

For an infinite sum, we may write

$$F(\mu) \sim \sum a_n \phi_n(\mu) \qquad \text{as} \quad \mu \to \mu_0 .$$

The successive coefficients a_n can be obtained from a given function $F(\mu)$ and a given asymptotic sequence by the successive application of the following limits:

$$a_1 = \lim_{\mu \to \mu_0} \frac{F(\mu)}{\phi_1(\mu)},$$

$$a_2 = \lim_{\mu \to \mu_0} \frac{F(\mu) - a_1\phi_1(\mu)}{\phi_2(\mu)}, \tag{1.2.3}$$

$$\vdots$$

$$a_k = \lim_{\mu \to \mu_0} \frac{F(\mu) - \sum_{n=1}^{k-1} a_n\phi_n(\mu)}{\phi_k(\mu)}.$$

Thus, the expansion of a given function $F(\mu)$ in terms of a given asymptotic sequence is unique. A different asymptotic expansion can result in terms of a different sequence ϕ_n. Various linear operations and multiplications can be performed with asymptotic expansions.

For certain purposes, a slightly more general asymptotic expansion can be defined.

GENERAL ASYMPTOTIC EXPANSION • A sequence of functions $\psi_n(\mu)$ forms an asymptotic expansion of $F(\mu)$ in terms of an asymptotic sequence of "gauge" functions $\phi_n(\mu)$ if

$$\lim_{\mu \to \mu_0} \frac{F(\mu) - \sum_{n=1}^{N} \psi_n(\mu)}{\phi_N(\mu)} = 0. \tag{1.24}$$

Corresponding to this last definition, a uniform general asymptotic expression exists to N terms if

$$\lim_{\mu \to \mu_0} \frac{F(\mu; x) - \sum_{n=1}^{N} \psi_n(u; x)}{\phi_N(\mu)} = 0 \qquad (N = 1, 2, \ldots) \tag{1.2.5}$$

uniformly for x in some range.

CHAPTER **2**

Limit Process Expansions Applied to Ordinary Differential Equations

In this Section a series of simple examples are considered, some model and some physical, in order to demonstrate the application of various perturbation procedures. In general, we expect analytic dependence on the small parameter ε, but one of the main tasks in the various problems is to discover the nature of this dependence by working with various approximate differential equations. Another problem is to systematize as much as possible the procedures for discovering suitable expansions.

In physical problems, the small parameter ε is considered dimensionless and is found by expressing the entire problem in suitable dimensionless coordinates. Physical problems have another advantage from the point of view of perturbation procedures: very often the general nature of the solution is known.

After the simple examples have been worked out, some of the mathematical questions raised are considered.

2.1 Linear oscillator: *Regular* problem

As a first example, consider a case for which the exact solution is easily found, the response of a linear spring-mass-damping system initially at rest to an impulse I_0 (see Figure 2.1). The equations and initial conditions are

$$m\frac{d^2y}{dt^2} + \beta\frac{dy}{dt} + ky = I_0\delta(t), \qquad y(0-) = \frac{dy}{dt}(0-) = 0. \qquad (2.1.1)$$

Problem (2.1.1) can be replaced by an equivalent (2.1.2) by considering an

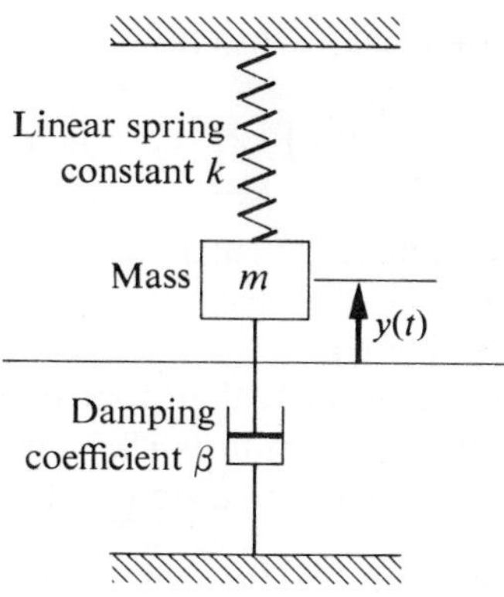

FIGURE 2.1 Spring-mass-damping system.

impulse–momentum balance across $t = 0$ or by integrating Equation (2.1.1) from $t = 0-$ to $t = 0+$:

$$m\frac{d^2y}{dt^2} + \beta\frac{dy}{dt} + ky = 0 \qquad (t \geq 0+), \qquad y(0+) = 0, \qquad \frac{dy}{dt}(0+) = \frac{I_0}{m}. \tag{2.1.2}$$

The solution defined by this problem is the fundamental solution of this linear problem.

The *regular* problem is concerned with an approximation for small damping coefficient β. For small β, we expect the motion to be a slightly damped oscillation close to the free simple harmonic oscillations of the system—the solutions of Equation (2.1.2) with $\beta = 0$. For the introduction of dimensionless coordinates, a suitable time scale is $1/\omega_N$ (ω_N = natural frequency of free motion $= \sqrt{k/m}$) since that scale remains in the limiting case $\beta = 0$. The length scale A, a measure of the amplitude, can be chosen arbitrarily, but it is actually chosen to normalize the initial conditions. Let

$$t^* = \omega_N t, \qquad \omega_N = \sqrt{k/m}, \qquad y^* = y/A. \tag{2.1.3}$$

Thus, we have

$$\frac{d^2y^*}{dt^{*2}} + 2\varepsilon^*\frac{dy^*}{dt^*} + y^* = 0, \tag{2.1.4}$$

where

$$\varepsilon^* = \beta\big/2\sqrt{km}.$$

In these variables, the initial conditions read

$$y^*(0+) = 0, \qquad \frac{dy^*}{dt^*}(0+) = 1, \qquad \text{when} \quad A = \frac{I_0}{\sqrt{km}}.$$

It is seen that only one parameter ε^* enters the differential equation. Small damping corresponds to ε^* small, so that an expansion connected with the limit process $\varepsilon^* \to 0$ is considered.

For this example, it seems evident that nontrivial correction terms can be obtained only if the first correction is $O(\varepsilon^*)$ and the higher terms are powers of ε^*. The assumed form of expansion is, thus,

$$y^*(t^*; \varepsilon) \cong f_0(t^*) + \varepsilon^* f_1(t^*) + \varepsilon^{*2} f_2(t^*) + \cdots. \tag{2.1.5}$$

By substituting the expansion Equation (2.1.5) into Equation (2.1.4) and the initial conditions or, equivalently, by repeatedly applying the limit ($\varepsilon^* \to 0$, t^* fixed), we obtain the following sequence of linear problems which can be solved in order:

$$\begin{aligned} &\frac{d^2 f_0}{dt^{*2}} + f_0 = 0, \qquad f_0(0) = 0, \qquad \frac{df_0}{dt^*}(0) = 1, \\ &\frac{d^2 f_1}{dt^{*2}} + f_1 = -2\frac{df_0}{dt^*}, \qquad f_1(0) = \frac{df_1}{dt^*}(0) = 0. \end{aligned} \tag{2.1.6}$$

The zero equation is that of the free undamped motion; the correction f_1 is computed by the damping acting on the velocity of the free motion f_0; and so on. The solutions are

$$f_0(t^*) = \sin t^*, \qquad f_1(t^*) = -t^* \sin t^*. \tag{2.1.7}$$

Thus, as far as the solution has been carried, the result is

$$y^*(t^*; \varepsilon) \cong \{1 - \varepsilon^* t^* + O(\varepsilon^{*2} t^{*2})\} \sin t^*. \tag{2.1.8}$$

The approximation to the decay is shown by Equation (2.1.8) whenever it is valid. It is clear that for any finite time interval $0 < t^* < T$, ε^* can be chosen sufficiently small so that Equation (2.1.8) is a good approximation but that the *regular* expansion is not uniformly valid for the infinite time interval. In fact, the exact solution for Equation (2.1.4) is

$$y^*(t^*; \varepsilon) = \frac{e^{-\varepsilon^* t^*}}{\sqrt{1 - \varepsilon^{*2}}} \sin\left(\sqrt{1 - \varepsilon^{*2}}\, t^*\right). \tag{2.1.9}$$

The term $\varepsilon^* t^*$ in Equation (2.1.8) is recognized as coming from the series representation of $e^{-\varepsilon^* t^*}$, so that this asymptotic expansion is good only if

$\varepsilon^* t^* \ll 1$. Later, we return to the problem of improving the approximation at infinity, but first we consider a perturbation problem for this system which is singular at $t = 0$.

2.2 Linear oscillator: singular problem

The singular problem is connected with approximations of Equation (2.1.1) for small values of the mass m. The difficulty near $t = 0$ arises from the fact that the limit equation with $m = 0$ is first order, so that both initial conditions (as in Equation 2.1.2) cannot be satisfied. The loss of an initial or boundary condition in a problem leads, in general, to the occurrence of a boundary layer.

First, a discussion of this problem is given based on physical reasoning. The general nature of the solution for small values of m is sketched in Figure 2.2 with each solid curve corresponding to a fixed m. After a short time interval, it can be expected that the motion of a system is described by the limit form of Equation (2.1.1) with $m = 0$. Thus, we have

$$\beta \frac{dy}{dt} + ky = I_0 \delta(t), \qquad y(0-) = 0. \tag{2.2.1}$$

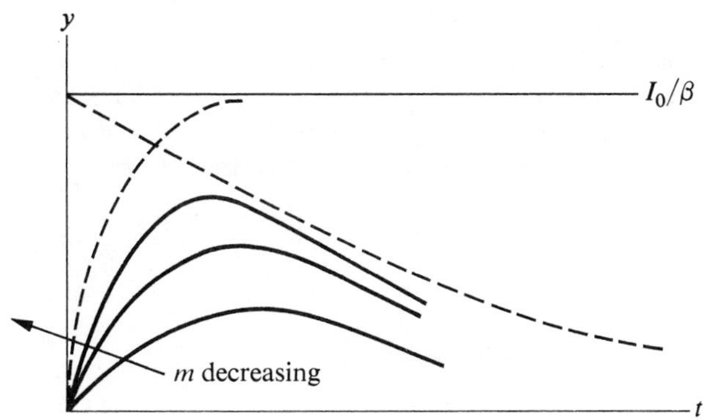

FIGURE 2.2 Solution curves, varying m.

The initial condition in velocity is lost, and the effect of the impulse is to jump the initial displacement

$$y(0+) = I_0/\beta. \tag{2.2.2}$$

The solution is

$$y = \frac{I_0}{\beta} e^{-kt/\beta}. \tag{2.2.3}$$

The solution demonstrates the exponential decay after the short initial interval in which the displacement increased infinitely rapidly from 0 to I_0/β. In order to describe the motion during the initial instants, we remark that inertia is certainly dominant at $t = 0$ (impulse–momentum balance) and that due to the large initial velocity, damping is important immediately but the spring is not, since deflection must be achieved before the spring is effective. Thus, in the initial instants, Equation (2.1.1) can be approximated by

$$m\frac{d^2y}{dt^2} + \beta\frac{dy}{dt} = I_0\delta(t), \qquad y(0-) = \frac{dy}{dt}(0-) = 0, \tag{2.2.4}$$

with the solution

$$y(t) = \frac{I_0}{\beta}\{1 - e^{-\beta t/m}\}. \tag{2.2.5}$$

This solution shows the approach of the deflection in a very short time ($m \to 0$) to the starting value for the decay solution of Equation (2.2.3). The curves are shown dashed in Figure 2.2 and give an overall picture of the motion.

Following our physical considerations, we aim to construct suitable asymptotic expansions for expressing these physical ideas and to show how to join these expansions. The first method uses expansions valid after a short time (away from the boundary) and expansions valid near the boundary.

For the expansion valid away from the boundary, we find that natural variables are those based on a time scale for decay (β/k) and on amplitude linear in I_0. Let

$$\bar{t} = \frac{kt}{\beta}, \qquad \bar{y} = \beta\frac{y}{I_0},$$

so that Equation (2.1.2) reads

$$\varepsilon\frac{d^2\bar{y}}{d\bar{t}^2} + \frac{d\bar{y}}{d\bar{t}} + \bar{y} = 0, \tag{2.2.6}$$

where $\varepsilon = mk/\beta^2$ with initial conditions

$$\bar{y}(0) = 0, \qquad \frac{d\bar{y}}{d\bar{t}}(0) = \frac{1}{\varepsilon}. \tag{2.2.7}$$

The expansion valid away from the boundary (outer expansion) is associated with the limit

$$\varepsilon \to 0, \qquad \bar{t} \text{ fixed} \qquad \text{(outer limit)}. \tag{2.2.8}$$

An asymptotic expansion in the form

$$\bar{y}(t;\varepsilon) \cong v_0(\varepsilon)h_0(\bar{t}) + v_1(\varepsilon)h_1(\bar{t}) + \cdots \quad \frac{v_{n+1}}{v_n} \to 0, \qquad \varepsilon \to 0 \tag{2.2.9}$$

is assumed.

The equations resulting from repeated application of the outer limit to Equation (2.2.6) or equating terms of the same order of magnitude when Equation (2.2.9) is substituted in Equation (2.2.6) are

$$\frac{dh_0}{d\bar{t}} + h_0 = 0, \tag{2.2.10}$$

$$\frac{dh_1}{d\bar{t}} + h_1 = \begin{cases} -\dfrac{d^2h_0}{d\bar{t}^2} & \text{if } \dfrac{v_0\varepsilon}{v_1} = 1, \\ 0 & \text{if } \dfrac{v_0\varepsilon}{v_1} \to 0. \end{cases} \tag{2.2.11}$$

The initial conditions for this set of equations, as well as the orders of the various $v_i(\varepsilon)$, are unknown and have to be found by matching with an expansion valid near $t = 0$ (inner expansion), which takes account of the initial conditions.

The solutions for the outer expansion are

$$h_0 = A_0 \exp(-\bar{t}), \tag{2.2.12}$$

$$h_1 = A_1 \exp(-\bar{t}) - A_0\bar{t}\exp(-\bar{t}). \tag{2.2.13}$$

The term $\bar{t}\exp(-\bar{t})$ above would be missing if it turned out that $v_0\varepsilon/v_1 \to 0$.

Various limits can be considered in which the representative time t_ϕ approaches the origin in the $\bar{t}$ space at varying rates. That is, limits and associated asymptotic expansions can be considered for which t_ϕ is fixed, where

$$t_\phi = \frac{\bar{t}}{\phi(\varepsilon)}, \qquad \phi(\varepsilon) \to 0.$$

In terms of this variable, Equation (2.2.6) is

$$\frac{\varepsilon}{\phi^2(\varepsilon)}\frac{d^2\bar{y}}{dt_\phi^2} + \frac{1}{\phi(\varepsilon)}\frac{d\bar{y}}{dt_\phi} + \bar{y} = 0. \tag{2.2.14}$$

Three cases evidently arise, yielding different limit equations, which would be satisfied by the dominant term of corresponding asymptotic expansions.

Case I. Inner–inner limit, ord $\phi < \varepsilon$ or $\varepsilon/\phi \to \infty$,

$$\frac{d^2\bar{y}}{dt_\phi^2} = 0. \tag{2.2.15}$$

This limit equation is second-order, so that the initial conditions can be accounted for. However, the use of an inner–inner limit is unnecessary for this problem since the expansion associated with it is contained in Case II. The expansion associated with this limit is valid only in a very small time interval, $t \leq k\phi(\varepsilon) < k$, around $t = 0$, the inertia-dominated regime.

Case II. Boundary-layer limit, $\phi = \varepsilon$,

$$\frac{d^2\bar{y}}{dt_\phi^2} + \frac{d\bar{y}}{dt_\phi} = 0. \tag{2.2.16}$$

This is called a *distinguished* limit, since ϕ cannot belong to a whole order case but is definitely $O(\varepsilon)$ as $t \to 0$. The initial conditions can be satisfied. This limit yields the boundary-layer equations derived previously by physical reasoning. As t_ϕ in Equation (2.2.16) approaches zero, the solutions of Equation (2.2.15) are obtained and, in that sense, Case I is contained in Case II.

Case III. Intermediate limit, ord $\varepsilon <$ ord $\phi < 1$, $(\varepsilon/\phi) \to 0$,

$$\frac{d\bar{y}}{dt_\phi} = 0. \tag{2.2.17}$$

Case III consists in limits (and expansions) intermediate to the boundary-layer limit and outer limit. Equation (2.2.17) can handle neither the initial conditions nor the expected behavior at infinity. In this example, limits of Case III are also superfluous since they are contained in both those of Case II and the outer limit.

Thus, consider the asymptotic expansion associated with the boundary-layer limit

$$\bar{y}(\bar{t}; \varepsilon) \cong \mu_0(\varepsilon) f_0(\tilde{t}) + \mu_1(\varepsilon) f_1(\tilde{t}) + \cdots \quad \frac{\mu_{n+1}}{\mu_n} \to 0, \qquad \varepsilon \to 0, \tag{2.2.18}$$

where $\tilde{t} = \bar{t}/\varepsilon$, and with the sequence of approximate equations which result,

$$\frac{d^2 f_0}{d\tilde{t}^2} + \frac{df_0}{d\tilde{t}} = 0, \tag{2.2.19}$$

$$\frac{d^2 f_1}{d\tilde{t}^2} + \frac{df_1}{d\tilde{t}} = \begin{cases} -f_0 & \text{if } \dfrac{\varepsilon\mu_0}{\mu_1} \to 1, \\ 0 & \text{if } \dfrac{\varepsilon\mu_0}{\mu_1} \to 0. \end{cases} \tag{2.2.20}$$

The initial conditions fix $\mu_0(\varepsilon)$ since

$$\frac{d\bar{y}}{d\tilde{t}} = \frac{\mu_0}{\varepsilon}\frac{df_0}{d\tilde{t}} + \frac{\mu_1}{\varepsilon}\frac{df_1}{d\tilde{t}} + \cdots = \frac{1}{\varepsilon} \qquad \text{as} \quad \tilde{t} \to 0.$$

Thus, $\mu_0 = 1$, and the initial conditions associated with (2.2.19) and (2.2.20) are

$$f_0(0) = 0, \qquad \frac{df_0}{d\tilde{t}} = 1, \tag{2.2.21}$$

$$f_1(0) = 0, \qquad \frac{df_1}{d\tilde{t}} = 0. \tag{2.2.22}$$

The solution of the boundary-layer equation (2.2.19) is thus

$$f_0 = 1 - \exp(-\tilde{t}). \tag{2.2.23}$$

A nonzero term is needed for f_1 if corrections to the first term are to be found. Thus, μ_1 must be chosen equal to ε, and Equation (2.2.20) reads

$$\frac{d^2 f_1}{d\tilde{t}^2} + \frac{df_1}{d\tilde{t}} = -(1 - \exp(-\tilde{t})),$$

$$\frac{df_1}{d\tilde{t}} + f_1 = B_1 - \tilde{t} - \exp(-\tilde{t}) = (1 - \exp(-\tilde{t})) - \tilde{t},$$

from (2.2.22). Thus, we have

$$f_1 = (2 - \tilde{t}) - (2 + \tilde{t})\exp(-\tilde{t}). \tag{2.2.24}$$

The inner expansion can be carried out in this way to any order. The matching of inner and outer expansions serves to determine both the orders of magnitude of various terms $\nu_0, \nu_1, \ldots$ and the constants of integration $A_0, A_1, \ldots$ in the outer expansion.

Crudely speaking, the idea of matching is that the behavior of the outer expansion as $\bar{t} \to 0$ and the inner expansion as $\tilde{t} \to \infty$ is in agreement. More formally, there is a domain in which both expansions are valid—an overlap domain—and in which these expansions agree. At first, the outer expansion is assumed valid, that is, truly asymptotic to the exact solution for $\bar{t} \geq k_1$ (and for as many terms as are considered). Correspondingly, the inner expansion is valid for $0 \leq \tilde{t} \leq k_2$ or $0 \leq \bar{t} < k_2\varepsilon$. If the regions of validity can be extended so that the outer expansion is valid in $\bar{t} \geq \eta_1(\varepsilon)$ and the inner expansion extended to cover $0 \leq \bar{t} \leq \eta_2(\varepsilon)$, where $\operatorname{ord} \eta_2 \geq \operatorname{ord} \eta_1$, then the expansions are valid in an overlap domain. If we assume that overlap exists in this case as already indicated for the first terms, an intermediate limit (corresponding to Case III) can be considered. Let

$$\varepsilon \to 0, \qquad t_\eta = \frac{\bar{t}}{\eta(\varepsilon)} \qquad \text{fixed},$$

where

$$\operatorname{ord} \varepsilon < \operatorname{ord} \eta < 1 \qquad \text{or} \qquad \frac{\eta}{\varepsilon} \to \infty, \qquad \eta \to 0.$$

Note that $\bar{t} = \eta t_\eta \to 0$, $\tilde{t} = (\eta/\varepsilon)t_\eta \to \infty$. Matching to order-one consists in the agreement of the two expansions to terms of order one; higher-order matching is defined correspondingly. Thus, to first order, we have

$$\lim_{t_\eta \text{ fixed}} \varepsilon \to 0\{v_0 h_0 + v_1 h_1 + \cdots - f_0 - \varepsilon f_1 - \cdots\} = 0$$

or

$$\lim_{t_\eta \text{ fixed}} \left\{ v_0(\varepsilon) A_0 e^{-\eta t_\eta} + \varepsilon v_0 [A_1 - A_0 \eta t_\eta] e^{-\eta t_\eta} + \cdots - [1 - e^{-(\eta/\varepsilon)t_\eta}] \right.$$
$$\left. - \varepsilon \left[\left(2 - \frac{\eta}{\varepsilon} t_\eta\right) - \left(2 + \frac{\eta}{\varepsilon} t_\eta\right) e^{-(\eta/\varepsilon)t_\eta} \right] + \cdots \right\} = 0. \quad (2.2.25)$$

This equation can be true only if, as before,

$$v_0(\varepsilon) = 1 \qquad \text{and} \qquad A_0 = 1. \quad (2.2.26)$$

Matching to the next order provides the value of A_1. Taking account of Equation (2.2.26), expanding the exponential $e^{-\eta t_\eta}$, and neglecting the transcendentally small terms $e^{-(\eta/\varepsilon)t_\eta}$, one finds, from Equation (2.2.25), that

$$\lim_{t_\eta \text{ fixed}} \frac{-\eta t_\eta + O(\eta^2) + \varepsilon[A_1] + \cdots + \eta t_\eta - 2\varepsilon + O(\eta^2)}{\gamma(\varepsilon)} = 0, \qquad \frac{\eta^2}{\gamma} \to 0. \quad (2.2.27)$$

The terms $O(\eta)$ cancel identically, that is, are already matched, and the terms $O(\varepsilon)$ can be made to cancel if

$$A_1 = 2.$$

The results achieved so far are summarized as follows:

$$\bar{y}(\bar{t}; \varepsilon) \cong e^{-\bar{t}} + \varepsilon[2 - \bar{t}]\, e^{-\bar{t}} + \cdots \qquad \text{(outer)},$$
$$(2.2.28)$$
$$\bar{y}(\tilde{t}; \varepsilon) \cong [1 - e^{-\tilde{t}}] + \varepsilon[(2 - \tilde{t}) - (2 + \tilde{t})\, e^{-\tilde{t}}] + \cdots \tilde{t} = \frac{\bar{t}}{\varepsilon} \qquad \text{(inner)}.$$

UNIFORMLY VALID ASYMPTOTIC EXPANSION • A uniformly valid asymptotic expansion, of the general form of Equation (1.2.5) can be constructed from Equation (2.2.28). The inner and outer expansions have some terms in common, namely those terms that are matched (cancel out in the matching). If the two expansions in Equation (2.2.28) are added together and the common part subtracted, then a uniformly valid ($0 \leq \bar{t} \leq \infty$) representation results. The common part (cp) is, for this case,

$$\text{cp} = 1 + \varepsilon(2 - \tilde{t}) + \cdots.$$

In boundary-layer problems such as this, it is possible and desirable to subtract the common part from the inner expansion, so that the part of the uniform expansion left in inner variables decays exponentially. The resulting expansion is

$$\bar{y}(\bar{t};\varepsilon) \cong \{e^{-\bar{t}} - e^{-\tilde{t}}\} + \varepsilon\{(2 - \bar{t})\,e^{-\bar{t}} - (2 + \tilde{t})\,e^{-\tilde{t}}\} + \cdots. \quad (2.2.29)$$

This expansion falls into the class of general asymptotic expansions of the form

$$\bar{y}(\bar{t};\varepsilon) \cong F_0(\bar{t};\varepsilon) + \varepsilon F_1(\bar{t};\varepsilon) + \cdots.$$

For this case, the general expansion takes the form of a composite expansion; each term is composed of an inner part ("defect" boundary layer) and an outer part:

$$\bar{y}(\bar{t};\varepsilon) \cong [h_0(\bar{t}) + g_0(\tilde{t})] + \varepsilon[h_1(\bar{t}) + g_1(\tilde{t})] + \cdots \quad \tilde{t} = \frac{\bar{t}}{\varepsilon}. \quad (2.2.30)$$

Such a form as Equation (2.2.30) can be assumed *a priori* in many boundary-layer problems. The $g_i(\bar{t}/\varepsilon)$ should have the property of correcting the incorrect (in general) boundary condition of the first outer solution h_0 and should decay exponentially from the boundary.

Finally, note that in this example the first term of the uniformly valid approximation gives a good description of the physical phenomenon for small m. In physical variables, we have

$$y \cong \frac{I_0}{\beta}\{e^{-kt/\beta} - e^{-\beta t/m}\}. \quad (2.2.31)$$

The motion shows a rapid rise to peak at $t \doteq (m/\beta)\log(\beta^2/km)$ and an eventual decay.

2.3 Singular perturbation problem with variable coefficients

The ideas of the previous Section are now applied to some general cases with the aim of showing how variable coefficients in the equation can affect the nature of the expansion.

Consider first a general boundary-value problem for a finite interval, $0 \leq x \leq 1$, say, for

$$\varepsilon \frac{d^2 y}{dx^2} + a(x)\frac{dy}{dx} + b(x)y = 0, \tag{2.3.1}$$

with the boundary conditions

$$y(0) = A, \qquad y(1) = B\dagger. \tag{2.3.2}$$

Assume that the solution to this boundary-value problem exists. In the limit problem ($\varepsilon = 0$), the equation drops down to first-order and, in general, both boundary conditions cannot be satisfied. A boundary layer can be expected to occur at either one of the ends (or possibly in the interior). As seen previously, the idea of the boundary layer is that the higher-order terms of Equation (2.3.1) dominate the behavior in the boundary layer. Thus, we have

$$\varepsilon \frac{d^2 y_{\mathrm{BL}}}{dx^2} + a(x)\frac{dy_{\mathrm{BL}}}{dx} = 0. \tag{2.3.3}$$

Exponential decay (rather than growth) is essential for boundary-layer behavior. Thus, if $a(x) > 0$ in $0 \leq x \leq 1$, the solutions of Equation (2.3.3) can be expected to have exponential decay near $x = 0$ ($\varepsilon > 0$), and the boundary layer occurs there; if $a(x) < 0$, the boundary layer occurs near $x = 1$. The case where $a(x)$ changes sign in the interval $0 \leq x \leq 1$ is evidently more complicated and is put aside here.

We can now make a few remarks about the general form the expansion takes. Assuming now that $a(x) > 0$, $0 \leq x \leq 1$, we see that the outer expansion valid away from $x = 0$ must be of the form of powers in ε, that is,

$$y(x; \varepsilon) \cong h_0(x) + \varepsilon h_1(x) + \varepsilon^2 h_2(x) + \cdots. \tag{2.3.4}$$

The various h_i all satisfy first-order differential equations and the boundary conditions

$$h_0(1) = B, \qquad h_i(1) = 0, \qquad i = 1, 2, 3, \ldots . \tag{2.3.5}$$

The sequence in powers of ε is necessary to ensure that the various h_i, $i = 1, 2, \ldots$, satisfy nonhomogeneous differential equations. If other orders of ε were used, the corresponding h_j would be identically zero. Thus, a

---

† In general, A and B can depend in a regular way on ε, but here it is assumed that they are independent of ε.

sequence of equations for the outer expansion is obtained:

$$
\begin{aligned}
a(x)\frac{dh_0}{dx} + b(x)h_0 &= 0, \\
a(x)\frac{dh_1}{dx} + b(x)h_1 &= -\frac{d^2h_0}{dx^2}, \\
&\vdots \\
a(x)\frac{dh_i}{dx} + b(x)h_i &= -\frac{d^2h_{i-1}}{dx^2}, \qquad i = 2, 3, \ldots .
\end{aligned}
\tag{2.3.6}
$$

The solution of the first equation of (2.3.6), if we take account of the boundary condition, is

$$h_0(x) = B\exp\left[\int_x^1 \frac{b(\xi)}{a(\xi)}\,d\xi\right]. \tag{2.3.7}$$

In order for the simple boundary layer to exist at $x = 0$, the first term $h_0(x)$ should be defined $0 \leq x \leq 1$; thus, it is assumed that the integral in Equation (2.3.7) exists and that $h_0(x)$ takes a value as $x \to 0$. Thus,

$$h_0(0) = B\exp\left[\int_0^1 \frac{b(\xi)}{a(\xi)}\,d\xi\right] = C \quad \text{(say)}. \tag{2.3.8}$$

In general, $h_0(0) \neq A$, so that a boundary layer exists at $x = 0$ (see Figure 2.3).

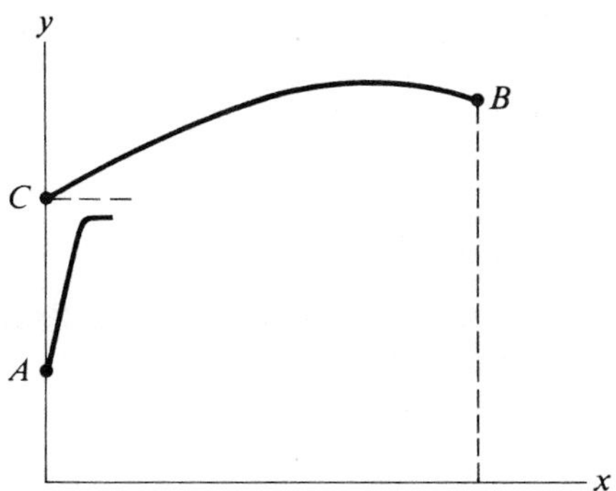

FIGURE 2.3 Boundary layer at $x = 0$.

Assuming now that the variable coefficients have regular expansions near $x = 0$,

$$a(x) = a^{(0)} + a^{(1)}x + \cdots, \qquad a^{(0)} > 0,$$
$$b(x) = b^{(0)} + b^{(1)}x + \cdots, \tag{2.3.9}$$

we can construct a boundary-layer expansion. The suitable inner variable is

$$\tilde{x} = \frac{x}{\varepsilon} \tag{2.3.10}$$

since the basic equation behaves near the boundary $x = 0$ in a way that is essentially the same as the constant-coefficient equation of the previous Section. The orders in ε of the terms in the asymptotic sequence for the inner expansion are found, strictly, from the condition of matching with the outer expansion. For the functions considered here, a power series in ε is adequate:

$$y(x;\varepsilon) \cong g_0(\tilde{x}) + \varepsilon g_1(\tilde{x}) + \cdots. \tag{2.3.11}$$

The coefficients in Equation (2.3.1) are also expressed in terms of the inner coordinate $\tilde{x}$ and, thus, have the expansion

$$a(x) = a(\varepsilon\tilde{x}) = a^{(0)} + \varepsilon a^{(1)}\tilde{x} + \cdots, \qquad b(x) = b(\varepsilon\tilde{x}) = b^{(0)} + \varepsilon b^{(1)}\tilde{x} + \cdots. \tag{2.3.12}$$

These expansions are useful for the inner-limit process $\varepsilon \to 0$, $\tilde{x}$ fixed. Thus, the equations satisfied by the g_i are

$$\frac{d^2 g_0}{d\tilde{x}^2} + a^{(0)}\frac{dg_0}{d\tilde{x}} = 0, \tag{2.3.13}$$

$$\frac{d^2 g_1}{d\tilde{x}^2} + a^{(0)}\frac{dg_1}{d\tilde{x}} = -b^{(0)}g_0(\tilde{x}) - a^{(1)}\tilde{x}\frac{dg_0}{d\tilde{x}}. \tag{2.3.14}$$

The boundary conditions at $x = 0$ are

$$g_0(0) = A, \tag{2.3.15}$$

$$g_1(0) = g_2(0) = \cdots = 0. \tag{2.3.16}$$

The solution of the boundary-layer equation (2.3.13) satisfying the initial condition, Equation (2.3.15), is

$$g_0(\tilde{x}) = Ae^{-a^{(0)}\tilde{x}} + B_0(1 - e^{-a^{(0)}\tilde{x}}). \tag{2.3.17}$$

The constant B_0 is found from matching with the first term of the outer expansion.

An intermediate limit for this problem is

$$\lim\,(\varepsilon \to 0,\, x_\eta \text{ fixed}) \quad x_\eta = \frac{x}{\eta(\varepsilon)},$$
$$\operatorname{ord}\varepsilon < \operatorname{ord}\eta < 1 \qquad \text{or} \qquad \frac{\eta}{\varepsilon} \to \infty, \qquad \eta \to 0. \tag{2.3.18}$$

Thus, in the intermediate limit, we have

$$x = \eta x_\eta \to 0, \qquad \tilde{x} = \frac{x}{\varepsilon} = \frac{\eta}{\varepsilon} x_\eta \to \infty. \tag{2.3.19}$$

Exactly as in the case of constant coefficients, the boundary layer $g_0(\tilde{x})$ goes asymptotically as $\tilde{x} \to \infty$ to a constant value, the deviation being transcendentally small in the intermediate limit. Thus, we have

$$\{h_0 - g_0\}$$
$$= \left\{B \exp\left[\int_{\eta x_\eta}^{1} \frac{b(\xi)}{a(\xi)}\, d\xi\right] - A \exp\left[-a^{(0)}\frac{\eta}{\varepsilon}x_\eta\right] - B_0\left(1 - \exp\left[-a^{(0)}\frac{\eta}{\varepsilon}x_\eta\right]\right)\right\}.$$

In the limit, this bracket approaches zero if

$$B_0 = B \exp\left[\int_0^1 \frac{b(\xi)}{a(\xi)}\, d\xi\right] = C. \tag{2.3.20}$$

Expressed simply, the matching is of the type

$$h_0(0) = g_0(\infty). \tag{2.3.21}$$

A uniformly valid approximation to order unity is obtained, as before, by adding h_0 and g_0 and subtracting the common part (Equation 2.3.20). Thus, the uniformly valid ($0 \le x \le 1$) first approximation is

$$y_{uv}(x;\varepsilon) = B \exp\left[\int_x^1 \frac{b(\xi)}{a(\xi)}\, d\xi\right] + \left\{A - B \exp\left[\int_0^1 \frac{b(\xi)}{a(\xi)}\, d\xi\right]\right\} e^{-a^{(0)}\tilde{x}} + o(1),$$
$$\tilde{x} = \frac{x}{\varepsilon}. \tag{2.3.22}$$

Higher approximations can be carried out, but these are illustrated below for a special simple case. Also, a composite form of expansion analogous to Equation (2.2.30) can be used in this problem to produce the result of Equation (2.3.22); the "defect" boundary-layer terms decay exponentially. Two illustrative examples with variable coefficients are now worked out, so that several features connected with the higher-approximation and non-regular behavior of the coefficients can be seen in concrete cases.

EXAMPLE 2.3.1

$$\varepsilon\frac{d^2y}{dx^2} + (1 + \alpha x)\frac{dy}{dx} + \alpha y = 0, \qquad 0 \le x \le 1, \qquad \alpha = \text{const} > -1 \quad (2.3.23)$$

with boundary conditions

$$y(0) = 0, \qquad y(1) = 1. \quad (2.3.24)$$

The outer expansion is

$$y(x;\varepsilon) = h_0(x) + \varepsilon h_1(x) + \cdots, \quad (2.3.25)$$

so that

$$(1 + \alpha x)\frac{dh_0}{dx} + \alpha h_0 = 0, \qquad h_0(1) = 1; \quad (2.3.26)$$

$$(1 + \alpha x)\frac{dh_1}{dx} + \alpha h_1 = -\frac{d^2h_0}{dx^2}, \qquad h_1(1) = 0. \quad (2.3.27)$$

The boundary conditions for the outer expansion are taken at the right-hand end of the interval, since the boundary layer occurs at $x = 0$. The solutions of Equations (2.3.26) and (2.3.27) are easily obtained as

$$h_0(x) = \frac{1 + \alpha}{1 + \alpha x}, \quad (2.3.28)$$

$$h_1(x) = -\alpha\left\{\frac{1}{(1 + \alpha)(1 + \alpha x)} - \frac{1 + \alpha}{(1 + \alpha x)^3}\right\}. \quad (2.3.29)$$

Note that $h_0(0) = 1 + \alpha > 0$. The inner expansion valid near the boundary is

$$y(x;\varepsilon) = g_0(\tilde{x}) + \varepsilon g_1(\tilde{x}) + \cdots, \qquad \tilde{x} = x/\varepsilon. \quad (2.3.30)$$

The basic equation (2.3.23) becomes

$$\frac{1}{\varepsilon}\left\{\frac{d^2g_0}{d\tilde{x}^2} + \varepsilon\frac{d^2g_1}{d\tilde{x}^2} + \cdots\right\} + \frac{1}{\varepsilon}\left\{1 + \alpha\varepsilon\tilde{x}\right\}\left\{\frac{dg_0}{d\tilde{x}} + \varepsilon\frac{dg_1}{d\tilde{x}} + \cdots\right\}$$
$$+ \alpha g_0 + \varepsilon\alpha g_1 + \cdots = 0, \quad (2.3.31)$$

so that we have

$$\frac{d^2g_0}{d\tilde{x}^2} + \frac{dg_0}{d\tilde{x}} = 0, \qquad g_0(0) = 0; \quad (2.3.32)$$

$$\frac{d^2 g_1}{d\tilde{x}^2} + \frac{dg_1}{d\tilde{x}} = -\alpha\tilde{x}\frac{dg_0}{d\tilde{x}} - \alpha g_0, \qquad g_1(0) = 0. \tag{2.3.33}$$

The constants of integration for the boundary-layer solutions are found from the boundary condition at $x = 0$ and by matching with the outer expansion. It is easily found that

$$g_0(\tilde{x}) = B_0(1 - e^{-\tilde{x}}). \tag{2.3.34}$$

The intermediate limit for matching is just that of the general example of Equation (2.3.19). Thus, we have

$$\lim_{\substack{\varepsilon \to 0, \\ x_\eta \text{ fixed}}} \{h_0(x) + \cdots - B_0(1 - e^{-\tilde{x}})\} = 0$$

or

$$(1 + \alpha) - B_0 = 0. \tag{2.3.35}$$

The boundary layer in this example rises from $x = 0$ to the value of $h_0(0) = 1 + \alpha$; $h_0(0)$ may be any positive value. Using this value of B_0, we find the solution for g_1:

$$g_1(\tilde{x}) = C_1 + B_1 e^{-\tilde{x}} - \alpha(\alpha + 1)\left\{(\tilde{x} - 1) - \frac{\tilde{x}^2}{2}e^{-\tilde{x}}\right\}. \tag{2.3.36}$$

The higher-order matching is again carried out by the intermediate limit Equation (2.3.19). Typically, the boundary-layer expansion contains terms that are transcendentally small and algebraic terms that must be matched. Taking account of the boundary condition at $\tilde{x} = 0$, we obtain

$$g_1(\tilde{x}) = C_1(1 - e^{-\tilde{x}}) - \alpha(\alpha + 1)\left\{e^{-\tilde{x}} + (\tilde{x} - 1) - \frac{\tilde{x}^2}{2}e^{-\tilde{x}}\right\}. \tag{2.3.37}$$

Thus, the matching condition is ($x = \eta x_\eta$, $\tilde{x} = (\eta/\varepsilon)x_\eta$)

$$\lim_{\substack{\varepsilon \to 0, \\ x_\eta \text{ fixed}}} \frac{(h_0(x) + \varepsilon h_1(x) +)\cdots - (g_0(\tilde{x}) + \varepsilon g_1(\tilde{x})\cdots)}{\varepsilon} = 0.$$

If we neglect the transcendentally small terms in g_0, g_1, the matching condition is

$$\lim_{\substack{\varepsilon \to 0, \\ x_\eta \text{ fixed}}} \left\{\frac{1}{\varepsilon}\frac{1 + \alpha}{1 + \alpha\eta x_\eta} - \varepsilon\alpha\left[\frac{1}{(1 + \alpha)(1 + \alpha\eta x_\eta)} - \frac{1 + \alpha}{(1 + \alpha\eta x_\eta)^3}\right] + O(\varepsilon^2)\right.$$
$$\left. -(1 + \alpha) - \varepsilon\left[C_1 - \alpha(\alpha + 1)\left(\frac{\eta x_\eta}{\varepsilon} - 1\right)\right]\right\} = 0 \tag{2.3.38}$$

or

$$\lim \frac{1}{\varepsilon}\left\{(1 + \alpha)(1 - \alpha\eta x_\eta) + O(\eta^2) - \varepsilon\alpha\left[\frac{1}{1 + \alpha} - (1 + \alpha) + O(\eta)\right] + O(\varepsilon^2)\right.$$

$$\left. -(1 + \alpha) - \varepsilon\left[C_1 - \alpha(\alpha + 1)\left(\frac{\eta x_\eta}{\varepsilon} - 1\right)\right]\right\} = 0.$$

The terms $O(\eta)$ are matched, so that choosing

$$C_1 + \alpha(\alpha + 1) = -\alpha\left[\frac{1}{1 + \alpha} - (1 + \alpha)\right]$$

or (2.3.39)

$$C_1 = -\frac{\alpha}{1 + \alpha}$$

completes the matching.

The intermediate class of limits is now restricted to $\eta^2/\varepsilon \to 0$, $\eta \to 0$, or $\varepsilon \ll \eta \ll \sqrt{\varepsilon}$. The common part (cp) contained in both inner and outer expansions which matches in this overlap region is, thus,

$$\text{cp} = (1 + \alpha) - \varepsilon\left(\frac{\alpha}{1 + \alpha} + \alpha(1 + \alpha)[\tilde{x} - 1]\right), \tag{2.3.40}$$

written in the inner variable $\tilde{x}$. Adding together the first two terms of inner and outer expansions and subtracting the common part yields the first two terms of a uniformly valid expansion. The inner expansion contributes only transcendentally small terms away from the boundary.

$$y(x;\varepsilon) = (1 + \alpha)\left\{\frac{1}{1 + \alpha x} - e^{-\tilde{x}}\right\}$$

$$-\varepsilon\left\{\frac{\alpha}{1 + \alpha}\left[\frac{1}{1 + \alpha x} - e^{-\tilde{x}}\right] - \alpha(1 + \alpha)\left[\frac{1}{(1 + \alpha x)^3} - e^{-\tilde{x}}\right]\right.$$

$$\left. + \alpha(\alpha + 1)\frac{\tilde{x}^2}{2}e^{-\tilde{x}}\right\} + O(\varepsilon^2), \qquad 0 \le x \le 1. \tag{2.3.41}$$

The uniformly valid expansion again has the form of a composite expression,

$$y(x;\varepsilon) = \sum_{k=0} \varepsilon^k\left\{h_k(x) + f_k\left(\frac{x}{\varepsilon}\right)\right\}. \tag{2.3.42}$$

This form could have been taken as the starting point with the requirements that $h_0 + f_0$ satisfy both boundary conditions, $(h_i + f_i, i \neq 0)$ satisfy zero boundary conditions, and all f_i are transcendentally small away from the boundary.

EXAMPLE 2.3.2 This example is chosen to illustrate the effect of coefficients that are not regular at the boundary point in modifying the form of the expansion. The basic assumption about the coefficients is that the first term of the outer expansion exists so that $h_0(x)$ is defined $0 \leq x \leq 1$ (cf. Equation 2.3.8).

$$\varepsilon \frac{d^2y}{dx^2} + \sqrt{x}\frac{dy}{dx} - y = 0, \qquad 0 \leq x \leq 1, \tag{2.3.43}$$

$$y(0) = 0, \qquad y(1) = e^2. \tag{2.3.44}$$

The outer expansion ($\varepsilon \to 0$, x fixed) is

$$y(x;\varepsilon) = h_0(x) + \varepsilon h_1(x) + \cdots, \tag{2.3.45}$$

with the corresponding equations and boundary conditions at $x = 1$,

$$\sqrt{x}\frac{dh_0}{dx} - h_0 = 0, \qquad h_0(1) = e^2; \tag{2.3.46}$$

$$\sqrt{x}\frac{dh_1}{dx} - h_1 = -\frac{d^2h_0}{dx^2}, \qquad h_1(1) = 0. \tag{2.3.47}$$

The solutions are

$$h_0(x) = e^{2\sqrt{x}}, \tag{2.3.48}$$

$$h_1(x) = e^{2\sqrt{x}}\left\{-\frac{1}{2x} + \frac{2}{\sqrt{x}} - \frac{3}{2}\right\}, \tag{2.3.49}$$

and the outer expansion is, thus,

$$y(x;\varepsilon) = e^{2\sqrt{x}}\left\{1 - \varepsilon\left(\frac{1}{2x} - \frac{2}{\sqrt{x}} + \frac{3}{2}\right) + O\left(\frac{\varepsilon^2}{x^{5/2}}\right)\right\}. \tag{2.3.50}$$

The second term has a singularity at $x = 0$; the first term $(e^{2\sqrt{x}})$ is a good approximation only for $x \gg \varepsilon$, the first two terms only for $x \gg \varepsilon^{4/5}$, etc. Nevertheless, the process of matching can be carried out.

In order to construct the inner or boundary-layer expansion, a suitable boundary-layer coordinate must be found, so that derivative terms in Equation (2.3.43) dominate Equation (2.3.43) and are of the same order. Let

$$\tilde{x} = \frac{x}{\varphi(\varepsilon)}, \qquad \varphi(\varepsilon) \to 0, \qquad \varepsilon \to 0,$$

be a general boundary-layer coordinate, and consider the boundary-layer expansion

$$y(x;\varepsilon) = \nu_0(\varepsilon)g_0(\tilde{x}) + \nu_1(\varepsilon)g_1(\tilde{x}) + \cdots = \sum_{j=0} \nu_j(\varepsilon)g_j(\tilde{x}), \tag{2.3.51}$$

where the $\nu_i(\varepsilon)$ are an asymptotic sequence. The basic equation (2.3.43) becomes

$$\frac{\varepsilon}{\varphi^2(\varepsilon)}\left\{\nu_0\frac{d^2g_0}{d\tilde{x}^2} + \nu_1\frac{d^2g_1}{d\tilde{x}^2} + \cdots\right\} + \frac{\sqrt{\varphi(\varepsilon)}}{\varphi(\varepsilon)}\sqrt{x}\left\{\nu_0\frac{dg_0}{d\tilde{x}} + \nu_1\frac{dg_1}{d\tilde{x}} + \cdots\right\}$$
$$-\nu_0 g_0 - \nu_1 g_1 - \cdots = 0. \tag{2.3.52}$$

Here $\varphi(\varepsilon)$ must be chosen so that

$$\frac{\varepsilon}{\varphi^2(\varepsilon)} = \frac{1}{\sqrt{\varphi(\varepsilon)}}$$

or

$$\varphi(\varepsilon) = \varepsilon^{2/3}, \qquad \tilde{x} = \frac{x}{\varepsilon^{2/3}}. \tag{2.3.53}$$

The dominant boundary-layer equation is

$$\frac{d^2g_0}{d\tilde{x}^2} + \sqrt{\tilde{x}}\frac{dg_0}{d\tilde{x}} = 0, \qquad g_0(0) = 0. \tag{2.3.54}$$

The solution, if we take account of the boundary condition at $\tilde{x} = 0$, is

$$g_0(\tilde{x}) = C_0\int_0^{\tilde{x}} \exp(-\tfrac{2}{3}\zeta^{3/2})\, d\zeta. \tag{2.3.55}$$

As $\tilde{x} \to \infty$, then g_0 approaches a constant which can be expressed in terms of the Γ-function (the integral in Equation 2.3.55 is an incomplete Γ-function). The approach of g_0 to its asymptotic value is exponential since we know that

$$\int_{\tilde{x}}^{\infty} \exp\left(-\frac{2}{3}\zeta^{3/2}\right) d\zeta = -\frac{\exp(-\frac{2}{3}\zeta^{3/2})}{\sqrt{\zeta}}\Bigg|_{\tilde{x}}^{\infty} - \frac{1}{2}\int_{\tilde{x}}^{\infty} \exp\left(-\frac{2}{3}\zeta^{3/2}\right)\frac{d\zeta}{\zeta^{3/2}}$$
$$= \frac{\exp(-\frac{2}{3}\tilde{x}^{3/2})}{\sqrt{\tilde{x}}} - \frac{1}{2}\int_{\tilde{x}}^{\infty} \exp\left(-\frac{2}{3}\zeta^{3/2}\right)\frac{d\zeta}{\zeta^{3/2}}. \tag{2.3.56}$$

The successive terms in the asymptotic expansion of the integral as $\tilde{x} \to \infty$ can be calculated by repeated partial integration or by substitution of the asymptotic series in Equation (2.3.54). Note only the estimate for the error term in Equation (2.3.56),

$$\int_{\tilde{x}}^{\infty} \exp\left(-\frac{2}{3}\zeta^{3/2}\right)\frac{\sqrt{\zeta}\,d\zeta}{\zeta^2} \le \frac{1}{\tilde{x}^2}\int_{\tilde{x}}^{\infty} \exp\left(-\frac{2}{3}\zeta^{3/2}\right)\sqrt{\zeta}\,d\zeta \le \frac{1}{\tilde{x}^2}\exp\left(-\frac{2}{3}\tilde{x}^{3/2}\right). \tag{2.3.57}$$

Matching of the first terms follows from the intermediate limit

$$\left(\varepsilon \to 0, \frac{x}{\eta} = x_\eta \text{ fixed}\right), \qquad \frac{\varepsilon^{2/3}}{\eta} \to 0, \qquad \eta \to 0,$$

so that

$$\tilde{x} = \frac{\eta}{\varepsilon^{2/3}} x_\eta \to \infty, \qquad x = \eta x_\eta \to 0.$$

Thus, the behavior of the $h_i(x)$ as $x \to 0$ is matched to the behavior of $g_i(\tilde{x})$ as $\tilde{x} \to \infty$. For the first terms, note that (from Equation 2.3.55) in the intermediate limit

$$g_0(\tilde{x}) \to kC_0 + \text{transcendentally small terms},$$

where

$$k = \int_0^{\infty} \exp(-\tfrac{2}{3}\xi^{3/2})\, d\xi,$$

while

$$h_0(x) \to 1 + O(\sqrt{\eta}).$$

For matching, we have

$$C_0 = \frac{1}{k},$$

so that $g_0(\tilde{x}) \to 1$ as $\tilde{x} \to \infty$.

For matching to higher orders, it is necessary to calculate further terms in the inner expansion, of the form

$$y(x;\varepsilon) = g_0(\tilde{x}) + \varepsilon^{1/3}g_1(\tilde{x}) + \varepsilon^{2/3}g_2(\tilde{x}) + \varepsilon g_3(\tilde{x}) + \cdots. \tag{2.3.58}$$

Each g_i satisfies

$$g_i'' + \sqrt{\tilde{x}}\, g_i' = g_{i-1}$$

or

$$\frac{d}{d\tilde{x}}(e^{2x^{3/2}/3}g_i) = e^{2\tilde{x}^{3/2}/3}g_{i-1}, \qquad i = 1, 2, \ldots, \quad g_i(0) = 0. \tag{2.3.59}$$

Only the asymptotic behavior as $\tilde{x} \to \infty$ is essential for matching, and this is easily found. For example, we have

$$g_0(\tilde{x}) \to 1 + \mathrm{TST}\dagger,$$

so that

$$\begin{aligned} g_1'(\tilde{x}) &= \exp\left(-\frac{2}{3}\tilde{x}^{3/2}\right)\int_1^{\tilde{x}} \exp\left(\frac{2}{3}\xi^{3/2}\right)d\xi + C_1 \exp\left(-\frac{2}{3}\tilde{x}^{3/2}\right) + \mathrm{TST} \\ &\cong \frac{1}{\sqrt{\tilde{x}}} + \frac{1}{2\tilde{x}^2} + O\left(\frac{1}{\tilde{x}^{7/2}}\right) + \mathrm{TST}, \end{aligned}$$

as shown by partial integration.

Thus, we have

$$g_1(\tilde{x}) \cong 2\sqrt{\tilde{x}} + \kappa_1 - \frac{1}{2\tilde{x}^2} + O\left(\frac{1}{\tilde{x}^{5/2}}\right) + \mathrm{TST}. \tag{2.3.60}$$

The calculation for g_2 and g_3 is carried out simply from the differential equation, noting that $g'' \ll \sqrt{\tilde{x}}\, g'$ as $\tilde{x} \to \infty$ (the reason the matching works), so that we have

$$g_2' \cong 2 + \frac{\kappa_1}{\sqrt{\tilde{x}}} - \frac{1}{2\tilde{x}^{3/2}} + O\left(\frac{1}{\tilde{x}^3}\right) - \frac{g_2''}{\sqrt{\tilde{x}}} + \mathrm{TST}.$$

It follows that

$$g_2'' \cong -\frac{\kappa_1}{2\tilde{x}^{3/2}} + \frac{3}{4}\frac{1}{\tilde{x}^{5/2}} + \cdots,$$

and

$$g_2' \cong 2 + \frac{\kappa_1}{\sqrt{\tilde{x}}} - \frac{1}{2\tilde{x}^{3/2}} + \frac{\kappa_1}{2\tilde{x}^2} + O\left(\frac{1}{\tilde{x}^3}\right) + \mathrm{TST},$$

$$g_2(\tilde{x}) \cong 2\tilde{x} + 2\kappa_1\sqrt{\tilde{x}} + \kappa_2 + \frac{1}{\sqrt{\tilde{x}}} - \frac{\kappa_1}{2\tilde{x}} + O\left(\frac{1}{\tilde{x}^2}\right) + \mathrm{TST}. \tag{2.3.61}$$

Similarly, we have

$$g_3(\tilde{x}) \cong \frac{4}{3}\tilde{x}^{3/2} + 2\kappa_1\tilde{x} + 2\kappa_2\sqrt{\tilde{x}} + \kappa_3 + \frac{\kappa_1}{\sqrt{\tilde{x}}} - \frac{\kappa_2}{\tilde{x}} + O\left(\frac{1}{\tilde{x}^{3/2}}\right) + \mathrm{TST}. \tag{2.3.62}$$

† TST = transcendentally small terms, always neglected for matching.

The constants of integration, κ_1, κ_2, and κ_3, are found from the matching. The second constant of integration for each solution is in the transcendentally small terms and is found from the boundary condition at the origin.

The matching condition is thus

$$\lim_{\substack{\varepsilon\to 0,\\ x_\eta \text{ fixed}}} \left\{ e^{2\sqrt{\eta x_\eta}}\left[1 - \varepsilon\left(\frac{1}{2\eta x_\eta} - \frac{2}{\sqrt{\eta x_\eta}} + \frac{3}{2}\right) + O\left(\frac{\varepsilon^2}{\eta^{5/2}}\right)\right] - g_0\left(\frac{\eta}{\varepsilon^{2/3}}x_\eta\right)\right.$$
$$\left. - \varepsilon^{1/3}g_1\left(\frac{\eta}{\varepsilon^{2/3}}x_\eta\right) - \varepsilon^{2/3}g_2\left(\frac{\eta}{\varepsilon^{2/3}}x_\eta\right) - \varepsilon g_3\left(\frac{\eta}{\varepsilon^{2/3}}x_\eta\right) - \cdots\right\} = 0.$$

Expanding the various terms and neglecting transcendentally small terms, we have

$$\left\{1 + 2\sqrt{\eta x_\eta} + 2\eta x_\eta + \frac{4}{3}(\eta x_\eta)^{3/2} + \cdots - \frac{\varepsilon}{2\eta x_\eta} + \frac{\varepsilon}{\sqrt{\eta x_\eta}} + \frac{3}{2}\varepsilon + \cdots\right.$$
$$-(1 + \cdots) - \varepsilon^{1/3}\left(\frac{2\sqrt{\eta x_\eta}}{\varepsilon^{1/3}} + \kappa_1 - \frac{\varepsilon^{2/3}}{2\eta x_\eta} + \cdots\right)$$
$$-\varepsilon^{2/3}\left(\frac{2\eta x_\eta}{\varepsilon^{2/3}} + \frac{2\sqrt{\eta x_\eta}}{\varepsilon^{1/3}}\kappa_1 + \frac{\varepsilon^{1/3}}{\sqrt{\eta x_\eta}} + \kappa_2 - \frac{\kappa_1\varepsilon^{2/3}}{2\eta x_\eta} + \cdots\right)$$
$$\left.-\varepsilon\left(\frac{4}{3}\frac{(\eta x_\eta)^{3/2}}{\varepsilon} + \frac{2\kappa_1\eta x_\eta}{\varepsilon^{2/3}} + \kappa_3 + \frac{2\kappa_2\sqrt{\eta x_\eta}}{\varepsilon^{1/3}} + \frac{\kappa_1\varepsilon^{1/3}}{\sqrt{\eta x_\eta}} - \frac{\kappa_2\varepsilon^{2/3}}{\eta x_\eta} + \cdots\right)\right\} = 0.$$

It can be seen how the first term in each g matches the expansion of the exponential function $\exp(2\sqrt{\eta x_\eta})$, that is h_0. All other terms are matched with the choice of constants

$$\kappa_1 = \kappa_2 = 0, \qquad \kappa_3 = \tfrac{3}{2}.$$

Further study shows that the g_i can be computed and are well behaved.

This example illustrates clearly how several terms in one expansion are needed to match one term of another expansion.

From these two expansions, a composite uniformly valid expansion can be constructed by addition of the two expansions and deletion of the common part. The common part is that part contained in both expansions which cancels out in the matching, so that in this case, expressed in inner variables, we have

$$\text{cp} = 1 + \varepsilon^{1/3}\left\{2\sqrt{\tilde{x}} - \frac{1}{2\tilde{x}^2}\cdots\right\} + \varepsilon^{2/3}\left\{2\tilde{x} + \frac{1}{\sqrt{\tilde{x}}}\cdots\right\} + \varepsilon\left\{\frac{4}{3}\tilde{x}^{3/2} + \frac{3}{2} + \cdots\right\}. \tag{2.3.63a}$$

Alternatively, the terms singular at the origin can be expressed in outer variables

$$\text{cp} = 1 + \varepsilon^{1/3}\{2\sqrt{\tilde{x}}\} + \varepsilon^{2/3}(2\tilde{x}) + \cdots + \varepsilon\left\{-\frac{1}{2x} + \frac{1}{\sqrt{x}} + \frac{3}{2}\right\} + \cdots. \tag{2.3.63b}$$

Thus, the uniformly valid expansion can be written, from Equations (2.3.50) and (2.3.58),

$$\begin{aligned} y_{\text{uv}}(x, \varepsilon) = e^{2\sqrt{x}} &+ \varepsilon^{1/3}\{g_1(\tilde{x}) - 2\sqrt{\tilde{x}}\} + \varepsilon^{2/3}\{g_2(\tilde{x}) - 2\tilde{x}\} \\ &+ \varepsilon\left\{g_3(\tilde{x}) - \frac{4}{6}\tilde{x}^{3/2} - e^{2\sqrt{x}}\left(+\frac{1}{2x} - \frac{2}{\sqrt{x}} + \frac{3}{2}\right) + \frac{1}{2x} - \frac{1}{\sqrt{x}} - \frac{3}{2}\right\} + \cdots. \end{aligned} \tag{2.3.64}$$

Problem

For

$$\varepsilon\frac{d^2y}{dx^2} + \frac{dy}{dx} - xy = 0, \qquad 0 \leq x \leq 1,$$

with

$$y(0) = 0, \qquad y(1) = e^{1/2},$$

construct the first term of a uniformly valid asymptotic expansion ($\varepsilon \to 0$) by using suitable inner and outer limits. Express the exact solution to the boundary-value problem in terms of Bessel functions of the $\frac{1}{3}$ order $\{I_{1/3}, K_{1/3}\}$. Using asymptotic properties of these Bessel functions, verify your result.

2.4 Theorem of A. Erdelyi

Recently A. Erdelyi (Reference 2.4.1) has stated and proved a theorem for a singular boundary-value problem for a general second-order nonlinear ordinary differential equation. Under certain assumptions, he is able to show rigorously that the solution has the composite form of an outer-solution, boundary-layer, and uniform-error term. Similar results have been given earlier by other authors (References 2.4.2, 2.4.3) under more restricted conditions. For example, in Reference (2.4.2) asymptotic expansions in terms of the small parameter are used, but in Reference (2.4.1) the proof is based on an integral representation of the solution, leading to a more general theorem. The theorem applies to the examples of the preceding Section 2.3 as well as to the example of the following Section which provides a test of the sharpness of the theorem. Here the theorem is stated without proof. For details, the reader is referred to the original paper.

The problem considered is denoted by P_ε.

$$P_\varepsilon: \qquad \varepsilon\frac{d^2y}{dx^2} + F\left(x, y, \frac{dy}{dx}; \varepsilon\right) = 0, \qquad 0 \le x \le 1, \tag{2.4.1}$$

$$y(0) = A(\varepsilon), \tag{2.4.2}$$

$$y(1) = B(\varepsilon). \tag{2.4.3}$$

The situation in mind is one where the boundary layer occurs at $x = 0$ as $\varepsilon \to 0$. Fundamental to the theorem is the limit problem P_0 for $\varepsilon = 0$, in which the boundary condition is satisfied at $x = 1$.

$$P_0: \qquad F(x, u(x), u'(x); 0) = 0, \tag{2.4.4}$$

$$u(1) = B(0), \tag{2.4.5}$$

where

$$(\;)' = d/dx.$$

Here $u(x)$ is our previous first term of an outer expansion. In terms of $u(x)$, a certain function $\phi(x)$ and domain D_δ are defined.

Let

$$\phi(x) = \int_0^x F_{y'}(\xi, u(\xi), u'(\xi); 0)\, d\xi \tag{2.4.6}$$

and

$$D_\delta: \left\{(x, y, y'; \varepsilon), \qquad 0 \le x \le 1 : |y(x) - u(x)| < \delta, \right.$$

$$\left. |y'(x) - u'(x)| < \delta\left(1 + \frac{e^{-\phi(x)/\varepsilon}}{\varepsilon}\right), \qquad 0 < \varepsilon < \varepsilon_0. \right\} \tag{2.4.7}$$

Under the following assumptions, a theorem can be stated and proved.

A1. Problem P_0 has a twice continuously differentiable solution $u(x)$ in $0 \le x \le 1$.

A2. For some $\delta > 0$, F has partial derivatives with respect to y, y' in D_δ and F, and these partial derivatives are continuous functions of (x, y, y') for fixed ε.

A3. As $\varepsilon \to 0$,

$$F(x, u(x), u'(x); \varepsilon) = O(\varepsilon),$$

$$q(x; \varepsilon) = F_y(x, u(x), u'(x); \varepsilon) = O(1),$$

$$p(x; \varepsilon) = F_{y'}(x, u(x), u'(x); \varepsilon) = \phi'(x) + \varepsilon p_1(x; \varepsilon),$$

where

$$\phi(x) \text{ is twice continuously differentiable in } 0 \leq x \leq 1,$$

$$\phi(0) = 0, \phi'(x) > 0 \qquad \text{and} \qquad p_1(x; \varepsilon) = O(1).$$

Also, we have

$$F_{yy}(x, y, y'; \varepsilon) = O(1), \qquad F_{yy'}(x, y, y'; \varepsilon) = O(1), \qquad F_{y'y'}(x, y, y'; \varepsilon) = O(\varepsilon).$$

A4. $B(\varepsilon) - B(0) = O(\varepsilon)$.

A5. $F_y(x, y, y'; \varepsilon) = O(1)$, $F_{y'}(x, y, y'; \varepsilon) \geq B > 0$ in D_δ.

The statement of theorem follows.

Under assumptions A1–A4, there exists a $\mu_0 > 0$ independent of ε, such that for $|A(\varepsilon) - u(0)| < \mu_0$, the problem P_ε has a solution

$$y = y(x; \varepsilon)$$

for all ε sufficiently small. The solution $y(x; \varepsilon)$ can be written

$$y(x; \varepsilon) = u(x) + v(x; \varepsilon) + w(x; \varepsilon), \tag{2.4.8}$$

where

$$y^*(x; \varepsilon) = u(x) + v(x; \varepsilon)$$

satisfies the differential equation and the boundary condition at $x = 1$. Furthermore, we have

$$v(x; \varepsilon) = O(\varepsilon), \qquad v'(x; \varepsilon) = O(\varepsilon), \qquad 0 \leq x \leq 1,$$

and

$$w(x; \varepsilon) = O\left(\exp\left[-\frac{\phi(x)}{\varepsilon}\right]\right), \quad \varepsilon w'(x; \varepsilon) = O\left(\exp\left[-\frac{\phi(x)}{\varepsilon}\right]\right), \qquad 0 \leq x \leq 1.$$

Under the additional assumption (A5), the solution $y(x; \varepsilon)$ is unique.

The significance of the various assumptions is fairly clear. The conditions on $\phi(x)$ in A3 are such to ensure a boundary layer at $x = 0$, and those on the partial derivatives of F to rule out certain nonlinearities.

The content of the theorem is that for $A(\varepsilon)$ sufficiently close to $u(0)$ (independent of ε), the solution can be expressed in the specified form. Here

$u(x)$ corresponds to the first term of an outer expansion, $w(x;\varepsilon)$ is that part of a boundary-layer solution which decays exponentially away from the boundary, and $v(x;\varepsilon)$ are all the remaining correction terms which are uniformly small.

The dependence on ε of the boundary-layer term here agrees with that of the previous Section if the boundary-layer variable $\tilde{x}$ is expressed in terms of x. In Example 2 of Section 2.3, we see that

$$F(x, y, y'; \varepsilon) = \sqrt{x}\, y' - y, \qquad F_{y'} = \sqrt{x},$$

so that

$$\phi(x) = \frac{2x^{3/2}}{3}.$$

Thus, according to the theorem, $w(x;\varepsilon) = O(\exp[-\frac{2}{3}(x/\varepsilon)^{3/2}])$. The decaying part of the boundary layer as calculated in Section 2.3 goes as

$$\frac{\exp(-\frac{2}{3}\tilde{x}^{3/2})}{\sqrt{\tilde{x}}} \qquad \text{for} \quad \tilde{x} \to \infty, \qquad \text{where} \quad \tilde{x} = \frac{x}{\varepsilon^{2/3}},$$

so that there is agreement in the exponential factor.

The example of the next Section shows that a boundary layer of this type may not occur if $A(\varepsilon)$ is too far away from $u(0)$, so that the result on the existence of μ_0 is sharp.

For further discussion, see Reference 2.4.4.

REFERENCES

2.4.1 A. Erdelyi, "Singular Perturbation," *Bull. Amer. Math. Soc. 68* (1962), 420–424.

2.4.2 E. A. Coddington and N. Levinson, "A Boundary Value Problem for a Nonlinear Differential Equation with a Small Parameter," *Proc. Amer. Math. Soc. 3* (1952), 73–81.

2.4.3 W. Wasow, "Singular Perturbations of Boundary Value Problems for Nonlinear Differential Equations of the Second Order," *Comm. Pure and Applied Math. 9* (1956), 93–113.

2.4.4 A. Erdelyi, "On a Nonlinear Boundary Value Problem Involving a Small Parameter," *J. Aust. Math. Soc. II*, Part 4 (1962), 425–439.

2.5 Model nonlinear example for singular perturbations

In this Section, a model nonlinear example is studied that illustrates the following points: (1) A consistent study of boundary layers in the general sense enables the correct limit ($\varepsilon = 0$) solutions to be isolated, and (2) a wide variety of phenomena can occur even in a simple-looking nonlinear problem. The example is

$$\varepsilon\frac{d^2y}{dx^2} + y\frac{dy}{dx} - y = 0, \qquad 0 \le x \le 1, \tag{2.5.1}$$

$$y(0) = A, \qquad y(1) = B.$$

Here A and B are not considered dependent on ε. The main problem of interest is the study of the dependence of the solutions on the end values A and B. Since the problem is nonlinear, the dependence on boundary conditions is nontrivial and can change the qualitative nature of the solution.

The (outer) limit solution ($\varepsilon = 0$) $y = h(x)$ satisfies

$$y\frac{dy}{dx} - y = 0. \tag{2.5.2}$$

Two branches appear in the limit solution:

(1) $$h = 0, \tag{2.5.3a}$$

(2) $$h = x + C. \tag{2.5.3b}$$

Only branch (2) has a chance to satisfy an arbitrary end condition. Note that if an asymptotic expansion is constructed in outer variables

$$y(x;\varepsilon) = h(x) + \varepsilon h_1(x) + \cdots, \tag{2.5.4}$$

then $h_1 = h_2 = \cdots = 0$; that is, $h(x)$ is an exact solution of (2.5.1). In this problem, it is not clear *a priori* where boundary layers will occur, so that various possibilities must be examined. Two special outer solutions are considered, h_R and h_L, which satisfy the boundary conditions at the right or left ends, respectively,

$$h_R(x) = x + B - 1, \tag{2.5.5}$$

$$h_L(x) = x + A. \tag{2.5.6}$$

These solutions take the values

$$h_R(0) = B - 1, \tag{2.5.7}$$

$$h_L(1) = A + 1 \tag{2.5.8}$$

at the other end of the interval. If $A \neq B - 1$, it is clear that a boundary layer may be needed at either one end of the interval or the other. A study of the possible boundary layers is now made with the aim of determining where boundary layers can occur and of what types they may be.

If $y \sim O(1)$, the simplest type of boundary can occur over an x scale of order ε. In such a boundary layer, the derivative terms in Equation (2.5.1) are dominant. The corresponding asymptotic expansion is of the form

$$y(x;\varepsilon) = g(\tilde{x}) + \varepsilon g_1(\tilde{x}) + \cdots, \tag{2.5.9}$$

where

$$\tilde{x} = \frac{x - x_d}{\varepsilon}.$$

Here x_d gives the location of the layer. We evidently have

$$\frac{d^2 g}{d\tilde{x}^2} + g\frac{dg}{d\tilde{x}} = 0. \tag{2.5.10}$$

The first integral is

$$\frac{dg}{d\tilde{x}} + \frac{g^2}{2} = C. \tag{2.5.11}$$

For boundary-layer-type solutions of Equation (2.5.11), we want solutions that go with exponential decay to asymptotic values as $\tilde{x} \to \pm\infty$. Thus, only $C > 0$ need be considered. If $C = 0$, algebraic decay occurs, which is fatal for matching in higher orders. We return later to this special solution $C = 0$. Let $C = \beta^2/2$, and write the solutions of Equation (2.5.11) as

$$g(\tilde{x}) = \beta \tanh \frac{\beta}{2}(\tilde{x} + k) \tag{2.5.12}$$

or

$$g(\tilde{x}) = \beta \coth \frac{\beta}{2}(\tilde{x} + k). \tag{2.5.13}$$

A sketch of these solutions is given in Figure 2.4; the various curves are obtained by translation with respect to $\tilde{x}$.

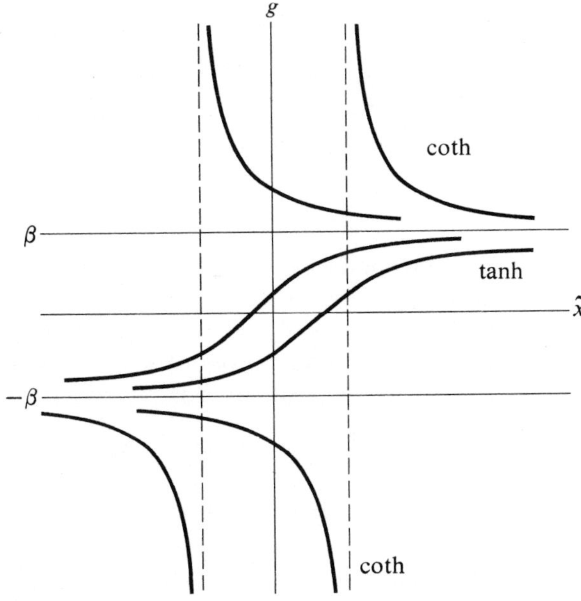

FIGURE 2.4 Solution curves of boundary layers.

The tanh solution, Equation (2.5.12), *increases* to its asymptotic value β as $\tilde{x} \to \infty$ and *decreases* to $(-\beta)$ as $\tilde{x} \to -\infty$. The approach is exponential:

$$g(\tilde{x}) \cong \beta\{1 - 2e^{-\beta(\tilde{x}+k)} + \cdots\} \qquad \text{for} \quad \tilde{x} \to \infty. \tag{2.5.14}$$

The coth solution, Equation (2.5.13), *decreases* from infinity at $\tilde{x} = -k$ to its asymptotic value β as $\tilde{x} \to +\infty$ and *increases* from $(-\infty)$ at $\tilde{x} = -k$ to its asymptotic value $(-\beta)$ as $\tilde{x} \to -\infty$.

Segments of these solutions can be used as boundary layers that match in a simple way with the outer solutions of Equations (2.5.5), (2.5.6):

$$h_R(x_d) = g(\infty) \qquad \text{or} \qquad h_L(x_d) = g(-\infty). \tag{2.5.15}$$

This type of simplified matching to order unity can be derived as in Section 2.2 by the consideration of suitable intermediate limits.

Before carrying out the discussion of the possibilities for various boundary conditions, notice that another distinguished limit exists for the model Equation (2.5.1) if the assumption that $y = O(1)$ is relaxed. The possibility of scaling y depends on the nonlinearity. In fact, if $y = \sqrt{\varepsilon}\, y^*$, $x^* = x/\sqrt{\varepsilon}$, the equation for y^* is free of ε. This transformation is not too useful, in general, because of the appearance of ε in the boundary conditions. Considered as a local solution derived from the exact equation by means of an asymptotic expansion,

$$y(x;\varepsilon) = \sqrt{\varepsilon} f(x^*) + \varepsilon f_1(x^*) + \cdots, \qquad x^* = (x - x_0)/\sqrt{\varepsilon}, \tag{2.5.16}$$

$f(x^*)$ should be an important element in some approximations. This statement is based on the idea that distinguished limits are always significant. The equation for f is essentially the same as Equation (2.5.1):

$$\frac{d^2 f}{dx^{*2}} + f\frac{df}{dx^*} - f = 0. \tag{2.5.17}$$

If the boundary conditions for Equation (2.5.17) are simplified, as is discussed later, then useful progress has been made.

Next, consider the range of values of A and B for which the solutions can be composed of h and g functions, that is, of outer solutions and boundary layers of order ε in thickness. The situation is represented on the (A, B) diagram of Figure 2.5. A distinguished line is $B = A + 1$, which represents solutions with no boundary layer. Next, consider region I of the diagram.

Case I. $A > B - 1 > 0$. The outer solution

$$h_R = x + B - 1$$

satisfies the right-hand boundary condition and takes a positive value at $x = 0$. A boundary layer at the left descending to a positive value can be

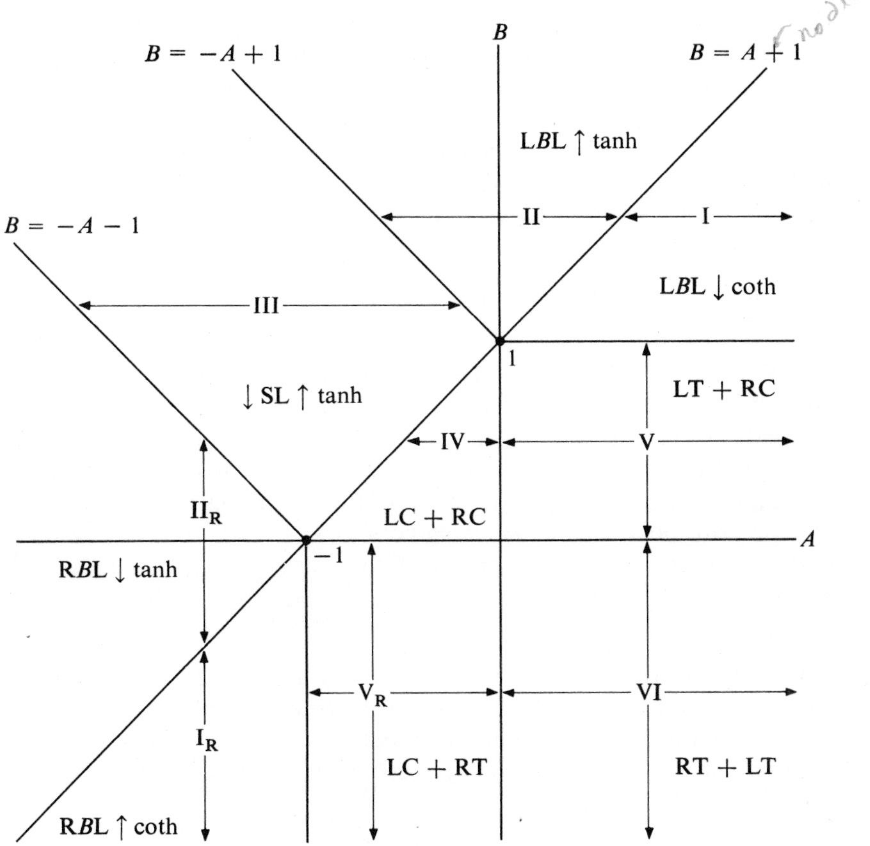

FIGURE 2.5 Domain of various solutions.

used to complete the solution. Such a boundary layer (cf. Figure 2.4) matched to h_R is

$$g_L(\tilde{x}) = (B - 1)\coth\frac{B-1}{2}(\tilde{x} + k), \qquad \tilde{x} = \frac{x}{\varepsilon}. \tag{2.5.18}$$

The value of k is chosen to satisfy the boundary condition at $\tilde{x} = 0$,

$$A = (B - 1)\coth\left(\frac{B-1}{2}k\right). \tag{2.5.19}$$

Note that the limiting case $B = 1$ brings us to the solution with algebraic decay, a case which is put aside temporarily. Note also that a reflected problem corresponds to this problem, region I_R in the diagram.

Case I_R. $B < A + 1 < 0$.

The left outer solution $h_L = x + A$ rises to the negative value $A + 1$ at the right-hand end of the interval. A coth boundary layer $g_R(\tilde{x})$, $\tilde{x} = (x - 1)/\varepsilon$ rises from B to $A + 1$.

Next, if $B > 1$ still but $A < B - 1$, it is possible to fit in a tanh-type boundary layer at the left end to match h_R, provided that $|A| < B - 1$. This is clearly seen from Figure 2.4. This type of reasoning applies as well to the following cases.

Case II. $0 \leq |A| < B - 1$ with a left boundary layer of tanh which rises from A to $B - 1$.

Case II_R. $|B| < |A + 1|$, $A + 1 < 0$. Case II_R has a right-end boundary layer of tanh type which descends from B to $A + 1$.

A case between II and II_R has $B > A + 1$, but a tanh boundary layer at the end cannot provide a sufficient rise (or descent) to match the end conditions. There is, however, the possibility of using the tanh solution at an interior point x_d and matching both as $\tilde{x} \to +\infty$ and $\tilde{x} \to -\infty$. The boundary layer is, so to speak, pushed off the ends and appears in the interior. This case is as follows.

Case III. Shock layer. $B > A + 1$, $-(B + 1) < A < 1 - B$.

The left and right boundary conditions are satisfied by outer solutions $h_L(x) = A + x$, $h_R(x) = (x - 1) + B$. The tanh solution of Equation (2.5.12) matches to values $(\pm B)$ symmetric about $y = 0$ as $x \to \pm\infty$. Thus, this solution can serve as a shock layer centered at $x = x_d$, where $h_L(x_d) = -h_R(x_d)$, $0 < x_d < 1$ or

$$A + x_d = -(x_d - 1 + B),$$

$$x_d = \frac{1 - A - B}{2}, \qquad h_R(x_d) = -h_L(x_d). \tag{2.5.20}$$

The inner solution is

$$g(\tilde{x}) = \frac{B - A - 1}{2} \tanh \frac{B - A - 1}{4} \tilde{x}, \qquad \tilde{x} = \frac{x - x_d}{\varepsilon}. \tag{2.5.21}$$

The possibilities for boundary layers of $O(\varepsilon)$ in thickness are now exhausted, but large parts of the AB-plane are still inaccessible; for example, $A > 0$, $B < 0$. A hint at the kind of solutions needed is obtained by considering the special case $A = 0$, $0 < B < 1$. In this example, outer solutions of different branches can be used to satisfy the end conditions

$$h_L(x) = 0, \qquad h_R = x + B - 1. \tag{2.5.22}$$

These solutions intersect in a corner at $x = x_C = 1 - B$. A smooth solution over the full interval can be found if a corner-layer solution centered about $x = x_C$ which matches to h_L and h_R can be found. Such a corner-layer solution, if it exists, must be contained in the solutions of Equation (2.5.17). The matching conditions for h_L, h_R are such that

$$f(x^*) \to 0, \qquad x^* \to -\infty; \qquad f(x^*) \to x^*, \qquad x^* \to +\infty. \tag{2.5.23}$$

To determine whether such solutions exist, study the phase plane of Equation (2.5.17),

$$v = \frac{df}{dx^*}, \tag{2.5.24}$$

$$\frac{dv}{df} = -\frac{f(v-1)}{v}. \tag{2.5.25}$$

The diagram of the paths of Equation (2.5.25) is Figure 2.6. Along any path, the direction of increasing x^* is indicated by an arrow, as found from Equation (2.5.24). It is clear that the paths which approach $v = 1 = df/dx^*$ are capable of matching of the type $f(x^*) \to x^*$ as $x^* \to +\infty$. The exceptional path labeled f_{RC}, which starts from the origin, has a chance also to satisfy $f(x^*) \to 0$, $x^* \to -\infty$, since the origin is a singular point. The nature of the singularity is found from the approximate form of Equation (2.5.25),

$$\frac{dv}{df} = \frac{f}{v}$$

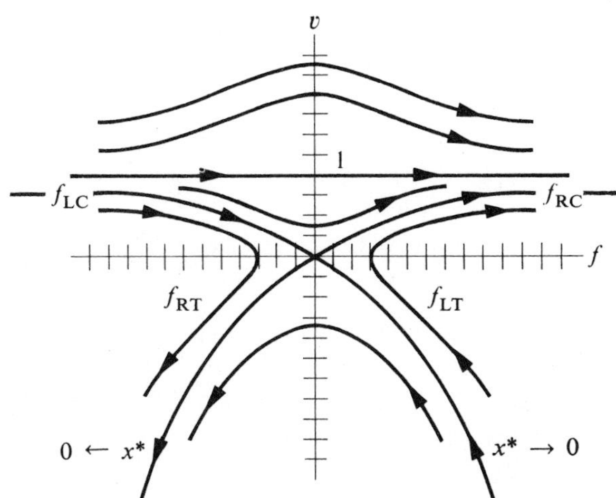

FIGURE 2.6 Phase plane of various solutions.

or

$$v^2 - f^2 = \text{const.}$$

The constant above is zero on the exceptional path, so that on f_{RC}

$$v = f + \cdots \qquad \text{as} \quad f \to 0.$$

The integration of Equation (2.5.24) shows that

$$f_{RC} = k_0 e^{x^*} + \cdots, \qquad x^* \to -\infty. \tag{2.5.26}$$

That is, the matching condition as $x^* \to -\infty$ is satisfied with an exponential approach. The constant k_0 is fixed from the requirement that the constant of integration (x^* shift) is zero at infinity ($f_{RC} = x^*$). Here f_{RC} is called a right-corner solution and can be used together with Equation (2.5.22) to complete the solution for $A = 0$, $0 < B < 1$. A reflection of this solution f_{LC} (left-corner layer) matches by

$$f_{LC}(x^*) \to x^*, \qquad x^* \to -\infty; \qquad f_{LC}(x^*) \to 0, \qquad x^* \to +\infty. \tag{2.5.27}$$

This can evidently be used in conjunction with

$$h_L = x + A, \qquad 0 \le x \le x_C, \qquad x_C = -A, \qquad h_R = 0, \qquad x_C < x < 1,$$

to satisfy $y(0) = A - 1 < A < 0$, $B = 0$. The path of f_{LC} is shown in Figure 2.6 as a reflection of f_{RC}.

The combination of these cases has solutions with both left and right corners and is the next case.

Case IV. $B - 1 < A < 0$, $0 < B < A + 1$. The outer solution has three pieces:

$$\begin{aligned} h_L(x) &= x + A, \qquad 0 \le x \le -A; \\ h_M(x) &= 0, \qquad -A < x \le 1 - B; \\ h_R(x) &= x - 1 + B, \qquad 1 - B \le x \le 1. \end{aligned}$$

Here f_{LC} provides the match between h_L and h_M and f_{RC} the match between h_M and h_R.

The other two exceptional paths in the phase plane of Figure 2.6 are also necessary to complete the coverage of the AB-plane. Consider, for example, that $B = 0, A > 0$. The outer solution satisfying the right-boundary condition is $h_R = 0$, and f_{LT} matches, with an exponential approach, to $h_R = 0$ as $x^* \to \infty$. It remains to see whether f_{LT} (left transition layer) can satisfy the boundary condition at $x = 0$. One way is to construct a boundary layer of thickness ε, the algebraic decay g, and match f_{LT} as $x^* \to 0$. However, this is not necessary, since the algebraic decay g is actually contained in f_{LT}. To see this and the details of the matching, first study the behavior of the exceptional path f_{LT} near infinity. Equation (2.5.25) can be written

$$\left(1 + \frac{1}{v - 1}\right) dv + f\, df = 0,$$

so that the first integral representing the paths through the origin is

$$v + \log|1 - v| + \frac{f^2}{2} = 0. \tag{2.5.28}$$

Thus, we see that, near infinity,

$$v \to -\frac{f^2}{2}$$

and

$$dx^* = -\frac{2df}{f^2}$$

or

$$x^* = \frac{2}{f} + \cdots, \qquad x^* \to 0^+, \qquad f \to \infty. \tag{2.5.29}$$

Equation (2.5.29) is the algebraic decay. The boundary condition at $x = 0$ is satisfied by choosing $x_{\mathrm{C}}(\varepsilon)$ since

$$x^* = \frac{x - x_{\mathrm{C}}(\varepsilon)}{\sqrt{\varepsilon}}.$$

The shift $x_{\mathrm{C}}(\varepsilon)$ removes the singularity of f as $x^* \to 0$. The asymptotic expansion near $x = 0$ is

$$y(x;\varepsilon) \cong \sqrt{\varepsilon}\, f_{\mathrm{LT}}(x^*) + \cdots,$$

$$y(x;\varepsilon) \cong \sqrt{\varepsilon}\, f_{\mathrm{LT}}\left(\frac{x - x_{\mathrm{C}}(\varepsilon)}{\sqrt{\varepsilon}}\right) + \cdots. \tag{2.5.30}$$

At $x = 0$, the argument of f_{LT} should approach $(0+)$, and Equation (2.5.29) holds, so that

$$A \cong \sqrt{\varepsilon} \cdot \left\{-\frac{2\sqrt{\varepsilon}}{x_{\mathrm{C}}(\varepsilon)}\right\} + \cdots. \tag{2.5.31}$$

Thus, to the order considered, we have

$$x_C(\varepsilon) = -\frac{2\varepsilon}{A}. \tag{2.5.32}$$

A reflection of this solution is f_{RT}, which can join zero to $B < 0$ at $x = 1$. It is now clear how the remainder of the AB-plane can be covered.

Case V. $0 < B < 1$, $A > 0$. Now f_{LT} brings the solution from A to $h_L = 0$, and f_{RC} brings the solution from $h_L = 0$ to $h_R = x - 1 + B$.

Case V_R. $-1 < A < 0$, $B < 0$—the reflection of Case V. Also $h_L = x + A$ is joined to $h_R = 0$ by f_{LC}, and $h_R = 0$ is joined to $B < 0$ by f_{RT}.

Case VI. $A > 0$, $B < 0$. Here the outer solution is $h_M = 0$, which is joined at the left to $A > 0$ by f_{LT} and to the right by f_{RT} to $B < 0$.

Thus, the systematic use of boundary-layer theory and matching can successfully cope with the wide variety of problems which can arise in a nonlinear case. While it is true that the full equation must be integrated to find f_{LT}, f_{RT}, f_{LC}, f_{RC}, the boundary conditions are canonical so that this integration can be done once for all problems.

2.6 Relaxation oscillations of the van der Pol oscillator

Relaxation oscillations are periodic motions with nearly discontinuous segments. The system typically operates in a fast phase and in a slow phase. In each phase, different physical processes dominate.

From the point of view of perturbation theory, the regions of rapid change in time are boundary layers or shock layers. The problem of perturbation theory is the problem of matching the rapid phases of motion to the slow phases.

A classical example is the relaxation oscillator of van der Pol illustrated in Figure 2.7. A linear oscillating circuit with resistance is coupled inductively to a triode which effectively provides a negative resistance for small currents. This negative resistance causes small currents to grow, but the eventual amplitude is limited due to saturation of the triode. An oscillation of definite amplitude and period, depending on the parameters, is produced. This oscillation, or limit cycle, is approached as time increases, independent of the initial conditions. For limiting values of the parameters, the limit cycle has the "jerky" character typical of relaxation oscillations.

The circuit equation corresponding to Figure 2.7 is

$$L\frac{dI}{d\tau} + RI + \frac{Q}{C} = M\frac{dI_a}{d\tau}. \tag{2.6.1}$$

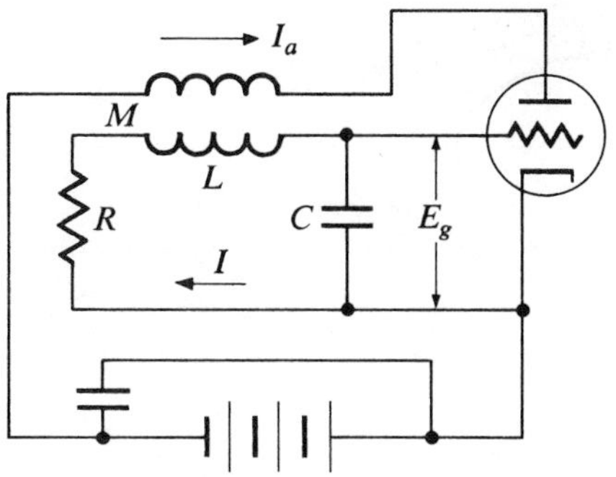

FIGURE 2.7 Circuit for van der Pol oscillator.

Here, τ is the physical time (sec), and the mutual inductance M is positive. The windings are arranged to oppose the voltage drop across L. The grid current is assumed to be negligibly small. The plate current I_a depends mainly on the grid voltage E_g and is given by the characteristic of the vacuum tube. An analytic form which approximates the tube characteristic well for $E_g/E_s < 1$ (E_s = characteristic saturation voltage) is

$$I_a = \sigma\left(E_g - \frac{1}{3}\frac{E_g^3}{E_s^2}\right), \tag{2.6.2}$$

where σ is the tube conductance (mho).

Now, $Q(\tau)$ is the charge on the capacitor, so that

$$E_g(\tau) = \frac{Q}{C}, \tag{2.6.3}$$

$$I = \frac{dQ}{d\tau} = C\frac{dE_g}{d\tau}. \tag{2.6.4}$$

Thus, Equation (2.6.1) can be expressed in terms of the dimensionless grid voltage $V = E_g(\tau)/E_s$ and dimensionless time $\bar{t}$, based on the natural frequency of oscillations of the linear system

$$\frac{d^2V}{d\bar{t}^2} + R\sqrt{\frac{C}{L}}\frac{dV}{d\bar{t}} + V = \frac{M\sigma}{\sqrt{LC}}(1 - V^2)\frac{dV}{d\bar{t}}, \tag{2.6.5}$$

$$\bar{t} = \omega\tau, \qquad \omega = \frac{1}{\sqrt{LC}}.$$

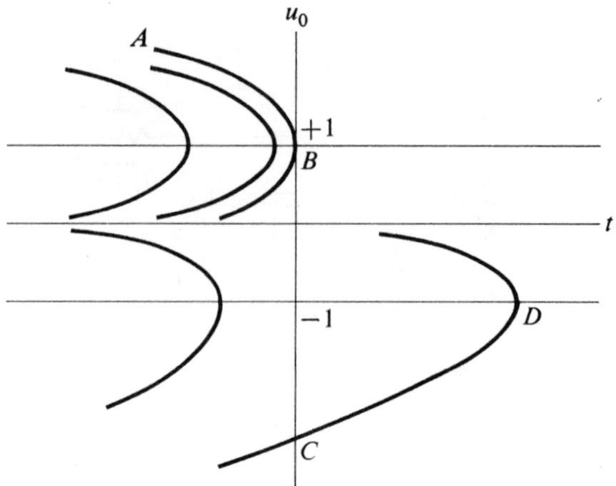

FIGURE 2.8 Outer solution curves.

By choosing a characteristic amplitude A,

$$V(\bar{t}) = Ay(\bar{t}),$$

Equation (2.6.5) can be brought to the form

$$\frac{d^2y}{d\bar{t}^2} - \nu(1 - y^2)\frac{dy}{d\bar{t}} + y = 0, \tag{2.6.6}$$

where

$$\nu = \frac{M\sigma}{\sqrt{LC}} - R\sqrt{\frac{C}{L}} = \frac{M\sigma A^2}{\sqrt{LC}}, \qquad A = \sqrt{1 - \frac{RC}{M\sigma}}.$$

This form is suitable for studying weak nonlinear effects; the motion is close to simple harmonic. The period is close to that of the linear oscillator $2\pi/\omega$. However, when ν becomes large, the time scale of the oscillations changes, and the problem assumes a singular form. Let

$$t = \frac{\bar{t}}{\nu} = \frac{\omega}{\nu}\tau. \tag{2.6.7}$$

Then Equation (2.6.6) is

$$\varepsilon\frac{d^2y}{dt^2} - (1 - y^2)\frac{dy}{dt} + y = 0, \qquad \varepsilon = \frac{1}{\nu^2} \ll 1. \tag{2.6.8}$$

We consider now the periodic solution of Equation (2.6.8) which corresponds to the limit cycle, and we study the limit of the limit cycles as $\varepsilon \to 0$, the relaxation oscillation.† Equation (2.6.8) with $\varepsilon = 0$ describes the motion over the main part of the cycle. However, the solution is necessarily discontinuous; the limit is singular. We sketch out below the various asymptotic expansions necessary to construct a uniformly valid approximation to the periodic solutions of Equation (2.6.8) as $\varepsilon \to 0$. The outer expansion is associated with the limit process

$$\varepsilon \to 0, \qquad t \text{ fixed.}$$

The equation has been scaled so that the limit solution is $O(1)$. Thus, the expansion has the following form.

OUTER EXPANSION

$$y(t;\varepsilon) = u_0(t) + \varepsilon u_1(t) + \cdots. \tag{2.6.9}$$

The sequence of equations that result is

$$(1 - u_0^2)\frac{du_0}{dt} - u_0 = 0, \tag{2.6.10}$$

$$\frac{d}{dt}[(1 - u_0^2)u_1] - u_1 = \frac{d^2u_0}{dt^2}. \tag{2.6.11}$$

The integral curves for u_0 have the form indicated in Figure 2.8. Both branches of the solution are represented by the integral

$$\log|u_0| - \frac{u_0^2}{2} = t + \text{const.} \tag{2.6.12}$$

The periodic solution must be constructed by piecing together segments of the different branches, such as AB and CD. In the periodic case, symmetry requirements demand that CD is a translation and reflection of AB. The branch AB is represented by

$$\log u_0 - \frac{u_0^2 - 1}{2} = t \qquad (AB). \tag{2.6.13}$$

The time origin has been taken at the jumping point B, where $u_0 = 1$. The period of the oscillations, even in the first approximation, is not yet evident. In the uniform approximation, the discontinuous segment, analogous to the shock layer of Section 2.5, is replaced by suitable boundary-layer expansions. Certain details of the solutions u_0, u_1 are necessary for the matching, and these are worked out now. The solutions for u_1 can be obtained by

† For the physical approximation to be valid, we need $E_g/E_s < 1$, that is $A < 1$ and $\nu \gg 1$.

considering $u_1 = u_1(u_0)$ and rewriting Equation (2.6.11) as

$$\frac{-u_0}{u_0^2 - 1}\frac{d}{du_0}[(u_0^2 - 1)u_1] + u_1 = -\frac{u_0}{u_0^2 - 1}\frac{d}{du_0}\left(\frac{u_0}{u_0^2 - 1}\right).$$

Various terms can be combined so that we have

$$\frac{d}{du_0}\left[\frac{u_0^2 - 1}{u_0}u_1\right] = \frac{u_0}{u_0^2 - 1} - \frac{1}{u_0} - \frac{2u_0}{(u_0^2 - 1)^2}.$$

Integration of the last equation yields

$$u_1 = \frac{u_0}{u_0^2 - 1}\left\{A_1 + \frac{1}{u_0^2 - 1} + \frac{1}{2}\log\frac{u_0^2 - 1}{u_0^2}\right\}. \tag{2.6.14}$$

For any given branches AB, and CD with $|u_0| > 1$, u_1 is defined by Equation (2.6.14) with an arbitrary constant of integration A_1.

The behavior of u_0, u_1 as $t \to 0-$ in branch AB is needed for the matching. From the expansion of Equation (2.6.12) near $t = 0$, we find that

$$u_0 = 1 + \sqrt{-t} + \tfrac{1}{6}(-t) + \tfrac{5}{72}(-t)^{3/2} + O((-t)^{5/2}), \tag{2.6.15}$$

$$u_1 = \frac{1}{4(-t)} + \frac{1}{4\sqrt{-t}}\log\sqrt{-t} + \frac{1}{4\sqrt{-t}}(2A_1 - \tfrac{1}{3} + \log 2) + \cdots. \tag{2.6.16}$$

Next, we consider joining the two branches AB and CD with a boundary layer of shock type. The thickness of the layer is chosen so that the second-derivative terms in Equation (2.6.8) remain, that is, the thickness is $O(\varepsilon)$. Since the time origin for this expansion is not fixed, the limit process associated with the expansion has

$$\left(\varepsilon \to 0, \qquad t^* = \frac{t - \delta(\varepsilon)}{\varepsilon}\ \text{fixed}\right); \qquad \delta(\varepsilon) \quad \text{is to be found.} \tag{2.6.17}$$

For matching to u_0 as $t \to 0$, the first term is $O(1)$. The inner expansion is, thus,

$$y(t; \varepsilon) = g_0(t^*) + \beta_1(\varepsilon)g_1(t^*) + \cdots, \tag{2.6.18}$$

and Equation (2.6.8) becomes

$$\frac{1}{\varepsilon}\left\{\frac{d^2g_0}{dt^{*2}} + \beta_1\frac{d^2g_1}{dt^{*2}} + \cdots\right\} - \frac{1}{\varepsilon}\{(1 - g_0^2) - 2\beta_1 g_0 g_1 - \cdots\}$$

$$\times\left\{\frac{dg_0}{dt^*} + \beta_1\frac{dg_1}{dt^*} + \cdots\right\} + g_0 + \beta_1 g_1 + \cdots = 0.$$

Thus, we have

$$\frac{d^2 g_0}{dt^{*2}} - (1 - g_0^2)\frac{dg_0}{dt^*} = 0 \tag{2.6.19}$$

and, if $O(\beta_1) > O(\varepsilon)$,

$$\frac{d^2 g_1}{dt^{*2}} - \frac{d}{dt^*}[(1 - g_0^2)g_1] = 0. \tag{2.6.20}$$

If $\beta_1 = \varepsilon$, the forcing term $-g_0$ appears on the right-hand side of Equation (2.6.20).

The first integral of Equation (2.6.19) is

$$\frac{dg_0}{dt^*} - g_0 + \frac{1}{3}g_0^3 = \text{const.} = k_0. \tag{2.6.21}$$

In the matching of the inner expansion to the outer expansion, an intermediate class of limits of the form

$$\left(\varepsilon \to 0, \quad t_\eta = \frac{t - \delta(\varepsilon)}{\eta} \text{ fixed}\right), \qquad \frac{\eta}{\varepsilon} \to \infty, \qquad \eta \to 0$$

would be considered, so that

$$t = \eta t_\eta + \delta(\varepsilon) \to (0-) \qquad (t_\eta < 0), \qquad t^* = \frac{\eta}{\varepsilon} t_\eta \to -\infty.$$

Since $u_0 \to 1$ as $t \to 0-$, it is clear that if matching is to be possible to the first order, $g_0 \to 1$ as $t^* \to -\infty$. Thus, the constant in Equation (2.6.21) is fixed as $-\frac{2}{3}$:

$$\frac{dg_0}{dt^*} - g_0 + \frac{1}{3}g_0^3 = -\frac{2}{3}$$

or

$$\frac{dg_0}{dt^*} = -\frac{1}{3}(1 - g_0)^2(g_0 + 2). \tag{2.6.22}$$

For matching to the other branch of the outer solution (CD), we expect that $t^* \to +\infty$, and it follows from Equation (2.6.22) that $g_0 \to -2$. Thus, for matching to first order, $u_0 \to -2$ as $t \to 0+$ (point C). These considerations give the first estimate of the size of the jump (u_0 goes from 1 to -2) and hence, the first approximation to the period. This same result can also be found directly from phase-plane or energy considerations. We now proceed to examine the matching in more detail. It is clear from Equation (2.6.22) that g_0 decays exponentially toward its asymptotic value (Equation 2.6.2) as $t^* \to +\infty$, but decays only algebraically as $t^* \to -\infty$. The form of the curves is indicated in Figure 2.9. Some difficulty in matching to higher order can be anticipated as $t^* \to -\infty$ because of the algebraic decay.

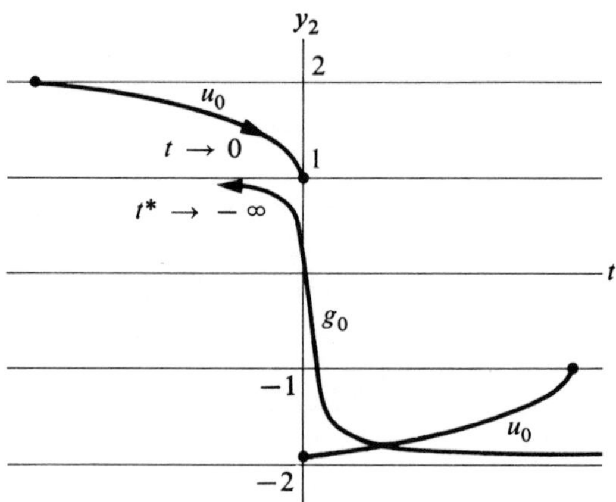

FIGURE 2.9 First-order boundary layer joining outer solutions.

The integral of Equation (2.6.22) is

$$\frac{1}{3}\log(1 - g_0) - \frac{1}{1 - g_0} - \frac{1}{3}\log(g_0 + 2) = -t^*, \tag{2.6.23}$$

with the constant of integration absorbed in $(-t^*)$. From Equations (2.6.23) or (2.6.22), the expansion as $t^* \to -\infty$ is easily worked out:

$$g_0(t^*) = 1 + \frac{1}{t^*} - \frac{1}{3}\log\frac{(-t^*)}{t^{*2}} + \cdots \qquad (t^* \to -\infty). \tag{2.6.24}$$

Correspondingly, the integral of Equation (2.6.20) is

$$\frac{dg_1}{dt^*} - (1 - g_0^2)g_1 = \text{const} = k_1. \tag{2.6.25}$$

The solution of the homogeneous part of Equation (2.6.25) can be written as (cf. Equation 2.6.19)

$$g_1 = h_1\frac{dg_0}{dt^*}, \qquad h_1 = \text{const},$$

so that

$$g_1 = h_1 \frac{dg_0}{dt^*} + g_{1_p}, \tag{2.6.26}$$

where g_{1_p} is a particular solution of Equation (2.6.25). Here h_1, k_1 are the two constants of integration. The behavior of the particular solution as $t^* \to -\infty$ is easily found from the form of Equation (2.6.25) as $t^* \to -\infty$,

$$\frac{dg_{1_p}}{dt^*} - \left(-\frac{2}{t^*} + \frac{2}{3}\frac{\log(-t^*)}{t^{*2}} - \frac{1}{t^{*2}} + \cdots\right) g_{1_p} = k_1,$$

so that

$$g_{1_p} = \frac{k_1}{3}\left\{t^* + \frac{1}{3}\log(-t^*) - \frac{1}{3} + O\left(\frac{\log^2(-t^*)}{t^{*2}}\right)\right\}, \qquad t^* \to -\infty. \tag{2.6.27}$$

Thus, if $k_1 \neq 0$, the particular solution g_{1_p} dominates as $t^* \to -\infty$, and

$$\begin{aligned} g_1 = \frac{k_1}{3}&\left\{t^* + \frac{1}{3}\log(-t^*) - \frac{1}{3} + O\left(\frac{\log^2(-t^*)}{t^{*2}}\right)\right\} \\ &+ h_1\left\{-\frac{1}{t^{*2}} + O\left(\frac{\log(-t^*)}{t^{*3}}\right)\right\}, \qquad t^* \to -\infty. \end{aligned} \tag{2.6.28}$$

Now, consider the attempt at matching the outer and inner expansions by writing both in intermediate variables

$$\begin{gathered} t = \eta t_\eta + \delta(\varepsilon) \to 0-, \qquad \frac{\eta}{\varepsilon} \to \infty, \qquad \eta \to 0; \\ t^* = \frac{\eta}{\varepsilon} t_\eta \to -\infty, \qquad t_\eta < 0. \end{gathered} \tag{2.6.29}$$

We have, from Equations (2.6.15), (2.6.16), (2.6.24), and (2.6.28), the following.

OUTER

$$\begin{aligned} y(t;\varepsilon) = 1 &+ \sqrt{-\eta t_\eta - \delta} + \tfrac{1}{6}(-\eta t_\eta - \delta) + \cdots \\ &+ \varepsilon\left\{\frac{1}{4(-\eta t_\eta - \delta)} + \frac{1}{8\sqrt{-\eta t_\eta - \delta}}[\log(-\eta t_\eta - \delta) + \cdots]\right\} + \cdots. \end{aligned} \tag{2.6.30}$$

INNER

$$y(t;\varepsilon) = 1 + \frac{\varepsilon}{\eta t_\eta} - \frac{1}{3}\varepsilon^2 \frac{\log(-\eta t_\eta/\varepsilon)}{\eta^2 t_\eta^2} + \cdots$$
$$+ \beta_1(\varepsilon)\left\{\frac{k}{3}\left(\frac{\eta t_\eta}{\varepsilon}\right) + \cdots - \frac{h_1\varepsilon^2}{\eta^2 t_\eta^2} + \cdots\right\}. \qquad (2.6.31)$$

It is clear that, even with $\delta \ll \eta$, there is no term in the outer expansion capable of matching the term $O(1/\eta t_\eta)$ in the inner expansion. In particular note that $y > 1$ in the outer expansion and $g_0 < 1$ in the inner.

The implication of the failure of matching to higher order is the existence of a distinguished limit and transition expansion between the inner and outer expansions. The transition expansion should match to the outer as $t \to 0-$ and the inner as $t^* \to -\infty$.

The thickness of the transition layer must be larger than that of the inner layer. Therefore, consider a limit process in which

$$\varepsilon \to 0, \qquad \tilde{t} = \frac{t - \rho(\varepsilon)}{\nu(\varepsilon)} \text{ is fixed}, \qquad 1 \gg \nu(\varepsilon) \gg \varepsilon.$$

Since the first term is already matched, the transition expansion has the form

$$y(t;\varepsilon) = 1 + \sigma_1(\varepsilon)f_1(\tilde{t}) + \sigma_2(\varepsilon)f_2(\tilde{t}) + \cdots. \qquad (2.6.32)$$

Thus, Equation (2.6.8) becomes

$$\frac{\varepsilon}{\nu^2}\left\{\sigma_1\frac{d^2f_1}{d\tilde{t}^2} + \sigma_2\frac{d^2f_2}{d\tilde{t}^2} + \cdots\right\} - \frac{1}{\nu}\{-2\sigma_1 f_1 - 2\sigma_2 f_2 - \sigma_1^2 f_1^2 - \cdots\}$$
$$\times\left\{\sigma_1\frac{df_1}{d\tilde{t}} + \sigma_2\frac{df_2}{d\tilde{t}} + \cdots\right\} + 1 + \sigma_1 f_1 + \sigma_2 f_2 + \cdots = 0. \qquad (2.6.33)$$

The orders of the terms associated with derivatives of each order are

$$\frac{\varepsilon\sigma_1}{\nu^2} \leftrightarrow \frac{\sigma_1^2}{\nu} \leftrightarrow 1. \qquad (2.6.34)$$

The distinguished limit is that in which all these orders are equal. The distinguished equation contains a representative of each of the three basic terms (y'', y', y) in Equation (2.6.8) [in contrast to the inner (y'', y') and outer (y', y) which contain only two]. Thus, we have

$$\nu = \varepsilon^{2/3}, \qquad \sigma_1 = \varepsilon^{1/3}. \qquad (2.6.35)$$

If the equation for f_2 is to contain forcing terms, it is necessary that

$$\sigma_2 = \varepsilon^{2/3}. \qquad (2.6.36)$$

The resulting expansion and equations are as follows.

TRANSITION EXPANSION

$$y(t'\varepsilon) = 1 + \varepsilon^{1/3} f_1(\tilde{t}) + \varepsilon^{2/3} f_2(\tilde{t}) + \cdots, \qquad \tilde{t} = \frac{t - \rho(\varepsilon)}{\varepsilon^{2/3}}, \tag{2.6.37}$$

$$\frac{d^2 f_1}{d\tilde{t}^2} + 2f_1 \frac{df_1}{d\tilde{t}} + 1 = 0, \tag{2.6.38}$$

$$\frac{d^2 f_2}{d\tilde{t}^2} + 2\frac{d}{d\tilde{t}}(f_1 f_2) = -f_1^2 \frac{df_1}{d\tilde{t}} - f_1 . \tag{2.6.39}$$

Typically, the equation for f_1 is nonlinear and that for f_2, f_3, etc. are linear. If necessary for matching, there is also the possibility of using a term f_{12} of order intermediate to $\varepsilon^{1/3}$ and $\varepsilon^{2/3}$; f_{12} satisfies the homogeneous version of Equation (2.6.39).

Next we study the properties of the solutions of Equations (2.6.38) and (2.6.39) with an eye to matching these with the inner and outer expansions as $t^* \to -\infty$ and $(t \to 0-, \tilde{t} \to -\infty)$, respectively. The first integral of Equation (2.6.38) is

$$\frac{df_1}{d\tilde{t}} + f_1^2 + \tilde{t} = 0, \tag{2.6.40}$$

where the constant of integration has been absorbed in the time shift $\rho(\varepsilon)$, which is still to be found. Equation (2.6.40) is of Riccati type and can be solved explicitly by means of the transformation

$$f_1 = \frac{V'(\tilde{t})}{V(\tilde{t})} = \frac{d}{d\tilde{t}} \log V. \tag{2.6.41}$$

Here $V(\tilde{t})$ satisfies the Airy equation

$$\frac{d^2 V}{d\tilde{t}^2} + \tilde{t} V = 0, \tag{2.6.42}$$

and, in terms of modified Bessel functions, the solution has the general form

$$V(\tilde{t}) = M\sqrt{-\tilde{t}}\, K_{1/3}(\tfrac{2}{3}(-\tilde{t})^{3/2}) + N\sqrt{-\tilde{t}}\, I_{1/3}(\tfrac{2}{3}(-\tilde{t})^{3/2}). \tag{2.6.43}$$

As $\tilde{t} \to -\infty$, these functions behave as

$$K_{1/3}\left(\frac{2}{3}(-\tilde{t})^{3/2}\right) = \frac{1}{2}\sqrt{3\pi}(-\tilde{t})^{-3/4} \exp\left[-\frac{2}{3}(-\tilde{t})^{3/2}\right]\left\{1 - \frac{5}{48(-\tilde{t})^{3/2}} + \cdots\right\}, \tag{2.6.44}$$

$$I_{1/3}\left(\frac{2}{3}(-\tilde{t})^{3/2}\right) = \frac{1}{2}\sqrt{\frac{3}{\pi}}(-\tilde{t})^{-3/4}\exp\left[\frac{2}{3}(-\tilde{t})^{3/2}\right]\left\{1 + \frac{5}{48(-\tilde{t})^{3/2}} + \cdots\right\}. \tag{2.6.45}$$

It is clear from Equation (2.6.40) that as $\tilde{t} \to -\infty$, $f_1 = \pm\sqrt{-\tilde{t}} + \cdots$. Further, if matching with the expansion of u_0 as $t \to 0-$ (Equation 2.6.15) is to be achieved, $f_1 = +\sqrt{-\tilde{t}}$ is the proper behavior. The asymptotic behavior of the $I_{1/3}$ and $K_{1/3}$ functions is such that

$$\log V(\tilde{t}) = \begin{cases} \frac{2}{3}(-\tilde{t})^{3/2} + \cdots & \text{if } N \neq 0, \\ -\frac{2}{3}(-\tilde{t})^{3/2} + \cdots & \text{if } N = 0. \end{cases}$$

Thus, from Equation (2.6.41), f_1 has the proper behavior only if $N = 0$, and Equation (2.6.43) becomes

$$V(\tilde{t}) = \begin{cases} M\sqrt{-\tilde{t}}\,K_{1/3}\left(\frac{2}{3}(-\tilde{t})^{3/2}\right), & \tilde{t} < 0; \\ M\frac{\pi}{\sqrt{3}}\sqrt{\tilde{t}}\left\{J_{1/3}\left(\frac{2}{3}\tilde{t}^{3/2}\right) + J_{1/3}\left(\frac{2}{3}\tilde{t}^{3/2}\right)\right\}, & \tilde{t} > 0. \end{cases} \tag{2.6.46}$$

Both constants of integration have now been accounted for in f_1. A sketch of the form of V and f_1 is shown in Figure 2.10. Here $\tilde{t}_0$ is the first zero of the Airy function.

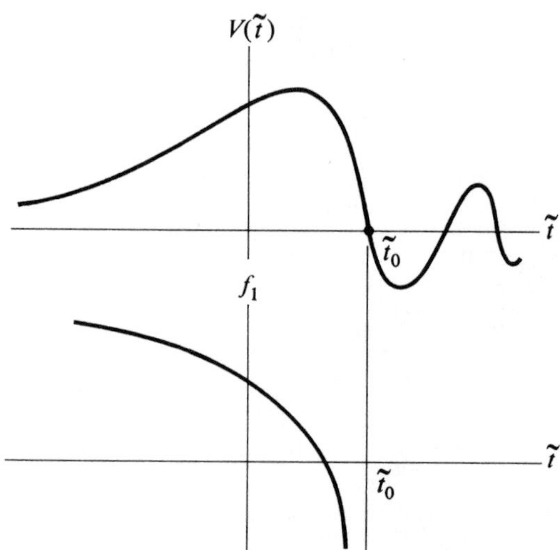

FIGURE 2.10 Transition layer.

We next construct a representation of the solution f_2. The first integral of Equation (2.6.39) is

$$\frac{df_2}{d\tilde{t}} + 2f_1 f_2 = C_2 - \frac{1}{3}f_1^3 - \log V(\tilde{t}), \tag{2.6.47}$$

where f_1, V are defined by Equations (2.6.41) and (2.6.46). Using Equation (2.6.41), we rewrite Equation (2.6.47) as

$$\frac{d}{d\tilde{t}}(V^2 f_2) + \frac{1}{3}\frac{V'^3}{V} + V^2 \log V = C_2 V^2,$$

so that

$$f_2 = \frac{D_2}{V^2} + \frac{C_2}{V^2}\int_{-\infty}^{\tilde{t}} V^2(\lambda)\, d\lambda - \frac{1}{V^2}\int_{-\infty}^{\tilde{t}} V^2 \log V\, d\lambda - \frac{1}{3V^2}\int_{-\infty}^{\tilde{t}} \frac{V'^3}{V}\, d\lambda. \tag{2.6.48}$$

Here C_2 and D_2 are the constants of integration. Integrating the last integral by parts, and using Equations (2.6.40) and (2.6.46), we can bring Equation (2.6.48) to the form

$$f_2 = \frac{D_2}{V^2} - \left(C_2 - \frac{1}{3}\log V\right)\frac{df_1}{d\tilde{t}} - \frac{1}{6}f_1^2 - \frac{2}{3V^2}\int_{-\infty}^{\tilde{t}} V^2 \log V\, d\lambda. \tag{2.6.49}$$

Now, as $\tilde{t} \to -\infty$, we have

$$V(\tilde{t}) = \frac{M}{2}\sqrt{3\pi}\,(-\tilde{t})^{-1/4} \exp[-\tfrac{2}{3}(-\tilde{t})^{3/2}] + \cdots,$$

$$\int_{-\infty}^{\tilde{t}} V^2 \log V\, d\lambda = \frac{M^2}{4}3\pi \int_{-\infty}^{\tilde{t}} \frac{\exp[-\tfrac{4}{3}(-\lambda)^{3/2}]}{\sqrt{-\lambda}}\left(-\frac{2}{3}(-\lambda)^{3/2} + \cdots\right) d\lambda$$

$$= -M^2\pi\sqrt{-\tilde{t}}\exp\left[-\frac{1}{3}(-\tilde{t})^{3/2}\right] + \cdots,$$

$$\frac{1}{V^2}\int_{-\infty}^{\tilde{t}} V^2 \log V\, d\lambda = -\frac{4}{3}(-\tilde{t}) + \cdots,$$

and

$$f_1 = \sqrt{-\tilde{t}} + \cdots, \qquad \frac{df}{d\tilde{t}} = -\frac{1}{2\sqrt{-\tilde{t}}} + \cdots.$$

Hence, to prevent exponential growth as $\tilde{t} \to -\infty$, D_2 is chosen to be zero, and the final form of f_2 is

$$f_2 = -\left(C_2 - \frac{1}{3}\log V\right)\frac{df_1}{d\tilde{t}} - \frac{1}{6}f_1^2 - \frac{2}{3V^2(\tilde{t})}\int_{-\infty}^{\tilde{t}} V^2(\lambda)\log V(\lambda)\,d\lambda. \qquad (2.6.50)$$

Thus, the asymptotic behavior of f_1, f_2 as $\tilde{t} \to -\infty$ can be found from V and its asymptotic behavior. We find that

$$f_1 = \sqrt{-\tilde{t}} + \frac{1}{4(-\tilde{t})} - \frac{5}{32}\frac{1}{(-\tilde{t})^{5/2}} + O\left(\frac{1}{\tilde{t}^4}\right), \qquad (2.6.51)$$

$$f_2 = \frac{1}{6}(-\tilde{t}) + \frac{1}{8\sqrt{-\tilde{t}}}\log(-\tilde{t}) + \frac{1}{\sqrt{-\tilde{t}}}\left\{\frac{C_2}{2} - \frac{1}{12} - \frac{1}{2}\log\frac{M\sqrt{3\pi}}{2}\right\} + O\left(\frac{\log(-\tilde{t})}{\tilde{t}^2}\right). \qquad (2.6.52)$$

Next, we consider the matching to the branch AB of the outer expansion. The intermediate limit is defined by

$$(\varepsilon \to 0,\ t_\eta \text{ fixed}), \qquad t_\eta = \frac{t - \rho(\varepsilon)}{\eta(\varepsilon)}, \qquad \varepsilon^{2/3} \ll \eta \ll 1,$$

so that we have

$$t = \eta t_\eta + \rho(\varepsilon) \to 0, \qquad \tilde{t} = \frac{\eta}{\varepsilon}t_\eta \to -\infty.$$

The outer expansion written in intermediate variables is as follows from Equations (2.6.16) and (2.6.16).

OUTER

$$y(t;\varepsilon) = 1 + \sqrt{-\eta t_\eta - \rho} + \frac{1}{6}(-\eta t_\eta - \rho) + \cdots$$
$$+\varepsilon\left\{\frac{1}{4(-\eta t_\eta - \rho)} + \frac{1}{8\sqrt{-\eta t_\eta - \rho}}\log(-\eta t_\eta - \rho)\right.$$
$$\left. + \left(\frac{A_1}{2} - \frac{1}{12} + \frac{\log 2}{4}\right)\frac{1}{\sqrt{-\eta t_\eta - \rho}} + \cdots\right\}. \qquad (2.6.53)$$

For $\rho \ll \eta$, we have the following.

OUTER

$$y(t;\varepsilon) = 1 + \sqrt{-\eta t_\eta} - \frac{1}{2}\frac{\rho}{\sqrt{-\eta t_\eta}} + \cdots + \frac{1}{6}(-\eta t_\eta) - \frac{\rho}{6} + \cdots$$

$$+ \varepsilon\left\{\frac{1}{4(-\eta t_\eta)} + \frac{\rho}{4(-\eta t_\eta)^2} + \cdots + \frac{1}{8\sqrt{-\eta t_\eta}}\log(-\eta t_\eta)\right.$$

$$-\frac{1}{8}\frac{\rho}{(\eta t_\eta)^{3/2}} + \frac{\rho}{16(-\eta t_\eta)^{3/2}}\log(-\eta t_\eta) + \cdots$$

$$\left. + \left(\frac{A_1}{2} - \frac{1}{12} + \frac{\log 2}{4}\right)\frac{1}{\sqrt{-\eta t_\eta}} + \cdots\right\}, \tag{2.6.54}$$

and the intermediate expansion is as follows from Equations (2.6.51) and (2.6.52).

TRANSITION

$$y(t;\varepsilon) = 1 + \varepsilon^{1/3}\left\{\frac{\sqrt{-\eta t_\eta}}{\varepsilon^{1/3}} + \frac{\varepsilon^{2/3}}{4(-\eta t_\eta)} + \cdots\right\}$$

$$+ \varepsilon^{2/3}\left\{\frac{1}{6}\frac{(-\eta t_\eta)}{\varepsilon^{2/3}} + \frac{1}{8}\frac{\varepsilon^{1/3}}{\sqrt{-\eta t_\eta}}\left(\log(-\eta t_\eta) - \frac{2}{3}\log\varepsilon\right)\right.$$

$$\left. + \frac{\varepsilon^{1/3}}{\sqrt{-\eta t_\eta}}\left(\frac{C_2}{2} - \frac{1}{12} - \frac{1}{2}\log\frac{M\sqrt{3\pi}}{2}\right) + \cdots\right\}. \tag{2.6.55}$$

A comparison of these two expressions shows that all the terms in Equation (2.6.55) can be matched exactly by those in Equation (2.6.54) if the time shift $\rho(\varepsilon)$ and A_1 are chosen so that

$$\rho = \frac{1}{6}\varepsilon\log\varepsilon, \qquad A_1 = C_2 - \log\frac{M\sqrt{3\pi}}{2} - \frac{1}{4}\log 2. \tag{2.6.56}$$

All the terms omitted vanish more rapidly than those matched. Thus, the constants of integration (ρ, C_2) of the first two terms in the transition expansion are found in terms of A_1, from the matching.

The next problem is the matching of the transition expansion to the inner expansion as $t^* \to -\infty$. It is clear from the behavior of f_1 (cf. Figure 2.10) that the matching will take place as $\tilde{t} \to \tilde{t}_0$, the first zero of the Airy function. To study the matching, we need to know the behavior of f_1, f_2 as $\tilde{t} \to \tilde{t}_0$. We know that $V(\tilde{t})$ has a simple zero at $\tilde{t} = \tilde{t}_0$; it follows from Equation (2.6.42) that $V(\tilde{t})$ has an expansion near $\tilde{t}_0$ of the form

$$V(\tilde{t}) = M\left\{-K(\tilde{t} - \tilde{t}_0) + \frac{K}{6}\tilde{t}_0(\tilde{t} - \tilde{t}_0)^3 + O((\tilde{t} - \tilde{t}_0)^5)\right\}, \tag{2.6.57}$$

where $K = \text{const}$. Thus, from Equation (2.6.41), as $\tilde{t} \to \tilde{t}_0$, we have

$$f_1(\tilde{t}) = \frac{1}{\tilde{t} - \tilde{t}_0} - \frac{1}{3}\tilde{t}_0(\tilde{t} - \tilde{t}_0) + O((\tilde{t} - \tilde{t}_0)^2), \tag{2.6.58}$$

$$\frac{df_1}{d\tilde{t}}(\tilde{t}) = \frac{1}{\tilde{t} - \tilde{t}_0} - \frac{1}{3}\tilde{t}_0 + O((\tilde{t} - \tilde{t}_0)). \tag{2.6.59}$$

Now, the integral in Equation (2.6.50) approaches a finite value as $\tilde{t} \to \tilde{t}_0$, so that the dominant term in f_2 comes from $\log V\, df_1/d\tilde{t}$, and we have

$$f_2 = -\frac{1}{3}\frac{\log(\tilde{t}_0 - \tilde{t})}{(\tilde{t}_0 - \tilde{t})^2} + O\left(\frac{1}{(\tilde{t}_0 - \tilde{t})^2}\right). \tag{2.6.60}$$

To express the intermediate limit for this case, we first write t^* in terms of $\tilde{t}$,

$$t^* = \frac{t - \delta(\varepsilon)}{\varepsilon} = \frac{\tilde{t} + \frac{1}{6}\varepsilon^{1/3}\log\varepsilon - \varepsilon^{-2/3}\delta(\varepsilon)}{\varepsilon^{1/3}} \tag{2.6.61}$$

and let

$$\delta(\varepsilon) = \varepsilon^{2/3}\{\tilde{t}_0 + \gamma(\varepsilon)\},$$

so that

$$t^* = \frac{\tilde{t} - \tilde{t}_0 - \gamma(\varepsilon) + \frac{1}{6}\varepsilon^{1/3}\log\varepsilon}{\varepsilon^{1/3}} = \frac{\tilde{t} - \tilde{t}_0 - \sigma(\varepsilon)}{\varepsilon^{1/3}}, \tag{2.6.62}$$

where

$$\sigma(\varepsilon) = \gamma(\varepsilon) - \tfrac{1}{6}\varepsilon^{1/3}\log\varepsilon.$$

The intermediate class of limits is, thus,

$$\varepsilon \to 0, \qquad t_\eta \text{ fixed}, \qquad \text{where } t_\eta = \frac{\tilde{t} - \tilde{t}_0 - \sigma(\varepsilon)}{\eta}, \quad \varepsilon^{1/3} \ll \eta \ll 1, \tag{2.6.63}$$

so that we have

$$t^* = \frac{\eta}{\varepsilon^{1/3}}t_\eta \to -\infty \qquad (t_\eta < 0), \qquad \tilde{t} - \tilde{t}_0 \to -\eta t_\eta + \sigma(\varepsilon).$$

Thus, using Equations (2.6.58) and (2.6.60), we find that the transition expansion is written in intermediate variables.

TRANSITION

$$y(t;\varepsilon) = 1 + \varepsilon^{1/3}\left\{\frac{1}{\eta t_\eta + \sigma} - \frac{1}{3}\tilde{t}_0(\eta t_\eta + \sigma) + \cdots\right\} + \varepsilon^{2/3}\left\{-\frac{\log(-\eta t_\eta - \sigma)}{3(\eta t_\eta + \sigma)^2} + \cdots\right\}. \tag{2.6.64}$$

For $\sigma \ll \eta$, we have the following.

TRANSITION

$$y(t;\varepsilon) = 1 + \varepsilon^{1/3}\left\{-\frac{1}{(-\eta t_\eta)} - \frac{\sigma}{(-\eta t_\eta)^2} + \cdots + \frac{1}{3}\tilde{t}_0(-\eta t_\eta) + \cdots\right\} - \frac{1}{3}\varepsilon^{2/3}\frac{\log(-\eta t_\eta)}{(-\eta t_\eta)^2} + \cdots. \tag{2.6.65}$$

For the inner expansion, using Equations (2.6.24) and (2.6.28), we find the following.

INNER

$$y(t;\varepsilon) = 1 - \frac{\varepsilon^{1/3}}{(-\eta t_\eta)} - \frac{1}{3}\frac{\varepsilon^{2/3}}{(-\eta t_\eta)^2}\log(-\eta t_\eta) + \frac{1}{9}\frac{\varepsilon^{2/3}\log\varepsilon}{(-\eta t_\eta)^2} + \cdots + \beta_1(\varepsilon)\left\{-\frac{k_1}{3}\frac{(-\eta t_\eta)}{\varepsilon^{1/3}} + \frac{k_1}{3}\log(-\eta t_\eta) + \frac{k_1}{9}\log\varepsilon + \cdots - h_1\frac{\varepsilon^{2/3}}{(-\eta t_\eta)^2} + \cdots\right\}. \tag{2.6.66}$$

The terms in Equation (2.6.65) can all be matched to terms in Equation (2.6.66) with the choices

$$\beta_1 = \varepsilon^{2/3}, \qquad k_1 = -\tilde{t}_0, \qquad -\sigma\varepsilon^{1/3} = \tfrac{1}{9}\varepsilon^{2/3}\log\varepsilon. \tag{2.6.67}$$

This is consistent with our previous assumption that $\beta_1 \gg \varepsilon$. It follows that

$$\gamma(\varepsilon) = \tfrac{1}{18}\varepsilon^{1/3}\log\varepsilon, \qquad \delta = \varepsilon^{2/3}\tilde{t}_0 + \tfrac{1}{18}\varepsilon\log\varepsilon. \tag{2.6.68}$$

Thus, the relationship of t^* and t, Equation (2.6.61), is

$$t^* = \frac{t - \varepsilon^{2/3}\tilde{t}_0 - \frac{1}{18}\varepsilon\log\varepsilon}{\varepsilon}. \tag{2.6.69}$$

Lastly, we need to close the cycle by matching the inner expansion as $t^* \to \infty$ to the branch CD of the outer expansion as $t \to 0+$, $u_0 \to -2$. From

Equation (2.6.13), we can write CD as a reflection and translation,

$$\log(-u_0) - \frac{u_0^2 - 1}{2} = t^+, \tag{2.6.70}$$

where $t^+ = t - \frac{1}{2}T(\varepsilon)$ and $T(\varepsilon) =$ period on t scale. The outer expansion now has t^+ fixed.

We can expand Equation (2.6.13) about $u_0 = -2$ to obtain

$$u_0(t^+) = -2 + \tfrac{2}{3}\{t^+ - \log 2 + \tfrac{3}{2}\} + \cdots. \tag{2.6.71}$$

Equation (2.6.14) shows that $u_1 \to$ const as $u_0 \to -2$.

It also follows from Equation (2.6.22) or (2.6.23) that, as $t^* \to \infty$, we have

$$g_0(t^*) = -2 + O(e^{-3t^*}), \tag{2.6.72}$$

and the particular solution g_{1_p} of Equation (2.6.26) satisfies an equation of the form

$$\frac{dg_{1_p}}{dt^*} + \{3 + O(e^{-3t^*})\}g_{1_p} = k_1 = -\tilde{t}_0. \tag{2.6.73}$$

Thus, we have

$$g_1(t^*) = g_{1p} = -\tfrac{1}{3}\tilde{t}_0 + \cdots, \qquad t^* \to \infty. \tag{2.6.74}$$

The relationship of t^* and t^+ comes from Equation (2.6.69),

$$t^* = \frac{t^+ + \frac{1}{2}T(\varepsilon) - \varepsilon^{2/3}\tilde{t}_0 - \frac{1}{18}\varepsilon\log\varepsilon}{\varepsilon}, \tag{2.6.75}$$

so that the intermediate limit for this matching has ($\varepsilon \to 0$, t_η fixed)

$$t_\eta = \frac{t^+ + \frac{1}{2}T(\varepsilon) - \varepsilon^{2/3}\tilde{t}_0 - \frac{1}{18}\varepsilon\log\varepsilon}{\eta(\varepsilon)}, \qquad \varepsilon \ll \eta \ll 1, \tag{2.6.76}$$

and

$$t^* = \frac{\eta}{\varepsilon}t_\eta \to \infty, \qquad t^+ = -\frac{1}{2}T(\varepsilon) + \varepsilon^{2/3}\tilde{t}_0 + \frac{1}{18}\varepsilon\log\varepsilon + \eta t_\eta.$$

Using Equation (2.6.71) we can write the outer expansion in t_η as follows.

OUTER

$$y(t;\varepsilon) = -2 + \tfrac{2}{3}\{-\tfrac{1}{2}T(\varepsilon) + \varepsilon^{2/3}\tilde{t}_0 + \tfrac{1}{18}\varepsilon\log\varepsilon + \eta t_\eta - \log 2 + \tfrac{3}{2}\} + \cdots + O(\varepsilon) \tag{2.6.77}$$

and from Equations (2.6.72) and (2.6.74), the inner expansion becomes the following.

INNER

$$y(t;\varepsilon) = -2 + \varepsilon^{2/3}(-\tfrac{1}{3}\tilde{t}_0) + \cdots + \beta_2(\varepsilon)(\ ) + \cdots, \qquad \beta_2 \ll \varepsilon^{2/3}. \tag{2.6.78}$$

The period $T(\varepsilon)$ is fixed by the requirement that the terms $O(1)$ and $O(\varepsilon^{2/3})$ match. Thus we have

$$T(\varepsilon) = 3 - 2\log 2 + 3\tilde{t}_0\varepsilon^{2/3} + O(\varepsilon \log \varepsilon). \tag{2.6.79}$$

As far as the result above has been carried out, it agrees with that of Dorodnitsyn in Reference 2.6.1. It is not worthwhile to carry out the period to $O(\varepsilon \log \varepsilon)$ without calculating the terms $O(\varepsilon)$ at the same time. The method followed by Dorodnitsyn involved the matching of asymptotic expansions constructed in various regions in the phase plane. Reference 2.6.2 corrects the higher terms in Dorodnitsyn's formula for the period and carries out numerical calculations which show close agreement with the asymptotic formula for the period. It would be possible to find more details of the expansion for the period by carrying out further terms. The basic ideas essential for this procedure have been illustrated in this section.

REFERENCES

2.6.1 A. A. Dorodnitsyn, "Asymptotic Solution of the van der Pol Equations," *Prik. Mat. i Mekh. 11* (1947), 313–328 (in Russian).

2.6.2 M. Urabe, "Numerical Study of Periodic Solutions of the van der Pol Equations," in *Proc. Int. Symp. on Non-Linear Differential Equations and Non-Linear Mechanics*, 184–195. Edited by J. P. LaSalle and S. Lefschitz. New York: Academic Press, 1963.

2.7 Singular boundary problems

In this Section, two problems are discussed in which the expansions in terms of a small parameter are not regular, not because of a lowering of the order of the equations in the limit but, rather, because of a difficulty associated with the behavior near the boundary point. Nevertheless, the same method as used in previous Sections enables the expansions of the solutions to be found in these cases. Different asymptotic expansions valid in different regions are constructed, and the matching of these expansions in an overlap domain enables all unknown constants to be found. Thus, a uniformly valid approximation can be found.

2.7.1 Navier–Stokes shock-wave structure at high Mach number

It is of physical interest to know the limiting form of shock-wave structure for high Mach number according to the Navier–Stokes equations. It is essential in such a calculation to account for the variation of the viscosity coefficient with temperature due to the large increase in the temperature of the gas passing through the shock wave. In suitable dimensionless variables, the main parameter is the free stream Mach number M_1, which is thus considered here to approach infinity. The work of this Section is a condensed version of the work in References 2.7.1 and 2.7.2.

Consider steady one-dimensional flow of a perfect gas (constant specific heats) from a uniform state (1) at upstream infinity through a shock wave to a uniform state (2) at downstream infinity. Assume the Navier–Stokes equations and Stokes relation between longitudinal and shear viscosities so that, practically, the results apply most closely for a monatomic gas.

The equations of motion are as follows.

$$\rho u = m = \text{const} = \rho_{1,2} u_{1,2} \qquad \text{(continuity)}, \tag{2.7.1}$$

$$p + \rho u^2 - \frac{4}{3}\mu \frac{du}{dx} = P = \text{const} = p_{1,2} + \rho_{1,2} u_{1,2}^2 \qquad \text{(momentum)}, \tag{2.7.2}$$

$$c_p T + \frac{u^2}{2} - \frac{4}{3}\frac{\mu}{\rho}\frac{du}{dx} - \frac{k}{m}\frac{dT}{dx} = H = \text{const} = c_p T_{1,2} + \frac{u_{1,2}^2}{2} \qquad \text{(energy)}. \tag{2.7.3}$$

Assuming that the (realistic) value of the Prandtl number $\mu c_p/k = \frac{3}{4}$, we see that constant total enthalpy is an integral of Equation (2.7.3),

$$c_p T + \frac{u^2}{2} = H. \tag{2.7.4}$$

In these equations, ρ = density, u = velocity, p = pressure, $\mu(T)$ = viscosity coefficient, k = thermal conductivity, c_p = specific heat at constant pressure = const. The momentum equation (2.7.2) can thus, after some elimination, be written

$$\frac{8\gamma}{3(\gamma+1)}\mu \frac{u}{m}\frac{du}{dx} = -(u_1 - u)(u - u_2), \qquad \gamma = \frac{c_p}{c_v} = \text{const}. \tag{2.7.5}$$

In the basic equations, the relationship between (p_1, ρ_1, T_1, u_1) and (p_2, ρ_2, T_2, u_2) lies in the over-all shock-jump conditions which hold, for example, when the shock is treated as a discontinuity, as in inviscid flow problems. Thus, we have

$$\frac{u_2}{u_1} = \frac{\gamma - 1}{\gamma + 1} + \frac{2}{\gamma + 1}\frac{1}{M_1^2}. \tag{2.7.6}$$

Here $M_1 = u_1/\sqrt{\gamma R T_1}$ is the Mach number at upstream infinity.

Introduce now the dimensionless variables based on conditions at upstream infinity,

$$\bar{u} = \frac{u}{u_1}, \qquad \bar{\mu} = \frac{\mu}{\mu_1}, \qquad \xi = \frac{mx}{\mu_1}, \tag{2.7.7}$$

so that Equation (2.7.5) becomes

$$\frac{d\xi}{d\bar{u}} = -\frac{4}{3}(1 + \varepsilon)\frac{\bar{\mu}\bar{u}}{(1 - \bar{u})\{\bar{u} - \varepsilon(1 + \delta)\}},$$

where

$$\varepsilon = \frac{\gamma - 1}{\gamma + 1}, \qquad \delta = \frac{1 - \varepsilon}{\varepsilon M_1^2}. \tag{2.7.8}$$

The boundary conditions are

$$\xi(\bar{u}) \to -\infty, \qquad \text{as} \quad \bar{u} \to 1, \tag{2.7.9a}$$

$$\xi(\bar{u}) \to +\infty, \qquad \text{as} \quad \bar{u} \to \varepsilon(1 + \delta). \tag{2.7.9b}$$

The simple zeroes in the denominator of Equation (2.7.8) imply a logarithmic behavior of the distance coordinate ξ with velocity (or an exponential approach of velocity to its asymptotic value) as the upstream and downstream boundary conditions are approached. It is this behavior that is lost at upstream infinity in the limit ($M_1 \to \infty$ or $\delta \to 0$, ε fixed), when a realistic viscosity law is used. Such a realistic law is the Sutherland Viscosity Law,

$$\bar{\mu} = \bar{T}^{3/2}\left\{\frac{1 + \theta}{\bar{T} + \theta}\right\}, \qquad \theta = \frac{T_c}{T_1}, \tag{2.7.10}$$

T_c = characteristic temperature for gas considered, and, from Equation (2.7.4),

$$\bar{T} = 1 + \frac{1 - \bar{u}^2}{\delta}. \tag{2.7.11}$$

Hence, within the shock $\bar{\mu} = \bar{\mu}(\bar{u})$,

$$\bar{\mu}(\bar{u}) = \left[(1 + \theta)\left\{1 + \frac{1 - \bar{u}^2}{\delta}\right\}^{3/2}\right] \Big/ \left(\theta + 1 + \frac{1 - \bar{u}^2}{\delta}\right). \tag{2.7.12}$$

Thus, redefining the length scale slightly for convenience, the basic equation to be studied is

$$\frac{d\eta}{d\bar{u}} = \frac{\bar{u}}{(1 - \bar{u})(\bar{u} - \varepsilon(1 + \delta))}\left\{\left[1 + \frac{1 - \bar{u}^2}{\delta}\right]^{3/2} \Big/ \left(1 + \frac{1 - \bar{u}^2}{\delta} + \theta\right)\right\}, \tag{2.7.13}$$

where

$$\eta = \tfrac{3}{4}[\xi/(1 + \varepsilon)(1 + \theta)].$$

The corresponding boundary conditions at upstream and downstream are

$$\eta(\bar{u}) \to -\infty \qquad \text{as} \quad \bar{u} \to 1, \tag{2.7.14a}$$

$$\eta(\bar{u}) \to +\infty \qquad \text{as} \quad \bar{u} \to \varepsilon(1 + \delta). \tag{2.7.14b}$$

In order to study the solution as $M_1 \to \infty$, it is necessary to consider ($\delta \to 0$) all other parameters, particularly ε, held fixed. The solution downstream is connected with an outer limit ($\delta \to 0$, $\bar{u}$ fixed). It is clear that the right-hand side of Equation (2.7.13) is $O(1/\sqrt{\delta})$ as $\delta \to 0$, so that the following form of asymptotic expansion is used.

$$\eta(t;\delta) = \frac{1}{\sqrt{\delta}}\{G_0(t) + \delta G_1(t) + \cdots\}. \tag{2.7.15}$$

The variable $t = \bar{u}/\varepsilon(1 + \delta)$ is convenient for the downstream boundary condition but is not an essential change from $\bar{u}$. Only the first term is considered here. Details of the calculation of higher-order corrections are in References 2.7.1, 2.7.2.

$$\frac{dG_0}{dt} = -\frac{\varepsilon t}{t - 1}\sqrt{\frac{1 + \varepsilon t}{1 - \varepsilon t}}. \tag{2.7.16}$$

Notice that the nature of the singularity at upstream infinity ($\bar{u} = 1$) is altered in this equation as compared to Equation (2.7.13), so that in fact the boundary condition at upstream infinity cannot be satisfied; the conditions downstream ($t = 1$) can still be satisfied.

The solution of Equation (2.7.16), if we take account of the downstream boundary condition, is

$$G_0(t) = (1 + \varepsilon)\cos^{-1}(\varepsilon t) + \sqrt{1 - \varepsilon^2 t^2} - \varepsilon\sqrt{(1 + \varepsilon)/(1 - \varepsilon)}\,\log \Lambda(t) + C, \tag{2.7.17}$$

where

$$\Lambda(t) = \frac{\sqrt{(1 - \varepsilon)/(1 + \varepsilon)} - \sqrt{(1 - \varepsilon t)/(1 + \varepsilon t)}}{\sqrt{(1 - \varepsilon)/(1 + \varepsilon)} + \sqrt{(1 - \varepsilon t)/(1 + \varepsilon t)}}. \tag{2.7.18}$$

$\Lambda(1) = 0$, so that $G_0(1) = +\infty$. At the point corresponding approximately to upstream infinity, $t = 1/\varepsilon$ and G_0 is finite.

Next a different expansion is constructed that has the possibility of satisfying the boundary condition at upstream infinity. In order to retain the proper kind of singularity at upstream infinity, it is necessary that $1 - \bar{u}/\delta$ be $O(1)$ or less. This fact suggests that

$$s = \frac{1 - \bar{u}}{\delta} \geq 0 \tag{2.7.19}$$

is a suitable variable for the upstream region, but this assumption must be checked by matching. Rewriting Equation (2.7.13) in terms of s, we have

$$\frac{d\eta}{ds} = \frac{(1 - \delta s)\{(1 + 2s) - \delta s^2\}^{3/2}}{s[1 - \varepsilon - \delta(s + \varepsilon)][(1 + 2s + \theta) - \delta s^2]}, \tag{2.7.20}$$

with the boundary condition at upstream infinity

$$\eta(s) \to -\infty \qquad \text{as} \quad s \to 0.$$

A suitable asymptotic expansion associated with the limit process ($\delta \to 0$, s fixed) is

$$\eta(s; \delta) = \frac{1}{1 - \varepsilon}\{F_0(s) + \delta F_1(s) + \cdots\}. \tag{2.7.21}$$

It follows that

$$\frac{dF_0}{ds} = \frac{(1 + 2s)^{3/2}}{s(1 + 2s + \theta)}. \tag{2.7.22}$$

Integration of Equation (2.7.22) yields

$$F_0(s) = 2\sqrt{1 + 2s} - \frac{1}{1 + \theta}\log\left|\frac{1 + \sqrt{1 + 2s}}{1 - \sqrt{1 + 2s}}\right| - 2\frac{\theta^{3/2}}{1 + \theta}\tan^{-1}\sqrt{\frac{1 + 2s}{\theta}} + K. \tag{2.7.23}$$

As expected, the first term of this expansion satisfies the boundary condition at upstream infinity but not at downstream infinity. The constant of integration C in Equation (2.7.17) can be put equal to zero, since the origin of the x-coordinate is arbitrary. However, the constant of integration K in Equation (2.7.23) must then be found from the matching of the two expansions, the first terms of which are (G_0, F_0).

For matching a class of intermediate limits in terms of an intermediate variable, we use

$$w = \frac{1 - \bar{u}}{D(\delta)}, \tag{2.7.24}$$

where w is fixed as $\delta \to 0$, and $D(\delta)/\delta \to \infty$, $D(\delta) \to 0$.

Thus, in the intermediate limit, we have

$$s = \frac{D(\delta)}{\delta} w \to \infty, \qquad \varepsilon t = \frac{1 - D(\delta)}{1 + \delta} w \to 1 - D(\delta)w. \tag{2.7.25}$$

Matching to order one means that

$$\lim_{\substack{\delta \to 0, \\ w \text{ fixed}}} \left\{ \frac{1}{\sqrt{\delta}} G_0(t) + \cdots - \frac{1}{1 - \varepsilon} F_0(s) \right\} = 0. \tag{2.7.26}$$

From the integrals of Equations (2.7.17) and (2.7.23), we have

$$F_0 \to 2\left(2\frac{D}{\delta}w\right)^{1/2} - \frac{\pi\theta^{3/2}}{1 + \theta} + K + O\left\{\left(\frac{\delta}{D}\right)^{1/2}\right\}, \tag{2.7.27}$$

$$\begin{aligned} G_0 &\to (1 + \varepsilon)(2Dw)^{1/2} + (2Dw)^{1/2} \\ &\quad - \varepsilon\left(\frac{1 + \varepsilon}{1 - \varepsilon}\right)^{1/2} \log\left[1 - (2Dw)^{1/2}\left(\frac{1 + \varepsilon}{1 - \varepsilon}\right)^{1/2}\right] + \cdots \\ &\to \frac{2}{1 + \varepsilon}(2Dw)^{1/2} + O(D). \end{aligned} \tag{2.7.28}$$

Thus, the matching condition is

$$\lim_{\substack{\delta \to 0, \\ w \text{ fixed}}} \left[\begin{matrix} \dfrac{2}{1 - \varepsilon}\left(2\dfrac{D}{\delta}w\right)^{-1/2} & - \dfrac{2}{1 - \varepsilon}\left(2\dfrac{D}{\delta}w\right)^{1/2} & - \left(\dfrac{\pi\theta^{3/2}}{1 + \theta} - K\right) \\ + O\left(\dfrac{D}{\delta^{1/2}}\right) & & + O\left(\dfrac{\delta}{D}\right)^{1/2} \end{matrix} \right] = 0. \tag{2.7.29}$$

The expansions are matched to order one if we have

$$K = \frac{\pi\theta^{3/2}}{1 + \theta}. \tag{2.7.30}$$

From the order estimates, the intermediate range of limits is that for which

$$\delta \ll D(\delta) \ll \delta^{1/2}. \tag{2.7.31}$$

A uniformly valid first approximation can also be constructed by subtracting the common part, which is matched in Equation (2.7.29), from the sum of inner and outer expansions. A sketch of the profile appears in Figure 2.11.

Details of matching to higher-order appear in References 2.7.1 and 2.7.2.

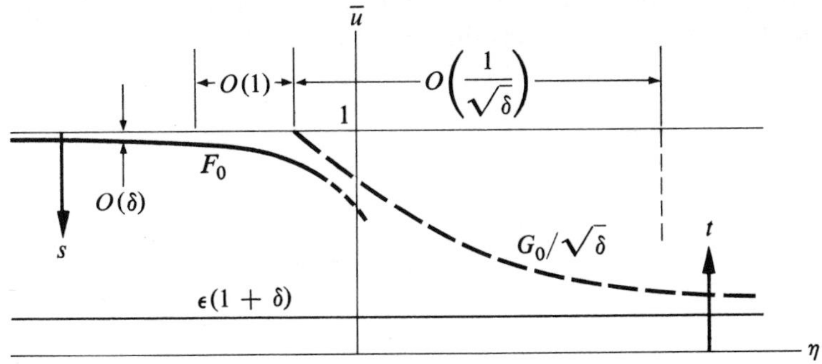

FIGURE 2.11 Shock-wave structure.

REFERENCES

2.7.1 W. B. BUSH, "The Hypersonic Approximation for the Shock Structure of a Perfect Gas with the Sutherland Viscosity Law," *AFOSR Rept.* 2257, California Institute of Technology, Feb. 1962.

2.7.2 W. B. BUSH, *Journ. de Mécanique*, 1. *3* (Sept. 1962).

2.7.2 Model example for Stokes–Oseen problem

The mathematical problem of low-Reynolds number flow past an object is outlined in Section 4.5.2. A model example for this flow is discussed here. The problem is a singular boundary-value problem. The form of the expansion comes not from a distinguished limit but from the behavior of the solution near the boundary points. In this simple example, it is possible to give a rigorous demonstration of the validity of the asymptotic expansions and matching.

Consider the equation

$$\frac{d^2u}{dr^2} + \frac{1}{r}\frac{du}{dr} + u\frac{du}{dr} = 0 \tag{2.7.32}$$

defined in

$$\varepsilon \leq r < \infty$$

with boundary conditions

$$u(\varepsilon) = 0, \qquad u(\infty) = 1. \tag{2.7.33}$$

We want the behavior of the solution $u(r; \varepsilon)$ as $\varepsilon \to 0$. The problem has an analogy with a cylindrically symmetric heat-flow problem having a heat source strength/area proportional to $u(du/dr)$. In these coordinates, as $\varepsilon \to 0$ the size of the cold ($u = 0$) cylinder shrinks to zero. The general shape of the expected solution is shown in Figure 2.12.

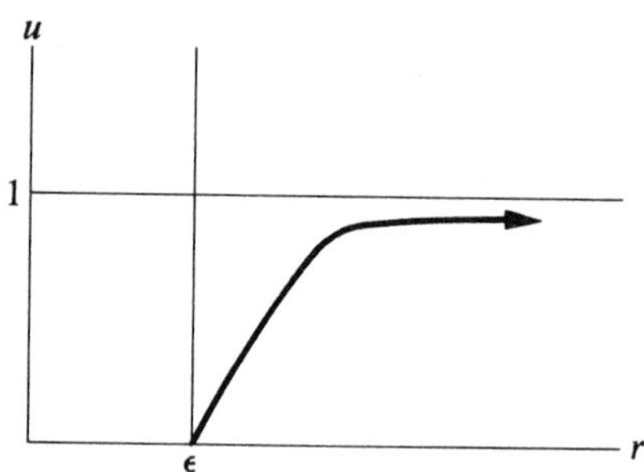

FIGURE 2.12 Stokes–model solution.

From this, the first term of the limiting solution connected with the outer limit ($\varepsilon \to 0$, r fixed) can be intuitively guessed as

$$u \to 1. \tag{2.7.34}$$

That is, the zero-size cold cylinder does not disturb the temperature field at all. Away from $r = \varepsilon$, one might expect only small perturbations to this solution. Thus, an outer expansion of the form

$$u(r; \varepsilon) = 1 + \mu_1(\varepsilon)h_1(r) + \mu_2(\varepsilon)h_2(r) + \cdots \tag{2.7.35}$$

is assumed, with the idea of satisfying the boundary conditions at infinity and matching to an inner expansion near $r = \varepsilon$. The first term of Equation (2.7.35) is not a good approximation in some neighborhood of $r = \varepsilon$, and the orders in the asymptotic sequence $\mu_i(\varepsilon)$ are not known *a priori*.

The equations satisfied by h_1 and h_2 are

$$\frac{d^2h_1}{dr^2} + \left(\frac{1}{r} + 1\right)\frac{dh_1}{dr} = 0, \tag{2.7.36}$$

$$\frac{d^2h_2}{dr^2} + \left(\frac{1}{r} + 1\right)\frac{dh_2}{dr} = \begin{cases} 0 & \text{if } \dfrac{\mu_1^2}{\mu_2} \to 0 \\ -h_1\dfrac{dh_1}{dr} & \text{if } \dfrac{\mu_1^2}{\mu_2} = O(1). \end{cases} \tag{2.7.37}$$

The boundary condition at infinity becomes

$$h_1(\infty) = 0, \qquad h_2(\infty) = 0. \tag{2.7.38}$$

An h_2 which is significantly different from h_1 appears only if $\mu_2 = \mu_1^2$, and we can assume that $\mu_2 = \mu_1^2$ with the option of inserting h_1 terms of various orders larger than μ_1^2.

The solutions for h_1 and h_2 satisfying the condition at infinity are easily found. Equation (2.7.36) can be written

$$\frac{d}{dr}\left(re^r\frac{dh_1}{dr}\right) = 0,$$

so that

$$h_1(r) = A_1 E_1(r), \tag{2.7.39}$$

where

$$E_1(r) = \int_r^\infty \frac{e^{-\rho}}{\rho}\,d\rho. \tag{2.7.40}†$$

Here E_1 is the well-known exponential integral and has the following expansion (useful for matching) as $r \to 0$.

$$E_1(r) = -\log r - \gamma + r + O(r^2), \qquad \gamma = \text{Euler's const} = .577215\ldots \tag{2.7.41}$$

Similarly, we have

$$\frac{d}{dr}\left(re^r\frac{dh_2}{dr}\right) = A_1^2 E_1(r). \tag{2.7.42}$$

Defining

$$E_n(r) = \int_r^\infty \frac{e^{-\rho}}{\rho^n}\,d\rho, \tag{2.7.43}$$

we can easily show that

$$\int_r^\infty E_n(\rho)\,d\rho = -rE_n(r) + E_{n-1}(r). \tag{2.7.44}$$

Hence, Equation (2.7.42) becomes

$$\frac{dh_2}{dr} = -A_1^2\frac{e^{-2r}}{r} + A_1^2 e^{-r}E_1(r) - A_2\frac{e^{-r}}{r}$$

† Sometimes denoted $-Ei(-r)$.

and

$$h_2(r) = A_2E_1(r) + A_1^2\{2E_1(2r) - e^{-r}E_1(r)\}. \tag{2.7.45}$$

Use has been made of the result

$$\int_r^\infty e^{-\rho}E_1(\rho)\,d\rho = e^{-r}E_1(r) - E_1(2r). \tag{2.7.46}$$

The expansion of $h_2(r)$ as $r \to 0$ is, thus,

$$h_2(r) = -(A_2 + A_1^2)\log r - (A_2 + A_1^2)\gamma - A_1^2\, 2\log 2 - A_1^2 r\log r$$
$$+ [A_2 + (3 - \gamma)A_1^2]r + O(r^2\log r). \tag{2.7.47}$$

Now an inner expansion has to be constructed that can take care of the boundary condition $u = 0$ on $r = \varepsilon$. A suitable inner coordinate is

$$r^* = \frac{r}{\varepsilon},$$

and the limit process has r^* fixed as $\varepsilon \to 0$. The form of this expansion is

$$u(r;\varepsilon) = \nu_0(\varepsilon)g_0(r^*) + \nu_1(\varepsilon)g_1(r^*) + \nu_2 g_2 + \cdots. \tag{2.7.48}$$

Again, choose $\nu_1 = \varepsilon\nu_0^2$ so that the equation for g_1 has a forcing term; other terms similar to g_0 but of order intermediate to ν_0, ν_1 can be inserted in the expansion if necessary. For g_0 we have

$$\frac{d^2g_0}{dr^{*2}} + \frac{1}{r^*}\frac{dg_0}{dr^*} = 0, \qquad g_0(1) = 0, \tag{2.7.49}$$

so that

$$g_0 = B_0\log r^*.$$

Then we have

$$\frac{d^2g_1}{dr^{*2}} + \frac{1}{r^*}\frac{dg_1}{dr^*} = -g_0\frac{dg_0}{dr^*} = -B_0^2\frac{\log r^*}{r^*}, \qquad g_1(1) = 0. \tag{2.7.50}$$

Integration of Equation (2.7.50) yields

$$g_1(r^*) = B_1\log r^* - B_0^2(r^*\log r^* - 2r^* + 2). \tag{2.7.51}$$

For matching the inner and outer expansions, we can consider an intermediate limit, denoted $\lim_\eta$,

$$\varepsilon \to 0, \qquad r_\eta = \frac{r}{\eta} \text{ fixed,}$$

where

$$\varepsilon \ll \eta \ll 1 \qquad \text{or} \qquad \eta/\varepsilon \to \infty, \quad \eta \to 0.$$

In the limit $r = \eta r_\eta \to 0$, $r^* = (\eta/\varepsilon)r_\eta \to \infty$. The first-order matching is

$$\lim_\eta \left[1 + \mu_1(\varepsilon)h_1(\eta r_\eta) + \cdots - v_0(\varepsilon)g_0\left(\frac{\eta}{\varepsilon}r_\eta\right)\cdots \right] = 0$$

or

$$\lim_\eta \left[1 + O(\mu_1 \log \eta) + \cdots - v_0(\varepsilon)B_0 \log\left(\frac{1}{\varepsilon}\right) + O(v_0 \log \eta) \right] = 0. \quad (2.7.52)$$

If we choose

$$v_0(\varepsilon) = \frac{1}{\log(1/\varepsilon)}, \qquad B_0 = 1, \qquad (2.7.53)$$

the first terms are matched since μ_1, $v_0 \to 0$. Matching to the next order demands that

$$\lim_\eta \frac{1}{\delta_1(\varepsilon)}\left[1 + \mu_1(\varepsilon)h_1(\eta r_\eta) + \mu_1^2(\varepsilon)h_2(\eta r_\eta) + \cdots - \frac{1}{\log(1/\varepsilon)}g_0\left(\frac{\eta}{\varepsilon}r_\eta\right) \right.$$
$$\left. - \frac{\varepsilon}{\log^2(1/\varepsilon)}g_1\left(\frac{\eta}{\varepsilon}r_\eta\right)\cdots \right] = 0 \quad (2.7.54)$$

for some suitable $\delta_1(\varepsilon) \to 0$. Writing out Equation (2.7.54), we have

$$\frac{1}{\delta_1}\Big\{1 + \mu_1(\varepsilon)[A_1(-\log \eta r_\eta) - A_1\gamma + A_1\eta r_\eta + O(\eta^2)]$$
$$+ \mu_1^2(\varepsilon)[-(A_1^2 + A_2)\log \eta r_\eta - (A_1^2 + A_2)\gamma - A_1^2\, 2\log 2 - A_1^2\eta r_\eta \log \eta r_\eta$$
$$+ [A_2 + 3 - \gamma]\eta r_\eta + \cdots] - \frac{1}{\log(1/\varepsilon)}\left[\log\frac{\eta r_\eta}{\varepsilon}\right] - \frac{\varepsilon}{\log^2(1/\varepsilon)}\left[B_1 \log\left(\frac{\eta r_\eta}{\varepsilon}\right)\right.$$
$$\left. - \left(\frac{\eta r_\eta}{\varepsilon}\log\frac{\eta r_\eta}{\varepsilon}\right) - 2\frac{\eta r_\eta}{\varepsilon} + 2\right]\cdots\Big\} \to 0. \quad (2.7.55)$$

The terms of order one are already matched. The terms ($\log \eta r_\eta$) can be matched by choosing

$$\mu_1(\varepsilon) = \frac{1}{\log(1/\varepsilon)}, \qquad A_1 = -1. \qquad (2.7.56)$$

A suitable δ_1 has $\mu_1/\delta_1 \to 0$. The next term to be matched (with a suitable function δ_2 replacing δ_1) is $-A_1\gamma\mu_1(\varepsilon)$ in the outer expansion, and we can see that there is no corresponding term in the inner expansion to match this term. Thus, a term

$$\nu^+(\varepsilon)g^+(r^*) = \nu^+(\varepsilon)B^+ \log r^*$$

has to be inserted between g_0, g_1 in the inner expansion with

$$\nu^+(\varepsilon) = \frac{1}{\log^2(1/\varepsilon)}.$$

Thus, omitting the already matched terms, we write Equation (2.7.55) with the intermediate term added in:

$$\frac{1}{\delta_2}\Bigg\{1 + \frac{1}{\log(1/\varepsilon)}[\gamma - \eta r_\eta + O(\eta^2)] + \frac{1}{\log^2(1/\varepsilon)}[-(1 + A_2)\log \eta r_\eta$$
$$-(1 + A_2)\gamma - 2\log 2 - \eta r_\eta \log \eta + \cdots] - \frac{B^+}{\log^2(1/\varepsilon)}\left[\log\frac{\eta r_\eta}{\varepsilon}\right]$$
$$-\frac{\varepsilon}{\log^2(1/\varepsilon)}\left[B_1 \log\frac{\eta r_\eta}{\varepsilon} - \left(\frac{\eta r_\eta}{\varepsilon}\log\frac{\eta r_\eta}{\varepsilon}\right) - 2\frac{\eta r_\eta}{\varepsilon} + 2\right] + \cdots\Bigg\} \to 0. \quad (2.7.57)$$

The γ term in h_1 is matched with the choice

$$B^+ = +\gamma. \quad (2.7.58)$$

This at the same time fixes A_2:

$$A_2 = \gamma - 1. \quad (2.7.59)$$

This procedure can evidently be continued, with the appropriate insertion of terms of intermediate order in the inner expansion. Summarizing the results, we see that the terms and orders of inner and outer expansions are as shown on page 67.

The term with g_1 is transcendentally small compared with the g_0 term; it does not enter the matching until further terms such as

$$[(-\gamma^2 + 2\log 2)/\log^2(1/\varepsilon)]$$

are matched by the introduction of an intermediate order $\nu^{++} = 1/[\log^3(1/\varepsilon)]$. This serves to determine A_3 associated with the log term of h_3, etc. The effect of the nonlinearity never appears in the inner expansion, but this effect is in the far field of the outer expansion. The outer expansion contains the inner expansion. In the analogy with viscous flow, the inner or Stokes flow is not adequate for finding the solution and evaluating the skin friction $(du/dr)_0$, but the outer or Oseen flow is.

In this example, we can give a proof that our guess of the first term in the

	ORDER	TERM
OUTER		
	1	1
	$\mu_1 = \dfrac{1}{\log(1/\varepsilon)}$	$h_1 = -E_1(r)$
	$\mu_2 = \dfrac{1}{\log^2(1/\varepsilon)}$	$h_2 = -(1-\gamma)E_1(r) + 2E_1(2r) - e^{-r}E_1(r)$
INNER		
	$\nu_0 = \dfrac{1}{\log(1/\varepsilon)}$	$g_0 = \log r^*$
	$\nu^+ = \dfrac{1}{\log^2(1/\varepsilon)}$	$g^+ = -\gamma \log r^*$
	$\nu_1 = \dfrac{\varepsilon}{\log^2(1/\varepsilon)}$	$g_1 = B_1 \log r^* - (r^* \log r^* - 2r^* + 2)$

outer expansion is really correct. We can write Equation (2.7.32) as

$$\frac{d}{dr}\left(r\frac{du}{dr}\right) + u\left(r\frac{du}{dr}\right) = 0, \qquad u(\varepsilon) = 0, \qquad u(\infty) = 1. \tag{2.7.60}$$

If we regard Equation (2.7.60) as a linear problem for $r(du/dr)$ and integrate, the problem can be formulated as an integral equation:

$$u(r;\varepsilon) = 1 - \frac{G(r;\varepsilon)}{G(\varepsilon;\varepsilon)}, \tag{2.7.61}$$

where

$$G(r;\varepsilon) = \int_r^\infty \frac{\exp[-\int_\varepsilon^\rho u(\sigma;\varepsilon)\,d\sigma}{\rho}\,d\rho.$$

Equation (2.7.60) is invariant under a group of transformations if $ru \sim$ const and can be reduced to the first-order system

$$\frac{dt}{ds} = \frac{t(1-s)}{t+s}, \qquad \frac{dr}{r} = \frac{dt}{t(1-s)}, \tag{2.7.62}$$

where

$$s = ru, \qquad t = r^2 \frac{du}{dr}.$$

From a study of the integral curves of Equation (2.7.62), we can conclude that the only possible solution of Equation (2.7.60) satisfying the boundary condition has $s > 0$, and hence $u \geq 0$. These phase-plane considerations also can be used to prove the existence of a unique solution. It follows from Equation (2.7.61) that

$$0 \leq u \leq 1, \qquad \varepsilon \leq r \leq \infty. \tag{2.7.63}$$

Thus, we have

$$G(\varepsilon;\varepsilon) \geq \int_\varepsilon^\infty \frac{e^{-(\rho-\varepsilon)}}{\rho}\,d\rho \geq \int_\varepsilon^\infty \frac{e^{-\rho}}{\rho}\,d\rho \qquad \text{or} \qquad G(\varepsilon;\varepsilon) \geq E_1(\varepsilon). \tag{2.7.64}$$

Now we can write

$$G(r;\varepsilon) = \int_r^{r_0} \frac{\exp[-\int_\varepsilon^\rho u(\rho;\varepsilon)\,d\rho}{\rho}\,d\rho + \int_{r_0}^\infty \frac{\exp[-\int_\varepsilon^\rho u(\rho;\varepsilon)\,d\rho}{\rho}\,d\rho.$$

Thus, we have

$$G(r;\varepsilon) \leq \log\frac{r_0}{r} + \frac{1}{r_0 u(r_0;\varepsilon)} \int_{r_0}^\infty u(r;\varepsilon)\exp\left[-\int_\varepsilon^\rho u(\rho;\varepsilon)\,d\rho\right]d\rho \tag{2.7.65}$$

if we use the fact that $u(r)$ is monotonic ($r > 0$). Integrating, we have

$$G(r;\varepsilon) \leq \log\frac{r_0}{r} + \frac{1}{r_0 u(r_0;\varepsilon)}\exp\left[-\int_\varepsilon^{r_0} u(\rho;\varepsilon)\,d\rho\right],$$

$$G(r;\varepsilon) \leq \log\frac{r_0}{r} + \frac{1}{r_0 u(r_0;\varepsilon)}.$$

Now, for any given δ and all $\varepsilon < \delta$, it follows that $u(r_0;\varepsilon) > u(r_0, \delta)$, so that

$$G(r;\varepsilon) \leq \log\frac{r_0}{r} + \frac{1}{r_0 u(r_0;\delta)}, \qquad \varepsilon < \delta. \tag{2.7.66}$$

Thus, in Equation (2.7.29) the outer limit $\varepsilon \to 0$, r fixed shows that

$$\frac{G(r;\varepsilon)}{G(\varepsilon;\varepsilon)} \leq \frac{1}{E_1(\varepsilon)}\left\{\log\frac{r_0}{r} + \frac{1}{r_0 u(r_0;\delta)}\right\} \to 0, \qquad \varepsilon \to 0. \tag{2.7.67}$$

The problem of finding the viscous, incompressible flow past a circular cylinder relies on considerations, such as these, although a rigorous proof has not been provided for that case. The considerations given above can actually be extended to demonstrate the overlapping of the two expansions used.

2.8 Higher-order example: beam string

In this section, an elementary example of a higher-order equation is constructed in order to show that the ideas of the previous sections have a natural and general validity.

The engineering theory of an elastic beam with tension which supports a given load distribution leads to the following differential equation, when it is assumed that the deflection W is small (linearized theory):

$$EI\frac{d^4W}{dX^4} - T\frac{d^2W}{dX^2} = P(X), \qquad 0 \le X \le L. \tag{2.8.1}$$

Here

E = constant modulus of elasticity,
I = constant moment of inertia of cross section about neutral axis,
T = constant external tension,
X = coordinate along beam,
W = deflection of neutral axis,
$P(X)$ = external load per length on the beam.

The derivation of an equation of this type from a more exact elastic theory is an example of the kind of approximation that is discussed in Chapter 5 of this book. In the engineering theory of bending, see for example Reference 2.8.1, a model is made for the deformation of the beam under load in which plane cross sections of the beam remain plane under load. The tension and compression forces due to bending which act along the beam are computed by Hooke's law from the stretching of the fibers; the neutral axis is unstressed. Adjacent sections exert a bending moment M on each other proportional to the beam curvature. For small deflections, we have

$$M(X) \doteq -EI\frac{d^2W}{dX^2}. \tag{2.8.2}$$

A vertical shear V at these sections produces a couple to balance the bending moment:

$$V = \frac{dM}{dX}. \tag{2.8.3}$$

The effect of this shear in supporting the external load is expressed in

Equation (2.8.1) by the fourth derivative term. The load is carried by the tension in the structure in the usual way in which a string or cable supports an external load. $[T(d^2W)/(dX^2)]$. When the deflection is known, the stresses of interest can be calculated.

Singular perturbation problems arise when the effect of bending rigidity is relatively small in comparison to the tension. In general, when a more complicated model of a physical phenomenon (for example, beam vs. string) is constructed, the order of the differential equations is raised. Correspondingly, the nature of the boundary conditions at the ends is more complicated; due to the higher order of the equations, more conditions are needed. For the string problem, for example, it is sufficient to prescribe the deflection. In a beam problem, the mode of support must also be given. The loss of a boundary condition in passage from the beam-string to the string implies the existence of a boundary layer near the support, a local region in which bending rigidity is important. A similar phenomenon can occur under a region of rapid change of the load, or near a concentrated load. Various types of boundary conditions can be used to represent the end of a beam of which the following are most common and important.

(1) Pin-end: no restoring moment M applied at the end, $d^2W/dX^2 = 0$; deflection prescribed, for example, $W = 0$.

(2) Built-in end: slope at end prescribed, for example, $dW/dX = 0$, deflection prescribed, for example, $W = 0$;

(3) Free end: no bending moment exerted on end $d^2W/dX^2 = 0$, no shear exerted on end $dW/dX = 0$.

Consider now the typical problem for a beam with built-in ends under the distributed load $P(X)$. The problem can be expressed in suitable dimensionless coordinates by measuring lengths in terms of L and using a characteristic load density $\mathscr{P}$, so that

$$P(X) = \mathscr{P}p(x), \qquad 0 \le x \le 1, \tag{2.8.4}$$

where $x = X/L$. The deflection is conveniently measured in terms of that characteristic of the string alone,

$$w(x) = \left(\frac{T}{\mathscr{P}L^2}\right)W(X), \tag{2.8.5}$$

and the resulting dimensionless equation and boundary conditions are

$$\varepsilon\frac{d^4w}{dx^4} - \frac{d^2w}{dx^2} = p(x), \qquad 0 \le x \le 1; \qquad w(0) = \frac{dw}{dx}(0) = w(1) = \frac{dw}{dx}(1) = 0. \tag{2.8.6}$$

The small parameter ε of the problem is

$$\varepsilon = \frac{EI}{TL^2} \tag{2.8.7}$$

and measures the relative importance of the bending rigidity in comparison to the tension.

Next we construct the inner and outer expansions. For the outer expansion ($x \to 0$, ε fixed), we expect the first term to be independent of ε, and we write

$$w(x;\varepsilon) = h_0(x) + \nu_1(\varepsilon)h_1(x) + \nu_2(\varepsilon)h_2(x) + \cdots. \tag{2.8.8}$$

The corresponding differential equations are

$$-\frac{d^2h_0}{dx^2} = p(x),$$

$$-\frac{d^2h_1}{dx^2} = \begin{cases} -\dfrac{d^4h_0}{dx^4} = p''(x) & \text{if } \dfrac{\nu_1}{\varepsilon} = 1, \\ 0 \quad \text{if } \dfrac{\nu_1}{\varepsilon} \to 0. \end{cases} \tag{2.8.9}$$

There are no boundary conditions for the h_i, but the constants of integration in the solutions must be obtained by matching with the boundary layers at each end. The solution for $h_0(x)$ is, thus,

$$h_0(x) = B_0 + A_0x - \int_0^x (x - \lambda)p(\lambda)\,d\lambda. \tag{2.8.10}$$

For purposes of matching, later it is useful to have the series expansions of $h_0(x)$ near $x = 0$ and $x = 1$.

NEAR $x = 0$

$$\begin{aligned} h_0(x) &= h_0(0) + xh_0'(0) + \frac{x^2}{2}h_0''(0) + \cdots \\ &= B_0 + A_0x - p(0)\frac{x^2}{2!} - p'(0)\frac{x^3}{3!} + O(x^4). \end{aligned} \tag{2.8.11}$$

NEAR $x = 1$

$$\begin{aligned} h_0(x) = B_0 + A_0 - \int_0^1 (1 - \lambda)p(\lambda)\,d\lambda + \left\{A_0 - \int_0^1 p(\lambda)\,d\lambda\right\}(x - 1) \\ -p(1)\frac{(x-1)^2}{2!} - p'(1)\frac{(x-1)^3}{3!} + O((x-1)^4). \end{aligned} \tag{2.8.12}$$

A suitable boundary-layer coordinate $\tilde{x}$ is chosen by the requirement that the bending and tension terms are of the same order of magnitude near $x = 0$:

$$\tilde{x} = x/\sqrt{\varepsilon}. \tag{2.8.13}$$

The corresponding asymptotic expansions near $x = 0$ is

$$w(x;\varepsilon) = \mu_0(\varepsilon)g_0(\tilde{x}) + \mu_1(\varepsilon)g_1(\tilde{x}) + \cdots. \tag{2.8.14}$$

Equation (2.8.6) thus becomes

$$\frac{1}{\varepsilon}\left\{\mu_0\frac{d^4g_0}{d\tilde{x}^4} + \mu_1\frac{d^4g_1}{d\tilde{x}^4} + \cdots\right\} - \frac{1}{\varepsilon}\left\{\mu_0\frac{dg_0}{d\tilde{x}^2} + \mu_1\frac{dg_1}{d\tilde{x}^2} + \cdots\right\}$$
$$= p(0) + \sqrt{\varepsilon}\,\tilde{x}p'(0) + \cdots. \tag{2.8.15}$$

Two possibilities arise: either $\mu_0/\varepsilon \to \infty$ or $\mu_0/\varepsilon = 1$. It can be shown that, in general, the second possibility does not allow matching, and thus only the first is considered here. The effect of the external load, then, does not appear in the first boundary-layer equation but enters at first only through the matching. Of course, it has to be verified that the assumption $\mu_0/\varepsilon \to \infty$ is correct after μ_0 is found from the matching. Thus, we have

$$O\left(\frac{\mu_0}{\varepsilon}\right): \qquad \frac{d^4g_0}{d\tilde{x}^4} - \frac{d^2g_0}{d\tilde{x}^2} = 0. \tag{2.8.16}$$

Both boundary conditions at $\tilde{x} = 0$ are to be satisfied by g_0:

$$\frac{dg_0}{d\tilde{x}} = g_0 = 0, \qquad \text{at} \quad \tilde{x} = 0. \tag{2.8.17}$$

Using the fact that exponential growth ($e^{\tilde{x}}$) cannot match as $\tilde{x} \to \infty$ and taking into account the boundary conditions, we obtain a solution with one arbitrary constant,

$$g_0(\tilde{x}) = C_0\{\tilde{x} - 1 + e^{-\tilde{x}}\}. \tag{2.8.18}$$

An intermediate limit suitable for matching near $\tilde{x} = 0$ is given by x_η fixed:

$$x_\eta = \frac{x}{\eta(\varepsilon)}, \qquad \eta \to 0, \qquad \frac{\eta}{\sqrt{\varepsilon}} \to \infty, \tag{2.8.19}$$

so that

$$\tilde{x} = \frac{\eta}{\sqrt{\varepsilon}}x_\eta \to \infty, \qquad x = \eta x_\eta \to 0. \tag{2.8.20}$$

Matching near $x = 0$ takes the form

$$\lim_{\substack{\varepsilon\to 0,\\ x_\eta \text{ fixed}}} \left\{ h_0(\eta x_\eta) + \nu_1(\varepsilon)h_1(\eta x_\eta) + \cdots - \mu_0(\varepsilon)g_0\left(\frac{\eta}{\sqrt{\varepsilon}}x_\eta\right) - \mu_1(\varepsilon)g_1\left(\frac{\eta x_\eta}{\sqrt{\varepsilon}}\right)\cdots \right\} = 0. \tag{2.8.21}$$

Using the expansion of Equations (2.8.11) and (2.8.18), we find that the first-order matching condition is

$$\lim\left\{ B_0 + A_0\eta x_\eta + \cdots - \mu_0(\varepsilon)C_0\left(\frac{\eta}{\sqrt{\varepsilon}}x_\eta - 1 + \exp\frac{-\eta x_\eta}{\sqrt{\varepsilon}}\right) + \cdots + \nu_1(\varepsilon)h_1(\eta x_\eta)\right\} = 0. \tag{2.8.22}$$

The term linear in x_η dominates g_0, so that matching is only possible if

$$B_0 = 0 \tag{2.8.23}$$

and

$$\mu_0 = \sqrt{\varepsilon}, \qquad A_0 = C_0. \tag{2.8.24}$$

This verifies the fact that $\mu_0/\varepsilon \to \infty$.

Another point can be noticed from Equation (2.8.22). The term $O(1)$ in g_0 can not be matched except by a suitable h_1. That is, we have $\nu_1(\varepsilon) = \sqrt{\varepsilon}$, and h_1 satisfies the equation of an unloaded string (cf. Equation 2.8.9):

$$d^2h_1/dx^2 = 0. \tag{2.8.25}$$

The solution is

$$h_1 = B_1 + A_1 x. \tag{2.8.26}$$

Thus, considering matching to the next order in Equation (2.8.22), we have

$$B_1 = -C_0. \tag{2.8.27}$$

The final determination of the unknown constants depends on the application of similar considerations at the other end of the beam. Summarizing, for the outer expansion we have thus far

$$w(X; \varepsilon) = h_0(x) + \sqrt{\varepsilon}h_1(x) + \cdots$$

where

$$h_0(x) = C_0 x - \int_0^x (x - \lambda)p(\lambda)\, d\lambda, \qquad h_1(x) = -C_0 + A_1 x. \tag{2.8.28}$$

The first approximation h_0 satisfies a zero-deflection boundary condition at $x = 0$ as might have been expected from physical consideration. Applying the same reasoning at $x = 1$, we find, for example, that

$$C_0 = \int_0^1 (1 - \lambda)p(\lambda)\, d\lambda = -M^{(1)}. \qquad (2.8.29)$$

Here $M^{(1)}$ represents the total moment of the applied load about $x = 1$. The result of Equation (2.8.29) is now verified by detailed matching, and the unknown constant A_1 is also found.

For the boundary layer near $x = 1$, the coordinate

$$x^+ = (x - 1)/\sqrt{\varepsilon} \qquad (2.8.30)$$

is used, and the boundary-layer expression is

$$w(x;\varepsilon) = \sqrt{\varepsilon} f_0(x^+) + \cdots. \qquad (2.8.31)$$

The equation for f_0 is the same as that for g_0, so that the solution satisfying the boundary condition at $x = 1$, $x^+ = 0$ is

$$f_0(x^+) = D_0\{x^+ + 1 - e^{x^+}\}. \qquad (2.8.32)$$

Exponential growth as $x^+ \to -\infty$ is ruled out near $X = 1$.

The intermediate limit near $x^+ = 1$ is defined in terms of X_ξ:

$$x_\xi = \frac{x - 1}{\xi(\varepsilon)} < 0, \qquad (2.8.33)$$

where

$$x = 1 + \xi x_\xi \to 1, \qquad x^+ = (\xi/\sqrt{\varepsilon})x_\xi \to -\infty .$$

The expansion of h_0 near $x = 1$ (Equation 2.8.12) is now

$$h_0(x) = C_0 + M^{(1)} + (C_0 - k)(x - 1) + \cdots, \qquad (2.8.34)$$

where

$$k = \int_0^1 p(\lambda)\, d\lambda = \text{total load on beam.}$$

The matching condition near $x = 1$ is, thus,

$$\lim_{\substack{\xi\to 0,\\ x_\xi \text{ fixed}}} \left\{C_0 + M^{(1)} + (C_0 - k)\xi x_\xi + \cdots + \sqrt{\varepsilon}(-C_0 + A_1 + A_1\xi x_\xi) + \cdots \right.$$
$$\left. - \sqrt{\varepsilon}D_0\left(\frac{\xi}{\sqrt{\varepsilon}}x_\xi + 1 - \exp(\xi x_\xi/\sqrt{\varepsilon}\right) + \cdots\right\} = 0. \qquad (2.8.35)$$

First-order matching shows that, indeed,

$$C_0 = -M^{(1)}$$

and

$$C_0 - k = D_0, \tag{2.8.36}$$

that is,

$$D_0 = \int_0^1 (1-\lambda)p\,d\lambda - \int_0^1 p\,d\lambda = -\int_0^1 \lambda p(\lambda)\,d\lambda = -M^{(0)}. \tag{2.8.37}$$

Further, the matching of the constant term in f_0 yields

$$A_1 = C_0 + D_0 = -[M^{(1)} + M^{(0)}]. \tag{2.8.38}$$

Thus, finally, the three expansions are fully determined to the orders considered.

$$w(X;\varepsilon) = -\sqrt{\varepsilon}M^{(1)}\{\tilde{x} - 1 + e^{-\tilde{x}}\} + \cdots \qquad \text{near} \quad x = 0,$$

$$w(X;\varepsilon) = -M^{(1)}x - \int_0^x (x-\lambda)p(\lambda)\,d\lambda + \sqrt{\varepsilon}\{M^{(1)} - (M^{(0)} + M^{(1)})x\} + \cdots 0$$

$$\text{away from the ends,} \tag{2.8.39}$$

$$w(X;\varepsilon) = -\sqrt{\varepsilon}M^{(0)}\{x^+ + 1 - e^{+x^+}\} + \cdots \qquad \text{near} \quad x = 1.$$

The uniformly valid approximation is constructed, as before, by adding together all three expansions and subtracting the common part, which has canceled out identically in the matching. Thus, we have

$$w_{\text{uv}} = -M^{(1)}x - \int_0^x (x-\lambda)p(\lambda)\,d\lambda$$

$$+\sqrt{\varepsilon}\{M^{(0)}e^{(x-1)/\sqrt{\varepsilon}} - M^{(1)}e^{-x/\sqrt{\varepsilon}} + M^{(1)} - (M^{(0)} + M^{(1)})x\} + O(\sqrt{\varepsilon}). \tag{2.8.40}$$

The uniformly valid expansion is again recognized as having the form of a composite expansion,

$$\sum \varepsilon^{n/2}\{h_n(x) + G_n(\tilde{x}) + F_n(x^+)\},$$

where the F_n and G_n decay exponentially.

From this expansion, the deflection curve, bending moment, and stresses are easily calculated. For example, the bending moment distribution near $x = 0$, proportioned to d^2w/dx^2, comes only from the boundary-layer term.

Near $x = 0$, the moment (and stress) decay exponentially:

$$M = -\frac{EI\mathscr{P}}{T}\frac{d^2w}{dx^2} = +\frac{M^{(1)}}{\sqrt{\varepsilon}}\frac{EI\mathscr{P}}{T}e^{-x/\sqrt{\varepsilon}} = M^{(1)}\sqrt{\frac{EI}{T}}L\mathscr{P}\exp\left(-X\sqrt{\frac{T}{EI}}\right). \tag{2.8.41}$$

Problem

In Reference 2.8.1 (pp. 277 ff), the deflection theory of suspension bridges is discussed, and the differential equation for the additional cable deflection $w(X)$ (or beam deflection) over that due to dead load is obtained. This equation is of the form studied in this Section,

$$EI\frac{d^4W}{dX^4} - (T + \tau)\frac{d^2W}{dX^2} = P - Q\frac{\tau}{T}, \qquad 0 \le x \le L,$$

where

T = dead load cable tension,
τ = increase in cable tension due to live load,
$Q(X)$ = dead load per length,
$P(X)$ = live load per length.

The increase of the main-cable tension depends on the stretching of the cable and is thus related to W. Assuming a linear elasticity for the cable (and small-cable slopes) we find that

$$\frac{TL_c}{E_cA_c}\tau = \int_0^L W(X)Q(X)\,dX,$$

where L_c, E_c, A_c are the original cable length, modulus of elasticity, and cross-section at area, respectively.

According to the usual boundary conditions, the truss (or beam) is considered pin-ended.

Using boundary-layer theory, calculate the deflection $W(X)$ due to a uniform dead load, Q = const, and a concentrated live load, $P = P_0S(X - L/2)$, at the center. Use either matched or composite expansions. Indicate what kind of problem must be solved to find the additional tension.

REFERENCES

2.8.1 T. VON KARMAN, and M. BIOT, *Mathematical Methods in Engineering*, New York: McGraw-Hill Book Co., 1940.

2.9 Extension theorem of S. Kaplun

In this Section, we give a brief discussion of the extension theorem first proposed by S. Kaplun as part of his basic study on the nature of asymptotic expansions and matching. Unfortunately, a large body of Kaplun's work was left unpublished at the time of his death, but P. A. Lagerstrom has taken the job of editing the manuscripts and preparing them for publication (Reference 2.9.1).

The theorem helps to explain the success of the matching procedure introduced in Section 2.7.2 and used subsequently. The idea is that if an asymptotic approximation is uniformly valid in an interval of a variable x, then it is uniformly valid in a wider interval depending on the parameter ε. The fact that the outer expansion contains the inner expansion in that problem is rather special, as the simple addition of a nonlinear term $(du/dr)^2$ to the equation shows. When this happens, recourse must be had to the more sophisticated matching procedure of Reference 2.9.1. An intermediate expansion, a solution of Stokes equations which is not a limit process expansion, is used. The success of this method depends on the ability to extend the domain of validity a little.

In order to prove the theorem, we assume the existence of a function $F(x;\varepsilon)$, for example the difference between some exact solution and its first (outer) approximation,

$$F(x;\varepsilon) = y(x;\varepsilon) - y_0(x;\varepsilon), \tag{2.9.1}$$

which is uniformly small as $\varepsilon \to 0$ for $x > 0$. Thus, we have the following statement of the theorem:

If $F(x;\varepsilon)$ exists such that

$$\lim_{\substack{\varepsilon\to 0,\\ x\,\text{fixed}}} F(x;\varepsilon) = 0 \qquad \text{for} \quad x > 0,$$

in particular uniformly in $x_0 \le x \le 1$ (any x_0), then there exists an interval $\sigma(\varepsilon) \le x \le 1$, $\sigma(\varepsilon) \to 0$, such that $F(x;\varepsilon) \to 0$ uniformly in this interval.

For a proof, first note the meaning of the hypothesis that given any δ, it is possible to find $\varepsilon = \varepsilon(\delta)$, independent of x for $x_0 \le x \le 1$, such that

$$|F(x;\varepsilon)| < \delta \qquad \text{for all} \quad \varepsilon < \varepsilon(\delta).$$

Thus, in particular, a decreasing sequence (δ_i), ε_i can be found with the following properties:

$$\text{all } \varepsilon \leq \varepsilon_1 |F(x;\varepsilon)| \leq \frac{1}{2} \qquad \text{for} \quad \frac{1}{2} \leq x \leq 1,$$

$$\varepsilon \leq \varepsilon_2 |F(x;\varepsilon)| \leq \frac{1}{2^2} \qquad \text{for} \quad \frac{1}{2^2} \leq x \leq 1,$$

$$\vdots$$

$$\varepsilon \leq \varepsilon_n |F(x;\varepsilon)| \leq \frac{1}{2^n} \qquad \text{for} \quad \frac{1}{2^n} \leq x \leq 1,$$

$$\vdots$$

Now construct a continuous function $\sigma(\varepsilon)$ such that at the points of the sequence ε_i we have

$$\sigma(\varepsilon_{i+1}) = 1/2^i,$$

and define $\sigma(\varepsilon)$ between the points by a smooth interpolation. Since, for any δ, there is an n such that

$$1/2^n \leq \delta < 1/2^{n-1},$$

there exists an ε_n such that for all $\varepsilon \leq \varepsilon_n$,

$$|F(x;\varepsilon)| \leq \frac{1}{2^n} \leq \delta \qquad \text{for} \quad \frac{1}{2^n} \leq x \leq 1.$$

Further, for all $m > n$,

$$|F(x;\varepsilon)| \leq \frac{1}{2^m} < \frac{1}{2^n} \leq \delta, \qquad \text{for} \quad \frac{1}{2^m} \leq x \leq 1.$$

Thus, the conclusion is that

$$F(x;\varepsilon) \to 0 \qquad \text{as} \quad \varepsilon \to 0 \quad \text{uniformly in} \quad \sigma(\varepsilon) \leq x \leq 1.$$

REFERENCES

2.9.1 Saul Kaplun, *Fluid Mechanics and Singular Perturbations*, edited by P. A. Lagerstrom, L. N. Howard, and C.-S. Liu, New York: Academic Press, 1967.

CHAPTER **3**

Two-variable Expansion Procedures

Various physical problems are characterized by the presence of a small force or disturbance which is active for a long time. The method outlined in this Chapter is one of several methods that have been devised in order to provide a systematic way of estimating this cumulative effect.

The main effort here is devoted to an exposition of the method by means of various examples. The aim of these methods is the construction of expansions uniformly valid over long time intervals.

A central feature of the method is the failure of expansions of the limit-process type, used so extensively in the previous chapter, to provide the proper description of the problem. In this case, an attempt must be made to construct an asymptotic expansion of the more general type discussed in Section 1.2 (cf. Equation 1.2.5). This means that the successive terms can not be calculated merely by the repeated applications of limits, and further that some new kind of reasoning must be introduced in order to provide rules for the calculations of these terms. Viewed in this light, the method of this chapter becomes a generalization of Poincaré's idea for the calculations of periodic motions of slightly nonlinear oscillations. Poincaré's method is sketched in the next Section.

A characteristic elementary example illustrating the kinds of problems which arise is the effect of a small damping on a linear oscillation. This example has been discussed previously in Section 2.1 (Equation 2.1.4). In that Section, an expression of the form

$$y(t;\varepsilon) = f_0(t) + \varepsilon f_1(t) + \cdots, \tag{3.1}$$

associated with the limit process ($\varepsilon \to 0$, t fixed), was constructed. It was shown that, due to the occurrence of a term (εt) in the expansion, the expansion is only initially valid. The errors can be made arbitrarily small in a fixed time interval $0 \leq t \leq t_1$. The physical phenomena described by this equation reflect themselves in the occurrence of two time scales, the period of free undamped oscillations $T = 2\pi/\omega_N$, and the damping time β/k. The more general asymptotic expansion mentioned above, when applied to this problem, makes explicit use of time variables based on these two time scales. This procedure can be extended to problems where several time (or space) scales are necessary. The idea is that both a long time scale, such as damping time, associated with slow changes of the system, and a fast time scale appear explicitly in the solution. In this simple example, the exact solution (Equation 2.1.9) shows that the damping of the oscillations is given by $e^{-\varepsilon t}$. The root of the difficulty in the limit-process expansion mentioned above is the expansion of this exponential function in power series. This procedure is, from the point of view of asymptotic expansions, only initially valid. Another difficulty which appears both in the Poincaré problem and in this elementary example is a shift in the frequency of the oscillatory part of the solution. The order of this change is manifest in the exact solution (Equation 2.1.9).

Any general method that is developed must, thus, be able to cope with both of these difficulties. In the case of damped or bounded oscillations, a typical behavior of the solution is that the oscillations on the short time scale are modulated on the long time scale. In general, the relation of the fast time variable t to the slow time variable $\tilde{t}$ (long scale) is given by

$$\tilde{t} = \phi(\varepsilon)t, \qquad \phi(\varepsilon) \to 0. \tag{3.2}$$

The general asymptotic form assumed here is, thus,

$$y(t;\varepsilon) \cong \nu_0(\varepsilon)F_0(t^*, \tilde{t}) + \nu_1(\varepsilon)F_1(t^*, \tilde{t}) + \cdots, \tag{3.3}$$

where the $\nu_i(\varepsilon)$ form an asymptotic sequence and where the fast variable t^* is related to t in a manner that expresses frequency changes. For example, we have

$$t^* = t\{1 + \mu_1(\varepsilon)\omega_1 + \mu_2(\varepsilon)\omega_2 + \cdots\}. \tag{3.4}$$

The $\mu_i(\varepsilon)$ are the members of an asymptotic sequence and the ω_i constants to be determined.

With this assumed form, the various equations for F_i become formally partial differential equations.† However, they are not solved as such, but

† In general, if we have $y = F(t, \tilde{t})$, then an ordinary differential equation for y becomes formally a partial differential equation for F. This partial differential equation can be exploited in various ways. For example, the results of limit-process expansions can be reproduced in other ways.

rather as a sequence of ordinary differential equations. Certain orders of magnitude, assumed uniformly valid, appear explicitly upon differentiation. For example, we have

$$\frac{dy}{dt}(t;\varepsilon) = \nu_0(\varepsilon)\left\{\frac{\partial F_0}{\partial t^*}[1 + \mu_1(\varepsilon)\omega_1 + \cdots] + \phi(\varepsilon)\frac{\partial F_0}{\partial \tilde{t}}\right\} + \nu_1(\varepsilon)\frac{\partial F_0}{\partial t^*} + \cdots. \tag{3.5}$$

Small changes are seen to occur on the slow scale $\partial/\partial\tilde{t}$. The orders of magnitude which occur explicitly are used to construct the sequence of equations to be solved.

But now the central idea is the formation of rules for the construction of the successive terms. The basic idea of the expansion of Equation (3.3) is that the first term be uniformly valid. The rules are a direct enforcement of this idea. Reasoning about the form of solution F_1 must be used to calculate F_0 and so on (Poincaré's idea). Further, since the first term F_0 is constructed to be uniformly valid ($0 \leq t < \infty$), it must contain the initially valid limit process expansion ($t, \tilde{t} \to 0$). Thus, the general expansion must satisfy the initial conditions. An extension of this idea involving matching appears in Section 3.7.

However, it is best to illustrate these ideas with the several examples of the following Sections.

A general discussion of the two-variable expansion procedure is given by Kevorkian in Reference 3.1, which is a revision of an earlier work by the same author. Many of the examples discussed here appear in that work, as do further problems in orbit theory. For many problems, the method applied here gives the same results as the averaging method of Krylov and Bogoliubov (Reference 3.2). The theoretical basis of the method of averaging is discussed in the book of Bogoliubov and Mitropolsky (Reference 3.3). Finally, the relationship between these two methods is studied in a paper by Morrison (Reference 3.4). For a wide class of problems, Morrison demonstrates the equivalence of both methods up to the second approximations. The averaging method is not discussed here.

Struble is another author who works out similar problems by more or less *ad hoc* arguments about the form of the solution (see Reference 3.5). Struble's results also agree exactly with those of the two-variable expansion procedure.

The main advantage of the two-variable procedure is the simplicity of the formalism. A second advantage is the explicit appearance of the variables which makes it possible to extend the ideas of matching to expansions of this type. A disadvantage of the method, however, is that the proper choice of fast and slow variables is not always obvious.

REFERENCES

3.1 J. KEVORKIAN, *The Two Variable Expansion Procedure for the Approximate Solution of Certain Non-Linear Differential Equations.* Seattle, University of Washington, 1965. To be published in *Proceedings of Yale University Summer Institution on Dynamical Astronomy.* This is a revised version of an earlier report of Douglas Aircraft Co. SM-42620 (1962). A brief version of the work of J. D. Cole and J. Kevorkian appears in *Nonlinear Differential Equations and Nonlinear Mechanics* (LaSalle and Lefachetz editors), New York: Academic Press, 1965.
3.2 N. M. KRYLOV, and N. N. BOGOLIUBOV, *Introduction to Nonlinear Mechanics,* Princeton: Princeton University Press, 1957.
3.3 N. N. BOGOLIUBOV, and Y. A. MITROPOLSKY, *Asymptotic Methods in the Theory of Non-linear Oscillations,* Hindustan Publishing Co., 1961.
3.4 J. A. MORRISON, Comparison of the Modified Method of Averaging and the Two Variable Expansion Procedure (to be published in S.I.A.M. review).
3.5 R. A. STRUBLE, Nonlinear Differential Equations, New York: McGraw-Hill Book Co., 1962.

3.1 Poincaré method: periodic solution

The Poincaré method is the modification of a straightforward asymptotic expansion necessary to obtain an approximation to the periodic solution of various nonlinear problems. Two essential ideas appear:

(1) The distortion of the time scale t, so that the frequency of the resulting periodic motion depends on the small parameter ε. For example, a very general form of this dependence is

$$t = \tau + \varepsilon f_1(\tau) + \varepsilon^2 f_2(\tau) + \cdots. \tag{3.1.1}$$

(2) Connected with Equation (3.1.1), the use of reasoning about the right-hand side of the *second* approximation equation, elimination of secular terms in the expansion, in order to fix f_1, f_2, etc., and sometimes to determine the *first* approximation solution.

EXAMPLE 3.1.1 Free oscillations of a mass on a nonlinear spring.
The equation of motion is

$$m\frac{d^2y}{d\tilde{t}^2} + k(y - \alpha y^3) = 0. \tag{3.1.2}$$

The perturbation is that of a weak nonlinearity in the restoring force due to the spring. For $\alpha = 0$, free linear oscillations exist with frequency $\omega_N = \sqrt{k/m}$ independent of the amplitude of the motion. Physical reasoning indicates that due to the variability of the spring force with amplitude, the period should depend on the amplitude—certainly for $\alpha > 0$, (soft spring) large amplitude motions are unbounded. It should be noted that Equation (3.1.2) is an approximation ($\alpha > 0$) to the motion of a simple pendulum. The exact solution of Equation (3.1.2) can also be expressed in terms of elliptic integrals, which can be used to check the perturbation procedure developed here. In order to identify the small parameter ε, write the equation in dimensionless coordinates (Y, t):

$$Y = y/A, \qquad t = \omega \bar{t}, \tag{3.1.3}$$

where A is a characteristic amplitude, that at zero velocity, say. Then Equation (3.1.2) reads

$$\frac{d^2 Y}{dt^2} + Y - \varepsilon Y^3 = 0 \tag{3.1.4}$$

where

$$\varepsilon = \alpha A^2. \tag{3.1.5}$$

Here ε is thus a measure of the nonlinear part of the spring force compared to the linear part.

The energy integral of Equation (3.1.4) giving the trajectories in the phase plane ($V = dY/dt$, Y) demonstrates the existence of periodic solutions. Thus, we have

$$\frac{V^2}{2} + \frac{Y^2}{2} - \varepsilon \frac{Y^4}{4} = \text{const} = E. \tag{3.1.6}$$

For $\varepsilon < 0$ ($\alpha < 0$), the spring is called hard, and all paths for different energies E are closed curves corresponding to periodic solutions. For $\varepsilon > 0$, there are closed paths in the neighborhood of the origin. These paths are separated from the large-amplitude divergent paths by the zero E trajectories passing through $V = 0$, $Y = \pm\sqrt{2/\varepsilon}$. Thus, for small ε positive or negative, there are always periodic solutions.

Consider first the attempt to calculate the effect of the nonlinearity on the linear periodic solution by a straightforward expansion in powers of ε†:

$$Y(t;\varepsilon) = h_0(t) + \varepsilon h_1(t) + \cdots. \tag{3.1.7}$$

Thus, we have

$$\frac{d^2 h_0}{dt^2} + h_0 = 0, \tag{3.1.8}$$

† This expansion is actually generated by the limit process $\varepsilon \to 0$, t fixed. A series in ε is evidently necessary if any corrections at all are to be found.

$$\frac{d^2h_1}{dt^2} + h_1 = h_0^3. \tag{3.1.9}$$

The first-approximation solution can be chosen as

$$h_0(t) = \cos t, \tag{3.1.10}$$

since both the amplitude A and the time origin are arbitrary. Now, the right-hand side of the correction equation (Equation 3.1.9) is periodic with the same period as the natural free period of Equation (3.1.9). That is, resonance terms growing with t can be expected in the solution of Equation (3.1.9). The representation is not suitable for finding an approximation to a periodic solution. Explicitly, we have

$$\cos^3 t = \frac{3}{4}\cos t + \frac{1}{4}\cos 3t, \tag{3.1.11}$$

so that

$$h_1(t) = \tfrac{1}{32}\cos 3t + \tfrac{3}{8}t\sin t + A_1\cos t + B_1\sin t. \tag{3.1.12}$$

The occurrence of the secular term $\varepsilon t \sin t$ in the representation of Equation (3.1.7) shows that this expansion is asymptotically valid only for a finite time; it is an *initially* valid expansion. As such, it could be used as an approximation for a finite time for an initial-value problem $Y(0) = 1$, $dY/dt(0) = 0$, but could not be carried sufficiently far to give information about the period.

The essential feature omitted from the assumed representation of Equation (3.1.7) is the dependence of period on amplitude. In dimensionless variables, this can be expressed by Equation (3.1.1), so that a solution periodic in τ has a period in t which depends on ε. The form is chosen so that $\tau = t$ for $\varepsilon \equiv 0$. Thus, a new expansion is assumed:†

$$Y(t;\varepsilon) \cong Y_0(\tau) + \varepsilon Y_1(\tau) + \cdots, \tag{3.1.13}$$

where the functions $f_1(\tau)$, $f_2(\tau)$ are to be found. Note that we have

$$\begin{aligned}\frac{dY}{dt} &= \frac{dY_0}{d\tau}\frac{1}{1+\varepsilon(df_1/d\tau)+\cdots} + \varepsilon\frac{dY_1}{d\tau}\frac{1}{1+\varepsilon(df_1/d\tau)-\cdots} \\ &= \left(1 - \varepsilon\frac{df_1}{d\tau} + \cdots\right)\frac{dY_0}{d\tau} + \varepsilon\frac{dY_1}{d\tau} + \cdots\end{aligned} \tag{3.1.14}$$

and

$$\frac{d^2Y}{dt^2} = \left(1 - 2\varepsilon\frac{df_1}{d\tau} + \cdots\right)\frac{d^2Y_0}{d\tau^2} - \varepsilon\frac{d^2f_1}{d\tau^2}\frac{dY_0}{d\tau} + \varepsilon\frac{d^2Y_1}{d\tau^2}. \tag{3.1.15}$$

---

* The associated limit process has $\varepsilon \to 0$, τ fixed.

Thus, we have

$$\frac{d^2Y_0}{d\tau^2} + Y_0 = 0, \tag{3.1.16}$$

$$\frac{d^2Y_1}{d\tau^2} + Y_1 = Y_0^3 + 2\frac{df_1}{d\tau}\frac{d^2Y_0}{d\tau^2} + \frac{d^2f_1}{d\tau^2}\frac{dY_0}{d\tau}. \tag{3.1.17}$$

The sequence of approximating equations again has the appearance of forced linear oscillators. Choosing

$$Y_0 = \cos\tau, \tag{3.1.18}$$

we find that the right-hand side of Equation (3.1.17) is

$$\cos^3\tau - 2\frac{df_1}{d\tau}\cos\tau - \frac{d^2f_1}{d\tau^2}\sin\tau,$$

and it again has the same period as the free oscillations of Equation (3.1.17) unless $f_1(\tau)$ can be chosen to eliminate these terms. Using Equation (3.1.11), we can write Equation (3.1.17) as

$$\frac{d^2Y_1}{d\tau^2} + Y_1 = \frac{3}{4}\cos\tau + \frac{1}{4}\cos 3\tau - 2\frac{df_1}{d\tau}\cos\tau - \frac{d^2f_1}{d\tau^2}\sin\tau. \tag{3.1.19}$$

A periodic solution of Equation (3.1.19)† can be found only if the ($\sin\tau$, $\cos\tau$) terms on right-hand side vanish, and this condition serves to determine $f_1(\tau)$. Thus, we have

$$\sin\tau\frac{d^2f_1}{d\tau^2} + 2\cos\tau\frac{df_1}{d\tau} = \frac{3}{4}\cos\tau,$$
$$\frac{d}{d\tau}\left(\sin^2\tau\frac{df_1}{d\tau}\right) = \frac{3}{4}\sin\tau\cos\tau, \qquad \sin^2\tau\frac{df_1}{d\tau} = \frac{3}{8}\sin^2\tau + C_1. \tag{3.1.20}$$

In order that the (t, τ) transformation be regular, it is necessary that $C_1 = 0$ and that

$$f_1(\tau) = \tfrac{3}{8}\tau. \tag{3.1.21}$$

Thus, we have

$$Y(t;\varepsilon) \cong \cos t(1 - \tfrac{3}{8}\varepsilon) + \cdots, \tag{3.1.22}$$

which clearly shows the dependence of period on amplitude, as well as the

†The only uniformly bounded solution; terms growing with τ must be ruled out, so that Y_0 is uniformly good.

fact that the motion is simple harmonic to this order. Higher harmonics appear in Y_1, and f_2 is found from similar considerations applied to the equation for Y_2, and so on.

EXAMPLE 3.1.2 Limit cycle of the van der Pol oscillator for small nonlinearity.

If we take a mechanical model of a mass-spring with both positive and negative damping, the equation of motion can be written as

$$m\frac{d^2y}{d\bar{t}^2} - \beta\frac{dy}{d\bar{t}} + \frac{\alpha}{3}\left(\frac{dy}{d\bar{t}}\right)^3 + ky = 0. \tag{3.1.23}$$

Phase-plane arguments show that a limit cycle exists to which all motions tend irrespective of initial conditions. This limit cycle is a periodic solution of Equation (3.1.23). If the nonlinearity is weak, the amplitude must adjust itself so that all damping is small and the motion is close to a free linear motion of frequency $\omega_N = \sqrt{k/m}$. This idea is verified by introducing dimensionless variables

$$Y = y/A, \qquad t = \omega\bar{t}. \tag{3.1.24}$$

For a suitable choice of the characteristic amplitude A, Equation (3.1.23) reads

$$\frac{d^2Y}{dt^2} - \varepsilon\left\{\frac{dY}{dt} - \frac{1}{3}\left(\frac{dY}{dt}\right)^3\right\} + Y = 0. \tag{3.1.25}$$

Thus, we have

$$\beta\omega/k = \varepsilon = (\alpha\omega^3/k)A^2. \tag{3.1.26}$$

The periodic solution is evidently close to a free linear motion, but it might again be expected that the period depends on amplitude. Thus, a general asymptotic expansion of the form

$$Y(t;\varepsilon) \cong Y_0(\tau) + \varepsilon Y_1(\tau) + \cdots, \tag{3.1.27}$$

$$t \cong \tau + \varepsilon f_1(\tau) + \cdots \tag{3.1.28}$$

is assumed. Now the successive approximate equations are

$$\frac{d^2Y_0}{d\tau^2} + Y_0 = 0, \tag{3.1.29}$$

$$\frac{d^2Y_1}{d\tau^2} + Y_1 = \frac{dY_0}{d\tau} - \frac{1}{3}\left(\frac{dY_0}{d\tau}\right)^3 + 2\frac{df_1}{d\tau}\frac{d^2Y_0}{d\tau^2} + \frac{d^2f_1}{d\tau^2}\frac{dY_0}{d\tau}, \tag{3.1.30}$$

$$\vdots$$

The first solution is again chosen:

$$Y_0 = A_0 \cos \tau.$$

The argument is the same as before: The right-hand side of Equation (3.1.30) must be adjusted so that no secular terms appear in the answer, but now both A_0 and $f_1(\tau)$ are at our disposal. Using the identity

$$\sin^3 \tau = \tfrac{3}{4} \sin \tau - \tfrac{1}{4} \sin 3\tau,$$

we find the right-hand side of Equation (3.1.30):

$$\left(\frac{A_0^3}{4} - A_0 - A_0 \frac{d^2 f_1}{d\tau^2}\right) \sin \tau - 2A_0 \frac{df_1}{d\tau} \cos \tau - \frac{A_0^3}{12} \sin 3\tau.$$

Thus, the elimination of secular terms is achieved by

$$\begin{aligned} \sin \tau \frac{d^2 f_1}{d\tau^2} + 2 \cos \tau \frac{df_1}{d\tau} &= \left(\frac{A_0^2}{4} - 1\right) \sin \tau, \\ \frac{d}{d\tau}\left(\sin^2 \tau \frac{df_1}{d\tau}\right) &= \left(\frac{A_0^2}{4} - 1\right) \sin^2 \tau, \qquad (3.1.31) \\ \sin^2 \tau \frac{df_1}{d\tau} &= C_1 + \left(\frac{A_0^2}{4} - 1\right)\left(\frac{\tau}{2} - \frac{1}{4} \sin^2 \tau\right). \end{aligned}$$

For a regular (t, τ) transformation, C_1 must be chosen zero and

$$A_0 = 2, \qquad (3.1.32)$$

which means that $f_1 = 0$. Thus, there is no frequency shift to first-order, but the *amplitude* of the simple harmonic oscillation is fixed by Equation (3.1.32). In physical variables, the first approximation to the limit cycle is

$$y(\bar{t}) \cong \sqrt{\frac{\beta}{\alpha}} \frac{1}{\omega} \cos(\omega \bar{t}) + O\left(\frac{\beta^{3/2}}{k\alpha}\right). \qquad (3.1.33)$$

This procedure also can be carried to higher orders.

In the next Section, details are given indicating the generalization of this method for the characteristic elementary example mentioned in the beginning of this Chapter. In the two examples just presented, it has been shown the frequency shift to be $f_1 \sim \tau$, and in the following Sections, it is assumed that $f_1, f_2, \ldots \sim \tau$. This turns out to be adequate for all examples considered.

3.2 Linear oscillator with small damping

Using a time scale made dimensionless with the natural frequency of free oscillations (cf. Section 2.1), we can write the equation of motion for the linear oscillator with small damping:

$$\frac{d^2y}{dt^2} + 2\varepsilon\frac{dy}{dt} + y = 0. \tag{3.2.1}$$

Some typical initial conditions independent of ε are

$$y(0) = 0, \qquad \frac{dy}{dt}(0) = 1, \tag{3.2.2}$$

where

$$\varepsilon = \frac{\beta}{2\sqrt{km}}, \qquad = \frac{1}{2}\frac{\beta}{k}\omega_N$$

is essentially the small ratio of damping time to period of linear oscillations. For this example, it is plausible that only powers of ε enter, so that we assume a general asymptotic expansion of the form of Equation (3.2.3). The expansion is to be constructed in such a way that it is uniformly valid

$$y(t;\varepsilon) \cong F_0(t^*, \tilde{t}) + \varepsilon F_1(t^*, \tilde{t}) + \varepsilon^2 F_2(t^*, \tilde{t}) + \cdots \tag{3.2.3}$$

with

$$\tilde{t} = \varepsilon t, \qquad t^* = t\{1 + \varepsilon^2\omega_2 + \cdots\}.$$

The term $\varepsilon\omega_1$ is omitted from t^*, since εt should always appear explicitly as $\tilde{t}$. Thus, we have

$$\frac{dy}{dt}(t;\varepsilon) \cong \frac{\partial F_0}{\partial t^*}[1 + \varepsilon^2\omega_2 + \cdots] + \varepsilon\frac{\partial F_0}{\partial \tilde{t}} + \varepsilon\frac{\partial F_1}{\partial t^*} + \varepsilon^2\frac{\partial F_1}{\partial \tilde{t}} + \varepsilon^2\frac{\partial F_2}{\partial t^*} + \cdots, \tag{3.2.4}$$

$$\frac{d^2y}{dt^2}(t;\varepsilon) \cong \frac{\partial^2 F_0}{\partial t^{*2}}[1 + 2\varepsilon^2\omega_2 + \cdots] + 2\varepsilon\frac{\partial^2 F_0}{\partial t^*\,\partial \tilde{t}} + \varepsilon^2\frac{\partial^2 F_0}{\partial \tilde{t}^2} + \varepsilon\frac{\partial^2 F_1}{\partial t^{*2}} + 2\varepsilon^2\frac{\partial^2 F_1}{\partial t^*\,\partial \tilde{t}} + \varepsilon^2\frac{\partial^2 F_2}{\partial t^{*2}} + \cdots. \tag{3.2.5}$$

Thus the sequence of equations approximating Equation (3.2.1) is

$$\frac{\partial^2 F_0}{\partial t^{*2}} + F_0 = 0, \tag{3.2.6}$$

$$\frac{\partial^2 F_1}{\partial t^{*2}} + F_1 = -2\frac{\partial^2 F_0}{\partial t^*\,\partial \tilde{t}} - 2\frac{\partial F_0}{\partial t^*}, \tag{3.2.7}$$

$$\frac{\partial^2 F_2}{\partial t^{*2}} + F_2 = -2\omega_2\frac{\partial^2 F_0}{\partial t^{*2}} - \frac{\partial^2 F_0}{\partial \tilde{t}^2} - 2\frac{\partial^2 F_1}{\partial t^*\,\partial \tilde{t}} - 2\frac{\partial F_0}{\partial \tilde{t}} - 2\frac{\partial F_1}{\partial t^*}. \tag{3.2.8}$$

The first of these is the equation for the free linear oscillation, while the remainder have the appearance of forced linear oscillations. However, since $F_0 = F_0(t^*, \tilde{t})$, the free linear oscillations which are the solutions to Equation (3.2.6) have the possibility of being slowly modulated. Thus, we have

$$F_0(t^*; \tilde{t}) = A_0(\tilde{t}) \cos t^* + B_0(\tilde{t}) \sin t^*. \tag{3.2.9}$$

The initial conditions, $y = 0$, $dy/dt = 1$, become, from Equations (3.2.3) and (3.2.4),

$$F_0(0, 0) = 0, \qquad \frac{\partial F_0}{\partial t^*}(0, 0) = 1, \tag{3.2.10}$$

$$F_1(0, 0) = 0, \qquad \frac{\partial F_0}{\partial \tilde{t}}(0, 0) + \frac{\partial F_1}{\partial t^*}(0, 0) = 0, \tag{3.2.11}$$

$$F_2(0, 0) = 0, \qquad \frac{\partial F_1}{\partial \tilde{t}}(0, 0) + \frac{\partial F_2}{\partial t^*}(0, 0) + \omega_2 \frac{\partial F_0}{\partial t^*}(0, 0) = 0. \tag{3.2.12}$$

Equation (3.2.10) yields initial conditions for $A_0(\tilde{t})$ and $B_0(\tilde{t})$:

$$A_0(0) = 0, \qquad B_0(0) = 1. \tag{3.2.13}$$

Nothing more can be found out about A_0 and B_0 without considering the equation for F_1, the same idea as used before,

$$\frac{\partial^2 F_1}{\partial t^{*2}} + F_1 = -2\left\{-\frac{dA_0}{d\tilde{t}} \sin t^* + \frac{dB_0}{d\tilde{t}} \cos t^*\right\} - 2\{-A_0 \sin t^* + B_0 \cos t^*\}. \tag{3.2.14}$$

The argument to be used now parallels that of the preceding Section. For a uniformly valid first approximation, no unbounded terms of the form

$$t^*\begin{Bmatrix} \sin t^* \\ \cos t^* \end{Bmatrix}$$

can be permitted in the solution—all such growth and decay is assumed slow and is to be accounted for in the $\tilde{t}$ variable. In another way, εt^* is not allowed to appear explicitly in the expansion since this is essentially $\tilde{t}$. Now, $A_0(\tilde{t})$ and $B_0(\tilde{t})$ must be chosen so that all the resonance-producing terms on the right-hand side of Equation (3.2.14) disappear. Thus, we have

$$\frac{dA_0}{d\tilde{t}} + A_0 = 0, \tag{3.2.15}$$

$$\frac{dB_0}{d\tilde{t}} + B_0 = 0. \tag{3.2.16}$$

Taking account of the initial conditions of Equation (3.2.13), we find that

$$A_0(\tilde{t}) = 0, \qquad B_0(\tilde{t}) = e^{-\tilde{t}}. \tag{3.2.17}$$

The uniformly valid expansion thus far is

$$y(t\,;\varepsilon) \cong e^{-\tilde{t}} \sin t^* + \varepsilon\{A_1(\tilde{t}) \cos t^* + B_1(\tilde{t}) \sin t^*\} + \cdots. \tag{3.2.18}$$

The first term of Equation (3.2.18) is seen to be a close approximation to the exact solution:

$$y(t\,;\varepsilon) = \frac{e^{-\varepsilon t} \sin \sqrt{1 - \varepsilon^2}\, t}{\sqrt{1 - \varepsilon^2}}. \tag{3.2.19}$$

Now, $A_1(\tilde{t})$, $B_1(\tilde{t})$, and the frequency shift ω_2 are to be found from similar considerations applied to the equation for $F_2(t^*, \tilde{t})$, Equation (3.2.8). Thus far, we have

$$F_0(t^*, \tilde{t}) = e^{-\tilde{t}} \sin t^*, \qquad F_1(t^*, \tilde{t}) = A_1(\tilde{t}) \cos t^* + B_1(\tilde{t}) \sin t^*,$$

and

$$\frac{\partial^2 F_2}{\partial t^{*2}} + F_2 = -2\omega_2(-e^{-\tilde{t}} \sin t^*) - e^{-\tilde{t}} \sin t^* - 2\left\{ -\frac{dA_1}{d\tilde{t}} \sin t^* + \frac{dB_1}{d\tilde{t}} \cos t^* \right\}$$

$$- 2\{-e^{-\tilde{t}} \sin t^*\} - 2\{-A_1(\tilde{t}) \sin t^* + B_1(\tilde{t}) \cos t^*\}. \tag{3.2.20}$$

First, repeating the argument that resonance-producing terms must vanish from the right-hand side of Equation (3.2.20), we find that

$$2\frac{dA_1}{d\tilde{t}} + 2A_1 + (2\omega_2 + 1)e^{-\tilde{t}} = 0, \tag{3.2.21}$$

$$2\frac{dB_1}{d\tilde{t}} + 2B_1 = 0. \tag{3.2.22}$$

The initial conditions for these equations follow from Equation (3.2.11):

$$A_1(0) = 0, \qquad B_1(0) = 0. \tag{3.2.23}$$

Now, unless the nonhomogeneous term of Equation (3.2.21) also vanishes, terms of the form $\tilde{t}e^{-\tilde{t}}$ appear in A_1. The occurrence of terms like these in the expansion again would make the expansion nonuniformly valid, now with respect to the variable $\tilde{t}$. Mathematically speaking, a boundedness condition $|y| < Ce^{-\tilde{t}}$ can be imposed on the solution. The frequency shift

ω_2 is thus found to be

$$\omega_2 = -\tfrac{1}{2} \tag{3.2.24}$$

and the amplitudes

$$A_1(\tilde{t}) = B_1(\tilde{t}) = 0. \tag{3.2.25}$$

All the necessary reasoning has now been explained to carry the solution to any order and, in fact, to solve a wide variety of even nonlinear problems. For this problem, the result

$$y(t; \varepsilon) \cong e^{-\tilde{t}} \sin(1 - \tfrac{1}{2}\varepsilon^2)t + O(\varepsilon^2) \tag{3.2.26}$$

has been found, and it is seen to be in precise accord with the exact solution, Equation (3.2.19).

Next we proceed to several weakly nonlinear examples of damped and bounded oscillations.

3.3 Oscillator with cubic damping

In suitable dimensionless variables, an oscillator with cubic damping can be represented by

$$\frac{d^2y}{dt^2} + \varepsilon\left(\frac{dy}{dt}\right)^3 + y = 0. \tag{3.3.1}$$

A uniformly valid approximation $0 \leq t < \infty$ is desired. It is sufficient to consider the special initial conditions

$$y(0) = 0, \qquad \frac{dy}{dt}(0) = 1, \tag{3.3.2}$$

although the general case is also easily handled. Since only the first term is considered, the frequency variation ω_2 is ignored, and the expansion is written

$$y(t; \varepsilon) \cong F_0(t, \tilde{t}) + \varepsilon F_1(t, \tilde{t}) + \cdots. \tag{3.3.3}$$

Thus, the approximate equations are

$$\frac{\partial^2 F_0}{\partial t^2} + F_0 = 0, \tag{3.3.4}$$

$$\frac{\partial^2 F_1}{\partial t^2} + F_1 = -2\frac{\partial^2 F_0}{\partial t\, \partial \tilde{t}} - \left(\frac{\partial F_0}{\partial t}\right)^3. \tag{3.3.5}$$

The basic solution is again

$$F_0(t, \tilde{t}) = A_0(\tilde{t}) \cos t + B_0(\tilde{t}) \sin t. \tag{3.3.6}$$

Now, using the identities

$$\begin{aligned} \sin^3 t &= \tfrac{3}{4} \sin t - \tfrac{1}{4} \sin 3t, \\ \sin^2 t \cos t &= \tfrac{1}{4} \cos t - \tfrac{1}{4} \cos 3t, \\ \sin t \cos^2 t &= \tfrac{1}{4} \sin t + \tfrac{1}{4} \sin 3t, \\ \cos^3 t &= \tfrac{3}{4} \cos t + \tfrac{1}{4} \cos 3t, \end{aligned} \tag{3.3.7}$$

we find the differential equations for A_0, B_0 from the requirement that $\sin t$ and $\cos t$ do not appear on the right-hand side of Equation (3.3.5):

$$\frac{dA_0}{d\tilde{t}} + \frac{3}{8} A_0(A_0^2 + B_0^2) = 0, \tag{3.3.8}$$

$$\frac{dB_0}{d\tilde{t}} + \frac{3}{8} B_0(A_0^2 + B_0^2) = 0. \tag{3.3.9}$$

For the special initial conditions,† Equation (3.3.2), we have

$$A_0(0) = 0, \qquad B_0(0) = 1. \tag{3.3.10}$$

Thus, it follows that

$$A_0(\tilde{t}) \equiv 0 \tag{3.3.11}$$

and

$$\frac{dB_0}{d\tilde{t}} + \frac{3}{8} B_0^3 = 0. \tag{3.3.12}$$

Integration yields the result

$$B_0(\tilde{t}) = \frac{1}{\sqrt{1 + (3\tilde{t}/4)}}. \tag{3.3.13}$$

The first term of the uniformly valid solution is

$$y(t; \varepsilon) \cong \frac{1}{\sqrt{1 + (3\tilde{t}/4)}} \sin t + O(\varepsilon). \tag{3.3.14}$$

The solution is seen to decay algebraically because of the relatively weaker damping than that in the linear case.

† This system is easily solved, in general, by constructing the equation for $R = A_0^2 + B_0^2$.

3.4 Approach to limit cycle of van der Pol oscillator

Here we study the generalization of the Problem in Section 3.1.

Using the notation of Section 3.1, the equation of the van der Pol oscillator is

$$\frac{d^2Y}{dt^2} - \varepsilon\left\{\left(\frac{dY}{dt}\right) - \frac{1}{3}\left(\frac{dY}{dt}\right)^3\right\} + Y = 0. \tag{3.4.1}$$

The expansion (Equation 3.3.3) is again used to obtain the first term, the solution (Equation 3.3.6) is valid, and the equation for F_1 is

$$\frac{\partial^2 F_1}{\partial t^2} + F_1 = -2\frac{\partial^2 F_0}{\partial t\,\partial \tilde{t}} - \frac{1}{3}\left(\frac{\partial F_0}{\partial t}\right)^3 + \frac{\partial F_0}{\partial t}. \tag{3.4.2}$$

The last term and the factor $\frac{1}{3}$ modify Equations (3.3.8, 3.3.9) slightly to produce

$$2\frac{dA_0}{d\tilde{t}} + \frac{1}{4}A_0(A_0^2 + B_0^2) - A_0 = 0, \tag{3.4.3}$$

$$2\frac{dB_0}{d\tilde{t}} + \frac{1}{4}B_0(A_0^2 + B_0^2) - B_0 = 0. \tag{3.4.4}$$

Multiplication of Equations (3.4.3) and (3.4.4) by A_0 and B_0, respectively, and addition yield the equation for $R(\tilde{t})$:

$$R = A_0^2 + B_0^2, \qquad \frac{dR}{d\tilde{t}} = \frac{1}{4}R(R-4). \tag{3.4.5}$$

Integration yields the result

$$R(\tilde{t}) = \frac{4}{1 - ke^{-\tilde{t}}}, \qquad k = \text{const}, \tag{3.4.6}$$

so that

$$A_0(\tilde{t}) = \frac{2\lambda}{\sqrt{1 - ke^{-\tilde{t}}}}, \qquad B_0(\tilde{t}) = \frac{2\sqrt{1-\lambda^2}}{\sqrt{1 - ke^{-\tilde{t}}}}, \qquad \lambda = \text{const}. \tag{3.4.7}$$

This result clearly shows the approach to the limit cycle of amplitude 2, found in the last Section, independent now of the initial condition. The approach is exponential over the long time scale. For example, if

$$A_0(0) = 0, \qquad B_0(0) = C, \tag{3.4.8}$$

then

$$y(t;\varepsilon) \cong \frac{2C}{\sqrt{C^2 - (C^2 - 4)e^{-\tilde{t}}}}\sin t + O(\varepsilon). \tag{3.4.9}$$

If the solution starts on the limit cycle ($C = 2$), it, of course, remains there. The frequency shift is also $O(\varepsilon^2)$ in this example and can be calculated at the same time that A_1 and B_1 are found.

Problem

Calculate the second term $F_1(t^*, \tilde{t})$ for the examples of the two preceding Sections. In particular, make specific the boundedness requirements used in the solution in order to obtain a uniformly valid approximation.

3.5 Mathieu equation

Another class of problems (involving bounded and even unstable oscillations) to which the two-variable procedure can be applied is exemplified by the Mathieu equation:

$$\frac{d^2y}{dt^2} + (\delta + \varepsilon \cos t)y = 0. \tag{3.5.1}$$

The general theory of differential equations with periodic coefficients (Floquet theory) yields the fundamental result that the (δ, ε)-plane is divided into regions of "stability"† and instability separated by transition curves (cf. Figure 3.1). The general theory shows that along the transition curves, periodic solutions of period 2π or 4π exist (as well as linearly increasing solutions).

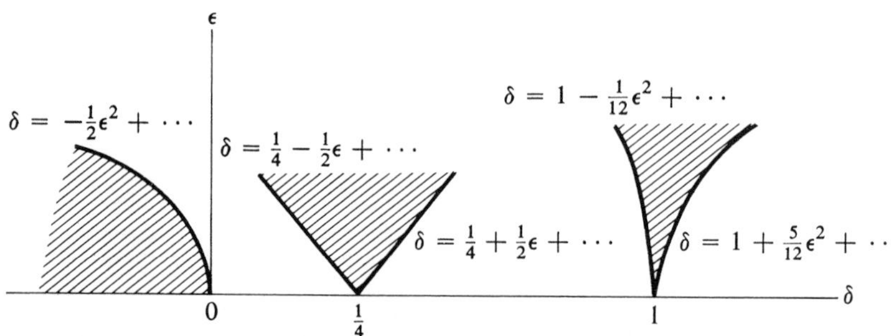

FIGURE 3.1 Shaded regions unstable, Mathieu equation.

An approximation to the transitional curves for small ε can thus be found by looking for $\delta(\varepsilon)$, such that periodic solutions of period 2π or 4π can be

† Stability here means boundedness as $t \to \infty$.

found. The general theory also states that the solutions in the unstable region have the form of exponentials times periodic (2π or 4π) functions. The transitional curves intersect $\varepsilon = 0$ at critical points:

$$\delta_c = \frac{n^2}{4}, \qquad n = 0, 1, 2, \ldots . \tag{3.5.2}$$

The application of the two-variable procedure to Equation (3.5.1) enables one to find not only the transitional curves but also the form of the solutions. A uniformly valid approximation $0 \le t < \infty$ is sought for general initial conditions, such that the first term in the asymptotic representation shows the transition from stability to instability.

Separate discussions have to be made for the various critical points, although $n = 1, 2, \ldots$, are very similar. Consider first the neighborhood of ($\delta = \frac{1}{4}$, $\varepsilon = 0$). A uniform approximation to Equation (3.5.1) as $\varepsilon \to 0$ is desired. If δ is held fixed ($\delta \neq \frac{1}{4}$), it is clear that only the stable solution consisting of harmonic oscillations will be obtained. Thus, it is necessary to consider $\delta \to \frac{1}{4}$ as $\varepsilon \to 0$ and to represent this limit as

$$\delta = \tfrac{1}{4} + \varepsilon\delta_1 + \varepsilon^2\delta_2 + \cdots . \tag{3.5.2a}$$

Here δ_1, δ_2 are parameters on which the solution depends, parameters indicating a path of approach to δ_c, and, in fact, a particular value of δ_1 corresponds to the transitional curve, $\delta_2 = \delta_2(\delta_1)$, and so on.

One time scale of this problem is associated with the simple harmonic oscillations at the critical points (t scale); the other is caused by small-scale fluctuations ($\varepsilon \cos t$) in the effective spring force. This small fluctuation can produce a cumulative or long time scale effect on the solution. It is certainly not clear *a priori* what the proper $\tilde{t}$ is, and the choice of $\tilde{t}$ is to be regarded as part of the problem. It will be seen, however, that there is a connection between the choice of $\tilde{t}$ and the two-variable expansion (Equation 3.2.3),

$$n = 1, \qquad \delta_c = \tfrac{1}{4}, \qquad \delta = \tfrac{1}{4} + \varepsilon\delta_1 + \varepsilon^2\delta_2 + \cdots,$$

$$\frac{d^2y}{dt^2} + \left\{\frac{1}{4} + \varepsilon(\delta_1 + \cos t) + \cdots\right\}y = 0, \tag{3.5.3}$$

$$y(0) = a, \qquad \frac{dy}{dt}(0) = b.$$

Let $\tilde{t} = \varepsilon t$, and try an expansion of the form

$$y(t;\varepsilon) \cong F_0(t, \tilde{t}) + \varepsilon F_1(t, \tilde{t}) + \cdots . \tag{3.5.4}$$

Thus, the successive equations replacing Equations (3.2.6) and (3.2.7) are

$$\frac{\partial^2 F_0}{\partial t^2} + \frac{1}{4} F_0 = 0, \tag{3.5.5}$$

$$\frac{\partial^2 F_1}{\partial t^2} + \frac{1}{4} F_1 = -2\frac{\partial^2 F_0}{\partial t\, \partial \tilde{t}} - (\delta_1 + \cos t) F_0. \tag{3.5.6}$$

The first solution, as usual, represents modulated oscillations:

$$F_0(t, \tilde{t}) = A_0(\tilde{t}) \cos\frac{t}{2} + B_0(\tilde{t}) \sin\frac{t}{2}, \tag{3.5.7}$$

where now $A_0(0) = a$, $B_0(0) = 2b$. The equation for F_1 thus reads

$$\frac{\partial^2 F_1}{\partial t^2} + \frac{1}{4} F_1 = -2\left\{-\frac{1}{2}\frac{dA_0}{d\tilde{t}} \sin\frac{t}{2} + \frac{1}{2}\frac{dB_0}{d\tilde{t}} \cos\frac{t}{2}\right\}$$
$$-(\delta_1 + \cos t)\left\{A_0(\tilde{t}) \cos\frac{t}{2} + B_0(\tilde{t}) \sin\frac{t}{2}\right\}. \tag{3.5.8}$$

Now we use the same argument as before: Unless all resonance producing terms ($\cos t/2$, $\sin t/2$) on the right-hand side are made to vanish, the solution grows on the t scale. Also, εt cannot be permitted to appear in a uniformly valid representation. Thus, using

$$\sin\frac{t}{2}\cos t = \frac{1}{2}\left\{\sin\frac{3t}{2} - \sin\frac{t}{2}\right\}, \qquad \cos\frac{t}{2}\cos t = \frac{1}{2}\left\{\cos\frac{3t}{2} + \cos\frac{t}{2}\right\}, \tag{3.5.9}$$

we find the differential equations for A_0, B_0:

$$\frac{dA_0}{d\tilde{t}} - \left(\delta_1 - \frac{1}{2}\right) B_0 = 0, \tag{3.5.10a}$$

$$\frac{dB_0}{d\tilde{t}} + \left(\delta_1 + \frac{1}{2}\right) A_0 = 0. \tag{3.5.10b}$$

This system has a solution of the form

$$A_0 = a_0 e^{\gamma \tilde{t}}, \qquad B_0 = b_0 e^{\gamma \tilde{t}}, \tag{3.5.11}$$

so that we have

$$\gamma a_0 - (\delta_1 - \tfrac{1}{2}) b_0 = 0, \qquad (\delta_1 + \tfrac{1}{2}) a_0 + \gamma b_0 = 0. \tag{3.5.12}$$

Thus, the characteristic exponent γ satisfies the equation

$$\gamma^2 + (\delta_1^2 - \tfrac{1}{4}) = 0. \tag{3.5.13}$$

It is immediately seen that real roots $\gamma_{1,2}$ occur for $|\delta_1| < \frac{1}{2}$. These values of δ_1 define, to this order, the region of instability. If, however, $|\delta_1| > \frac{1}{2}$, the roots are purely imaginary, so that the solutions are bounded and have the form of modulated oscillations. The transitional curve is given by $\delta_1 = \pm\frac{1}{2}$, a case of equal zero roots. The solutions of Equations (3.5.10) are easily constructed once $\gamma_{1,2}$ are found. If the initial conditions $A_0(0) = a$, $B_0(0) = 2b$ are accounted for, it is found that

$$A_0(\tilde{t}) = \left(\frac{a}{2} - b\sqrt{\frac{\frac{1}{2} - \delta_1}{\frac{1}{2} + \delta_1}}\right)\exp\left(\sqrt{\frac{1}{4} - \delta_1^2}\,\tilde{t}\right) + \left(\frac{a}{2} + b\sqrt{\frac{\frac{1}{2} - \delta_1}{\frac{1}{2} + \delta_1}}\right)\exp\left(-\sqrt{\frac{1}{4} - \delta_1^2}\,\tilde{t}\right),$$

$$B_0(\tilde{t}) = \left(b - \frac{a}{2}\sqrt{\frac{\frac{1}{2} + \delta_1}{\frac{1}{2} - \delta_1}}\right)\exp\left(\sqrt{\frac{1}{4} - \delta_1^2}\,\tilde{t}\right) + \left(b + \frac{a}{2}\sqrt{\frac{\frac{1}{2} + \delta_1}{\frac{1}{2} - \delta_1}}\right)\exp\left(-\sqrt{\frac{1}{4} - \delta_1^2}\,\tilde{t}\right),$$

$$|\delta_1| < \frac{1}{2}. \qquad (3.5.14)$$

This form of solution is in precise agreement with the general theory for equations with periodic coefficients. The solution on the transitional boundary which satisfies the same initial conditions is easily obtained from Equation (3.5.14) by the limit $\delta_1 \to \frac{1}{2}$. Thus, we have

$$A_0(\tilde{t}) = a, \qquad B_0(\tilde{t}) = 2b - a\tilde{t} \qquad (\delta_1 = \tfrac{1}{2}); \qquad (3.5.15)$$

$$A_0(\tilde{t}) = (a - 2b)\tilde{t}, \qquad B_0(\tilde{t}) = 2b \qquad (\delta_1 = -\tfrac{1}{2}). \qquad (3.5.16)$$

The continuation of this solution across the transition curve $|\delta_1| = \frac{1}{2}$ yields the modulated oscillation (cf. Equation 3.5.7) of the stable region $|\delta_1| > \frac{1}{2}$:

$$A_0(\tilde{t}) = a\cos\sqrt{\delta_1^2 - \frac{1}{4}}\,\tilde{t} \pm 2b\sqrt{\frac{\delta_1 - \frac{1}{2}}{\delta_1 + \frac{1}{2}}}\sin\sqrt{\delta_1^2 - \frac{1}{4}}\,\tilde{t},$$

$$B_0(\tilde{t}) = 2b\cos\sqrt{\delta_1^2 - \frac{1}{4}}\,\tilde{t} \mp a\sqrt{\frac{\delta_1 + \frac{1}{2}}{\delta_1 - \frac{1}{2}}}\sin\sqrt{\delta_1^2 - \frac{1}{4}}\,\tilde{t}. \qquad (3.5.17)$$

(Upper sign $\delta_1 > \frac{1}{2}$, lower sign $\delta_1 < -\frac{1}{2}$.)

This approximation, however is not valid down to $\varepsilon = 0$, since $\varepsilon = 0$ corresponds to $|\delta_1| \to \infty$. Validity of the expansion can be expected in a wedge-like region $|\delta_1| < k$, including the transition curve.

Similar considerations apply near the critical point $\delta_c = 1$. However, in this case the slow variable and the associated expansion $\delta(\varepsilon)$ must be chosen:

$$\tilde{t} = \varepsilon^2 t, \qquad (3.5.18)$$

$$\delta(\varepsilon) = 1 + \delta_2\varepsilon^2 + \cdots. \tag{3.5.19}$$

Thus, Equation (3.5.1) can be written as

$$\frac{d^2y}{dt^2} + (1 + \varepsilon\cos t + \varepsilon^2\delta_2 + \cdots)y = 0. \tag{3.5.20}$$

The expansion for y is of the same form as before,

$$y(t;\varepsilon) \cong F_0(t,\tilde{t}) + \varepsilon F_1(t,\tilde{t}) + \varepsilon^2 F_2(t,\tilde{t}) + \cdots, \tag{3.5.21}$$

but now

$$\frac{dy}{dt} = \frac{\partial F_0}{\partial t} + \varepsilon^2\frac{\partial F_0}{\partial \tilde{t}} + \varepsilon\frac{\partial F_1}{\partial t} + \varepsilon^2\frac{\partial F_2}{\partial t}, \tag{3.5.22}$$

$$\frac{d^2y}{dt^2} = \frac{\partial^2 F_0}{\partial t^2} + 2\varepsilon^2\frac{\partial^2 F_0}{\partial t\,\partial\tilde{t}} + \varepsilon\frac{\partial^2 F_1}{\partial t^2} + \varepsilon^2\frac{\partial^2 F_2}{\partial t^2}. \tag{3.5.23}$$

Using this expression in Equation (3.5.20), we see that the sequence of approximating equations is

$$\frac{\partial^2 F_0}{\partial t^2} + F_0 = 0, \tag{3.5.24}$$

$$\frac{\partial^2 F_1}{\partial t^2} + F_1 = -F_0\cos t, \tag{3.5.25}$$

$$\frac{\partial^2 F_2}{\partial t^2} + F_2 = -2\frac{\partial^2 F_0}{\partial t\,\partial\tilde{t}} - \delta_2 F_0 - F_1\cos t. \tag{3.5.26}$$

The basic solution is a modulation of the oscillations near ($\varepsilon = 0, \delta = 1$):

$$F_0 = A_0(\tilde{t})\cos t + B_0(\tilde{t})\sin t. \tag{3.5.27}$$

In this case, however, the equation for F_1 does not provide the information necessary to find A_0, B_0. The right-hand side of Equation (3.5.25) is

$$-F_0\cos t = -A_0\cos^2 t - B_0\sin t\cos t = -\frac{A_0}{2}(1+\cos 2t) - \frac{B_0}{2}\sin 2t. \tag{3.5.28}$$

Equation (3.5.28) contains no resonance producing terms. Equation (3.5.26) must be considered if A_0 and B_0 are to be found. The particular solution of Equation (3.5.25) due to F_0 is F_{1_p},

$$F_{1_p} = \frac{A_0(\tilde{t})}{6}\cos 2t - \frac{A_0(\tilde{t})}{2} + \frac{B_0(\tilde{t})}{6}\sin 2t. \tag{3.5.29}$$

Thus, Equation (3.5.26) becomes

$$\frac{\partial^2 F_2}{\partial t^2} + F_2 = -2\left\{-\frac{dA_0}{d\tilde{t}}\sin t + \frac{dB_0}{d\tilde{t}}\cos t\right\} - \delta_2\{A_0 \cos t + B_0 \sin t\}$$
$$-\frac{A_0}{12}\{\cos 3t + \cos t\} + \frac{B_0}{12}\{\sin 3t + \sin t\}$$
$$-\cos t\{A_1 \cos t + B_1 \sin t\}. \tag{3.5.30}$$

Now, the argument about resonance-producing terms can be applied, and it must be required that

$$2\frac{dA_0}{d\tilde{t}} - \left(\delta_2 + \frac{1}{12}\right)B_0 = 0, \qquad A_0(0) = a; \tag{3.5.31a}$$

$$2\frac{dB_0}{d\tilde{t}} + \left(\delta_2 - \frac{5}{12}\right)A_0 = 0, \qquad B_0(0) = b. \tag{3.5.31b}$$

This pair of equations is of the same form as those found for $\delta_c = \frac{1}{4}$ (Equation 3.5.10), and the same form of solution (3.5.11) can be used. Now, we have

$$\gamma^2 + \tfrac{1}{4}(\delta_2 - \tfrac{5}{12})(\delta_2 + \tfrac{1}{12}) = 0. \tag{3.5.32}$$

Real roots corresponding to the unstable region occur for $-\frac{1}{12} < \delta_2 < \frac{5}{12}$.

Finally, consider the behavior of the solutions to the Mathieu equation near the stability boundary through the origin $\delta = -\frac{1}{2}\varepsilon^2 + \cdots$. The behavior near this boundary is qualitatively different from that to be expected near the other stability boundaries which occur in pairs. Nevertheless, the two-variable method provides an approach to this problem. The expression for the stability boundary again takes the form

$$\delta = \varepsilon\delta_1 + \varepsilon^2\delta_2 + \cdots, \tag{3.5.33}$$

where in fact it is to be shown that $\delta_1 = 0$. The Mathieu equation (Equation 3.5.1) is

$$\frac{d^2y}{dt^2} + \{\varepsilon(\delta_1 + \cos t) + \varepsilon^2\delta_2 + \cdots\}y = 0. \tag{3.5.34}$$

Consider the general initial conditions

$$y(0) = a, \qquad \frac{dy}{dt}(0) = b$$

as before. In this case, the two-variable expression is of the form

$$y(t, \tilde{t}; \varepsilon) = \frac{1}{\varepsilon}F_{-1}(t, \tilde{t}) + F_0(t, \tilde{t}) + \varepsilon F_1(t, \tilde{t}) + \cdots, \tag{3.5.35}$$

where now $\tilde{t} = \varepsilon t$ and, hence,

$$\frac{dy}{dt}(t, \tilde{t}; \varepsilon) = \frac{1}{\varepsilon}\frac{\partial F_{-1}}{\partial t} + \left(\frac{\partial F_0}{\partial t} + \frac{\partial F_{-1}}{\partial \tilde{t}}\right) + \cdots,$$

and the equations of the approximating sequence are

$$\frac{\partial^2 F_{-1}}{\partial t^2} = 0, \tag{3.5.36}$$

$$\frac{\partial^2 F_0}{\partial t^2} = -2\frac{\partial^2 F_{-1}}{\partial t\, \partial \tilde{t}} - (\delta_1 + \cos t)F_{-1}, \tag{3.5.37}$$

$$\frac{\partial^2 F_1}{\partial t^2} = -2\frac{\partial^2 F_0}{\partial t\, \partial \tilde{t}} - (\delta_1 + \cos t)F_0 - \frac{\partial^2 F_{-1}}{\partial \tilde{t}^2} - \delta_2 F_{-1}. \tag{3.5.38}$$

The solution of Equation (3.5.36) is

$$F_{-1}(t, \tilde{t}) = A_{-1}(\tilde{t})t + B_{-1}(\tilde{t}), \tag{3.5.39}$$

and all the solutions of homogeneous equations $\partial^2 F_i/\partial t^2 = 0$ are of this form. Assuming boundedness on the fast time scale means that $A_{-1}(\tilde{t}) = 0$. This is, near the stability boundary we expect solutions to have the form,

$$F_{-1}(t, \tilde{t}) = B_{-1}(\tilde{t}), \tag{3.5.40}$$

of slowly varying functions. This explains why the initial term is $O(1/\varepsilon)$ in order to produce a velocity $O(1)$.

Now the equation for F_0, (Equation 3.5.37), reads

$$\frac{\partial^2 F_0}{\partial t^2} = -(\delta_1 + \cos t)B_{-1}(\tilde{t}). \tag{3.5.41}$$

Again, unless $\delta_1 = 0$, rapidly unbounded terms appear in the solutions of Equation (3.5.41). Thus, we have $\delta_1 = 0$ and

$$F_0(t, \tilde{t}) = B_0(\tilde{t}) + B_{-1}(\tilde{t}) \cos t. \tag{3.5.42}$$

The function $B_{-1}(\tilde{t})$, the basic uniformly valid solution, is still unknown, and the equation for F_1 must be considered in this example. Equation (3.5.38) now reads

$$\frac{\partial^2 F_1}{\partial t^2} = 2\frac{dB_{-1}}{d\tilde{t}} \sin t - \cos t\{B_0(\tilde{t}) + B_{-1}(\tilde{t}) \cos t\} - \frac{d^2 B_{-1}}{d\tilde{t}^2} - \delta_2 B_{-1}(\tilde{t}). \tag{3.5.43}$$

Using the same argument that terms independent of t must not appear on the right-hand side of Equation (3.5.43) (and using $\cos^2 t = \frac{1}{2}\{\cos 2t + 1\}$), we obtain the required differential equation (in this case *second*-order) for B_{-1},

$$\frac{d^2B_{-1}}{d\tilde{t}^2} + \left(\delta_2 + \frac{1}{2}\right)B_{-1} = 0. \tag{3.5.44}$$

It is clear, then, that in this case there is only one stability boundary and that unstable solutions exist for $\delta_2 < -\frac{1}{2}$ and bounded solutions exist for $\delta_2 > -\frac{1}{2}$. The original initial conditions are now

$$F_{-1}(0, 0) = 0, \qquad \frac{\partial F_{-1}}{\partial \tilde{t}}(0, 0) = b, \tag{3.5.45}$$

so that the dominant unbounded term depends only on the initial dy/dt. The solution of Equation (3.5.44) is

$$\begin{aligned} B_{-1}(\tilde{t}) &= \frac{b}{\sqrt{\delta_2 + \frac{1}{2}}} \sin \sqrt{\delta_2 + \frac{1}{2}}\,\tilde{t}, \qquad \delta_2 > -\frac{1}{2} \quad \text{(stable)}, \\ B_{-1}(\tilde{t}) &= \frac{b}{\sqrt{-(\delta_2 + \frac{1}{2})}} \sinh \sqrt{-\left(\delta_2 + \frac{1}{2}\right)}\,\tilde{t}, \qquad \delta_2 < -\frac{1}{2} \quad \text{(unstable)}. \end{aligned} \tag{3.5.46}$$

In the limit $\delta_2 = -\frac{1}{2}$, the solution $B_{-1}(\tilde{t}) = b\tilde{t}$, so that $y = bt + \cdots$. The solution actually does grow linearly in t, due to the fact that the average of $\cos t$ is $\frac{1}{2}$.

This expression can be carried to higher orders to represent also the effect of $y(0)$.

These few examples have served to introduce the idea of the two-variable procedures. Several more complicated examples are discussed in the later sections.

Problems

3.5.1 Consider the classical case of beats for a linear oscillator in which the driver frequency ω is close to the natural frequency ω_N:

$$\frac{d^2y}{dt^2} + \omega_N^2 y = F_0 \cos \omega t.$$

The small parameter of this problem is

$$\varepsilon = \frac{\omega_N - \omega}{\omega_N}.$$

Construct the exact solution of this problem, and compare it with the result of the formal application of the two-variable expansion procedure.

3.5.2 Consider

$$\frac{d^2y}{dt^2} + \left(\frac{1}{4} + \varepsilon\delta_1 + \varepsilon^2\delta_2 + \varepsilon\cos t\right)y = 0$$

with the boundary conditions $y(0) = a$, $y'(0) = b$. Assume that the solution is of the form

$$y = F_0(t, \tilde{t}) + \varepsilon F_1(t, \tilde{t}) + \varepsilon^2 F_2 + \cdots, \qquad \tilde{t} = \varepsilon t.$$

(a) Give the complete solution for F_0 and F_1. This involves considering the equation for F_2.

(b) Determine stability boundaries to order ε^2.

(c) Determine, by a limiting procedure, the solution right at the stability boundaries, in particular the normalized solutions y_1 and y_2 satisfying $y_1(0) = 1$, $y_1'(0) = 0$, $y_2(0) = 0$, $y_2'(0) = 1$.

(d) With y_1 and y_2 as above, verify that the discriminant D, defined by $y_1(2\pi) + y_2'(2\pi)$, is equal to $-2 + O(\varepsilon^2)$. Also construct solutions y_1^*, y_2^* such that $y_1^*(t + 2\pi) = -y_1^*(t)$, $y_2^*(t + 2\pi) = -y_2^*(t) + y_1^*(t)$. Verify the general theorem that an arbitrary solution y has the property

$$y(t + 2\pi) = -y(t) + \theta p(t), \qquad \theta = \text{const}, \qquad p(t) \text{ periodic}.$$

(Note that all questions in (d) refer to solutions at the stability boundaries.)

3.5.3 Consider the damped motion of an oscillator with quadratic friction:

$$\frac{d^2y}{dt^2} + \varepsilon\left|\frac{dy}{dt}\right|\frac{dy}{dt} + y = 0.$$

Apply the two-variable method to find an asymptotic representation valid $(0 \le t < \infty)$ if $y(0) = 0$, $(dy/dt)(0) = 1$. Compare your answer with an expansion of the exact solution obtained by quadratures.

3.6 Adiabatic invariance

A natural extension of the two-variable method is to those problems which contain a slowly varying function explicitly. However, the simple example of this Section shows that some thought must be given to the proper choice of variables. The classical example is the motion of a pendulum under slow variations in its length. In this context, of course, "slow" means over a time scale long compared to the natural period. In the version corresponding to small amplitudes, the following equation would apply:

$$\frac{d^2y}{dt^2} + \mu^2(\tilde{t})y = 0, \qquad (3.6.1)$$

where $\tilde{t} = \varepsilon t$ is the slow variable, $\mu^2 > 0$, and $\mu = O(1)$. Arbitrarily initial conditions can be chosen, for example, as

$$y(0) = a, \qquad \frac{dy}{dt}(0) = b. \tag{3.6.2}$$

An attempt to apply the two-variable expansion procedure directly to Equation (3.6.1) fails, because the instantaneous frequency of the basic oscillation is not really $\mu(\tilde{t})$, but rather some average value of μ decides about the basic oscillation. However, by a reconsideration of the fast variable, Equation (3.6.1) can be brought to a form where a procedure very close to that of the previous sections applies. Let

$$t^+ = f(t), \qquad \text{where} \quad f(0) = 0, \tag{3.6.3}$$

be a new fast variable; $\tilde{t}$ is a suitable slow variable. Then, Equations (3.6.1) and (3.6.2) become

$$\frac{d^2y}{dt^{+2}} + \frac{f''(t)}{f'^2(t)}\frac{dy}{dt^+} + \frac{\mu^2(\tilde{t})}{f'^2(t)}y = 0, \tag{3.6.4}$$

$$y(0) = a, \qquad f'(0)\frac{dy}{dt^+}(0) = b. \tag{3.6.5}$$

On the t^+ scale, the frequency is constant with the choice

$$f'(t) = \mu(\tilde{t}), \qquad t^+ = f(t) = \int_0^t \mu(\varepsilon t)\, dt, \qquad f''(t) = \varepsilon\mu'(\tilde{t}). \tag{3.6.6}$$

Thus, the problem now appears as one with small, slowly variable damping:

$$\frac{d^2y}{dt^{+2}} + \varepsilon g(\tilde{t})\frac{dy}{dt^+} + y = 0, \qquad g(\tilde{t}) = \frac{\mu'(\tilde{t})}{\mu^2(\tilde{t})}, \tag{3.6.7}$$

$$y(0) = 0, \qquad \frac{dy}{dt^+}(0) = \frac{b}{\mu(0)}. \tag{3.6.8}$$

Now, to apply the method, let

$$y(t^+; \varepsilon) = F_0(t^+, \tilde{t}) + \varepsilon F_1(t^+, \tilde{t}) + \cdots \tag{3.6.9}$$

and note that

$$\frac{dy}{dt^+} = \left(\frac{\partial F_0}{\partial t^+} + \frac{\partial F_0}{\partial \tilde{t}}\frac{d\tilde{t}}{dt}\frac{dt}{dt^+}\right) + \varepsilon\frac{\partial F_1}{\partial t^+} + \cdots = \frac{\partial F_0}{\partial t^+} + \varepsilon\left\{\frac{1}{\mu(\tilde{t})}\frac{\partial F_0}{\partial \tilde{t}} + \frac{\partial F_1}{\partial t^+}\right\} \tag{3.6.10}$$

and

$$\frac{d^2y}{dt^{+2}} = \frac{\partial^2 F_0}{\partial t^{+2}} + \frac{2\varepsilon}{\mu}\frac{\partial^2 F_0}{\partial \tilde{t}\,\partial t^+} + \varepsilon\frac{\partial^2 F_1}{\partial t^{+2}} + \cdots. \tag{3.6.11}$$

Thus, the sequence of approximating equations is

$$\frac{\partial^2 F_0}{\partial t^{+2}} + F_0 = 0, \tag{3.6.12}$$

$$\frac{\partial^2 F_1}{\partial t^{+2}} + F_1 = -g(\tilde{t})\frac{\partial F_0}{\partial t^+} - \frac{2}{\mu(\tilde{t})}\frac{\partial^2 F_0}{\partial t^+\,\partial \tilde{t}}. \tag{3.6.13}$$

Using

$$F_0(t^+, \tilde{t}) = A_0(\tilde{t})\cos t^+ + B_0(\tilde{t})\sin t^+ \tag{3.6.14}$$

to describe the basic oscillation, we see that the right-hand side of Equation (3.6.13) is

$$\left(A_0\frac{\mu'(\tilde{t})}{\mu^2(\tilde{t})} + \frac{2}{\mu(\tilde{t})}\frac{dA_0}{d\tilde{t}}\right)\sin t^+ - \left(B_0\frac{\mu'(\tilde{t})}{\mu^2(\tilde{t})} + \frac{2}{\mu(\tilde{t})}\frac{dB_0}{d\tilde{t}}\right)\cos t^+.$$

These terms must be made to vanish for uniformity of the approximation, so that

$$A_0(\tilde{t}) = A_0(0)\sqrt{\mu(0)/\mu(\tilde{t})}, \qquad B_0(\tilde{t}) = B_0(0)\sqrt{\mu(0)/\mu(\tilde{t})}. \tag{3.6.15}$$

Equation (3.6.15) shows how the amplitude of the basic oscillation changes with the frequency. The adiabatic invariant is $\mu(\tilde{t})(A_0^2 + B_0^2)$. For sufficiently slow external changes, this quantity does not change. The general solution of the initial value problem is

$$F_0(t^+, \tilde{t}) = \sqrt{\frac{\mu(0)}{\mu(\tilde{t})}}\left\{a\cos t^+ + \frac{b}{\mu(0)}\sin t^+\right\}. \tag{3.6.16}$$

A practical problem leading to Equation (3.6.1) is the motion of a charged particle in a magnetic field almost homogeneous in space and varying slowly in time (cf. Reference 3.6.1). The equations of motion of the particle in the xy-plane, with a magnetic field $B(t)$ in the z-direction, are

$$m\frac{d^2x}{dt^2} = qB\frac{dy}{dt} + qE_x, \qquad m\frac{d^2y}{dt^2} = -qB\frac{dx}{dt} + qE_y, \qquad q = \text{charge}. \tag{3.6.17}$$

The Maxwell equation

$$\text{curl}\,\mathbf{E} = -\frac{\partial \mathbf{B}}{\partial t} \tag{3.6.18}$$

has the local solution

$$E_x = -\frac{y}{2}\frac{dB}{dt} + \cdots, \qquad E_y = \frac{x}{2}\frac{dB}{dt} + \cdots, \tag{3.6.19}$$

which can be used in Equation (3.6.17) near the origin. Letting

$$u = x + iy, \tag{3.6.20}$$

we find that the system (Equation 3.6.17) becomes

$$\frac{d^2u}{dt^2} + i\omega\frac{du}{dt} + \frac{i}{2}\frac{d\omega}{dt}u = 0, \tag{3.6.21}$$

where

$$\omega(t) = \frac{qB(t)}{m}$$

is the cyclotron frequency. For $B = \text{const}$, the particle motion is a circular orbit about the origin with this frequency. Now, if we introduce the amplitude $\phi(t)$ by

$$u = x + iy = \phi(t)\exp[-(i/2)\int_0^t \omega\, dt], \tag{3.6.22}$$

$\phi(t)$ satisfies

$$\frac{d^2\phi}{dt^2} + \frac{\omega^2(t)}{4}\phi = 0. \tag{3.6.23}$$

The result (Equation 3.6.16) shows precisely in what sense the magnetic moment proportional to $\phi_{\max}\sqrt{\omega}$ is constant.

REFERENCES

3.6.1 L. F. J. Broer, and L. Wijngaarden, "On the Motion of a Charged Particle in an Almost Homogeneous Magnetic Field." *Applied Scientific Research B*, 8, *3* (1960), 159–176.

3.7 Sturm–Liouville equation; differential equation with a large parameter

The classical problem of the approximate solution of a differential equation with a large parameter (cf. Equation 3.7.1 below) falls naturally into the discussion of this chapter. The usual asymptotic expansion valid away from turning points turns out not to be a limit-process expansion but, rather, one of the two-variable type. However, near a turning point, the local behavior dominates, so that a limit-process expansion, valid locally, can be constructed. These two expansions, however, can be matched by the same procedure used for purely limit-process expansions. This extension of our previous ideas should prove useful for many similar problems.

For the consideration of asymptotic distribution of eigenvalues and eigenfunctions and for various other reasons, it is often necessary to obtain the asymptotic behavior of the solutions to the general self-adjoint second-order equation

$$\frac{d}{dx}\left(p(x)\frac{dy}{dx}\right) + [\lambda q(x) - r(x)]y = 0 \tag{3.7.1}$$

as

$$\lambda \to \infty.$$

A standard method is the transformation (Liouville, Green, 1837) of Equation (3.7.1) to an equation of canonical type by the introduction of

$$y(x) = f(x)w(z), \qquad z = g(x). \tag{3.7.2}$$

Over an interval of x where p, q individually have one sign (say positive), Equation (3.7.1) is transformed to

$$\frac{d^2w}{dz^2} + \lambda w = \phi(z)w \tag{3.7.3}$$

by a suitable choice of (f, g). For large λ, the right-hand side of Equation (3.7.3) makes a small contribution that can be estimated by iteration (cf. Reference 3.7.1). Since for $\lambda \to \infty$ the solutions of Equation (3.7.3) have the form of slowly varying oscillations, it is natural to expect the two-variable procedure to apply to this part of the problem. Besides having a certain unity with what has gone before, the two-variable method has the advantage that higher approximations are more easily calculated.

When the original equation (3.7.1) has a simple turning point ($q(x) = 0$), the extension of the previous method uses a comparison equation,

$$\frac{d^2w}{dz^2} + \lambda z w = \psi(z)w, \tag{3.7.4}$$

which gives the results of the WKBJ ... method. The procedure here is different. A local expansion valid near the turning point is constructed and matched to the expansions valid away from the turning point.

The method used here is similar to that of the previous Section (adiabatic invariants), of a slowly varying frequency. The equation is transformed to the form for an oscillator of constant frequency and small damping. A fast variable is $x^* = \sqrt{\lambda}\,x$, and x itself is a slow variable. Thus, Equation (3.7.1) can be written

$$\frac{d^2y}{dx^{*2}} + \varepsilon\frac{p'(x)}{p(x)}\frac{dy}{dx^*} + \left\{\frac{q(x)}{p(x)} - \varepsilon^2\frac{r(x)}{p(x)}\right\}y = 0, \tag{3.7.5}$$

where $\varepsilon = 1/\sqrt{\lambda} \to 0$. Consider, first, Equation (3.7.5) over an interval $(0 < x < l)$, where p, $q > 0$, and consider also that $\lambda > 0$, as would be typical for an eigenvalue problem. Then, introduce a new fast variable $\bar{x}$,

$$\bar{x} = \psi(x^*), \tag{3.7.6}$$

in order to bring Equation (3.7.5) to the desired form. We have

$$\psi'^2(x^*)\frac{d^2y}{d\bar{x}^2} + \psi''(x^*)\frac{dy}{d\bar{x}} + \varepsilon\frac{p'(x)}{p(x)}\psi'(x^*)\frac{dy}{d\bar{x}} + \left\{\frac{q(x)}{p(x)} - \varepsilon^2\frac{r(x)}{p(x)}\right\}y = 0. \tag{3.7.7}$$

It is clear that $\psi'(x^*)$ should be chosen so that

$$\psi'(x^*) = \sqrt{q(x)/p(x)} = O(1), \tag{3.7.8}$$

and the relationship of the new fast variable $\bar{x}$ to the slow variable is

$$\bar{x} = \int_0^{x^*}\sqrt{\frac{q(\varepsilon z)}{p(\varepsilon z)}}\,dz = \frac{1}{\varepsilon}\int_0^{x}\sqrt{\frac{q(\xi)}{p(\xi)}}\,d\xi. \tag{3.7.9}$$

With this choice, we have

$$\psi''(x^*) = \varepsilon\frac{1}{2}\sqrt{\frac{p}{q}}\left\{\frac{q'(x)}{p} - \frac{qp'(x)}{p^2}\right\}, \tag{3.7.10}$$

and Equation (3.7.5) is

$$\frac{d^2y}{d\bar{x}^2} + \varepsilon f(x)\frac{dy}{d\bar{x}} + \left\{1 - \varepsilon^2\frac{r(x)}{p(x)}\right\}y = 0, \tag{3.7.11}$$

where

$$f(x) = \frac{1}{2}\frac{p^{1/2}q'}{q^{3/2}} + \frac{1}{2}\frac{p'}{p^{1/2}q^{1/2}}. \tag{3.7.11a}$$

Now, for the two-variable expansion, we assume an expansion of the type

$$y(\bar{x};\varepsilon) = F_0(\bar{x}, x) + \varepsilon F_1(\bar{x}, x) + \varepsilon^2 F_2(\bar{x}, x) + \cdots, \tag{3.7.12}$$

$$\frac{dy}{d\bar{x}} = \frac{\partial F_0}{\partial \bar{x}} + \frac{dx}{d\bar{x}}\frac{\partial F_0}{\partial x} + \varepsilon\frac{\partial F_1}{\partial \bar{x}} + \varepsilon\frac{dx}{d\bar{x}}\frac{\partial F_1}{\partial x} + \varepsilon^2\frac{\partial F_2}{\partial x} + \cdots, \tag{3.7.13}$$

$$\frac{d^2y}{d\bar{x}^2} = \frac{\partial^2 F_0}{\partial \bar{x}^2} + 2\frac{dx}{d\bar{x}}\frac{\partial^2 F_0}{\partial \bar{x}\,\partial x} + \left(\frac{dx}{d\bar{x}}\right)^2 \frac{\partial^2 F_0}{\partial x^2} + \frac{d^2x}{d\bar{x}^2}\frac{\partial F_0}{\partial x}$$
$$+\varepsilon\frac{\partial^2 F_1}{\partial \bar{x}^2} + 2\varepsilon\frac{dx}{d\bar{x}}\frac{\partial^2 F_1}{\partial x\,\partial \bar{x}} + \cdots. \quad (3.7.14)$$

Note, from Equation (3.7.9), that

$$\frac{dx}{d\bar{x}} = \varepsilon\sqrt{\frac{p(x)}{q(x)}}, \quad (3.7.15)$$

and $d^2x/d\bar{x}^2$ can similarly be calculated. Thus, from Equation (3.7.11), the first two approximate equations are

$$O(1) \; : \; \frac{\partial^2 F_0}{\partial \bar{x}^2} + F_0 = 0, \quad (3.7.16)$$

$$O(\varepsilon) \; : \; \frac{\partial^2 F_1}{\partial \bar{x}^2} + F_1 = -2\sqrt{\frac{p}{q}}\frac{\partial^2 F_0}{\partial \bar{x}\,\partial x} - f(x)\frac{\partial F_0}{\partial \bar{x}}. \quad (3.7.17)$$

Thus, we have

$$F_0(\bar{x}, x) = A_0(x)\cos\bar{x} + B_0(x)\sin\bar{x}. \quad (3.7.18)$$

Using the same argument as before, namely that fast growth ($\bar{x}$ scale) is not permitted, we obtain differential equations for A_0, B_0 from the right-hand side of Equation (3.7.17). We have

$$\frac{\partial^2 F_1}{\partial \bar{x}^2} + F_1 = -2\sqrt{\frac{p}{q}}\left\{-\frac{dA_0}{dx}\sin\bar{x} + \frac{dB_0}{dx}\cos\bar{x}\right\}$$
$$-f(x)\{-A_0\sin\bar{x} + B_0\cos\bar{x}\}. \quad (3.7.19)$$

Here A_0, B_0 satisfy the same differential equation (using the definition of f in Equation 3.7.11a):

$$2\frac{dA_0}{dx} + \frac{1}{2}\left(\frac{q'}{q} + \frac{p'}{p}\right)A_0 = 0. \quad (3.7.20)$$

The general solution of Equation (3.7.20) is, thus,

$$A_0(x) = a_0[p(x)q(x)]^{-1/4}, \quad (3.7.21)$$

and the first approximation is the same as that usually found,

$$y(\bar{x};\varepsilon) = \frac{a_0\cos\bar{x} + b_0\sin\bar{x}}{[p(x)q(x)]^{1/4}} + \varepsilon F_1(\bar{x}, x) + \cdots, \quad (3.7.22)$$

where

$$F_1 = A_1(x)\cos\bar{x} + B_1(x)\sin\bar{x}$$

and

$$\bar{x} = \frac{1}{\varepsilon}\int_0^x \frac{q(\xi)}{p(\xi)}\,d\xi.$$

The same formulation can also be applied to an interval in which $p > 0$, $q < 0$, but $\lambda > 0$, and the sin and cos are replaced by exponential functions. In such a region, we have

$$y(\bar{x};\varepsilon) = \frac{c_0 e^{-\bar{x}} + d_0 e^{\bar{x}}}{[-p(x)q(x)]^{1/4}} + \varepsilon F_1(x,\bar{x}) + \cdots, \tag{3.7.23}$$

where

$$\bar{x} = \frac{1}{\varepsilon}\int_0^x \sqrt{\frac{-q(\xi)}{p(\xi)}}\,d\xi.$$

Next we consider the behavior of the original equation (3.7.1) near a simple turning point (say $x = 0$), where

$$q(x) = \alpha x + \cdots, \qquad p(x) = \beta + \beta_1 x + \cdots, \qquad r(x) = \rho + \cdots. \tag{3.7.24}$$

The idea is to construct a limit-process expansion valid near $x = 0$. Introduce

$$\tilde{x} = \frac{x}{\delta(\varepsilon)}, \tag{3.7.25}$$

and consider an expansion procedure in which $\tilde{x}$ is fixed and $\delta, \varepsilon \to 0$. The form of the expansion is

$$y(x,\varepsilon) = \sigma(\varepsilon)g(\tilde{x}) + \sigma_1(\varepsilon)g_1(\tilde{x}) + \cdots, \tag{3.7.26}$$

so that Equation (3.7.1) becomes

$$\varepsilon^2\frac{p(\delta\tilde{x})}{\delta^2}\frac{d^2g}{d\tilde{x}^2} + \varepsilon^2\frac{p'(\delta\tilde{x})}{\delta}\frac{dg}{d\tilde{x}} + [q(\delta\tilde{x}) - \varepsilon^2 r(\delta\tilde{x})]g + \cdots = 0. \tag{3.7.27}$$

The dominant terms are

$$\frac{\varepsilon^2}{\delta^2}\beta\frac{d^2g}{d\tilde{x}^2} + \delta(\varepsilon)\,\alpha\tilde{x}g = 0, \tag{3.7.28}$$

so that both terms are of the same order if $\varepsilon^2/\delta^2 = \delta$ or

$$\delta(\varepsilon) = \varepsilon^{2/3}. \tag{3.7.29}$$

Thus, the basic turning-point equation is obtained for $g(\tilde{x})$,

$$\frac{d^2g}{d\tilde{x}^2} + k^2\tilde{x}g = 0, \qquad k^2 = \frac{\alpha}{\beta}. \tag{3.7.30}$$

The problem is thus reduced to knowing the properties of the solution of Equation (3.7.30), and, since these solutions are expressed in terms of Airy functions or ordinary Bessel functions, further progress toward matching can be made. The general solution of Equation (3.7.30) can be written

$$g(\tilde{x}) = \sqrt{\tilde{x}}\{CJ_{-1/3}(\tfrac{2}{3}k\tilde{x}^{3/2}) + DJ_{1/3}(\tfrac{2}{3}k\tilde{x}^{3/2})\}, \tag{3.7.31}$$

with the corresponding analytic continuation to $\tilde{x} < 0$. The function $g(\tilde{x})$ is well behaved at $\tilde{x} = 0$, the D term in Equation (3.7.31) varies like $\tilde{x}$, and the C term is constant. (No branches!)

The two-variable expansion (Equation 3.7.22) is valid in some region $x > x_0$ excluding the turning point. For the matching of Equations (3.7.22) and (3.7.26), consider an intermediate limit x_η fixed, where

$$x_\eta = \frac{x}{\eta(\varepsilon)} \qquad \text{such that} \quad \eta \to 0, \qquad \frac{\eta}{\varepsilon^{2/3}} \to \infty. \tag{3.7.32}$$

Thus, we have

$$x = \eta x_\eta \to 0, \qquad \tilde{x} = \frac{\eta x_\eta}{\varepsilon^{2/3}} \to \infty, \tag{3.7.33}$$

and

$$\bar{x} = \frac{1}{\varepsilon}\int_0^{\eta x_\eta} \sqrt{\frac{q(\xi)}{p(\xi)}}\, d\xi \to \frac{1}{\varepsilon}\sqrt{\frac{\alpha}{\beta}}\int_0^{\eta x_\eta} \sqrt{\zeta}\, d\zeta + \cdots, \qquad x \to \frac{2}{3}\sqrt{\frac{\alpha}{\beta}}\frac{(\eta x_\eta)^{3/2}}{\varepsilon} + \cdots. \tag{3.7.34}$$

The two-variable expansion should contain all limit-process expansions valid in restricted x neighborhoods and so be able to be matched to Equation (3.7.31). Now the behavior of Equation (3.7.31) for large $\tilde{x}$ is necessary for the matching, but the usual asymptotic expressions for $J_\nu(z)$ can be used:

$$J_\nu(z) = \sqrt{\frac{2}{\pi z}}\cos\left(z - \frac{\nu\pi}{2} - \frac{\pi}{4}\right) + O\left(\frac{1}{z}\right). \tag{3.7.35}$$

Thus, in terms of intermediate variables, we have the following.

TRANSITION

$$y(x;\varepsilon) = \sigma(\varepsilon)\left\{\sqrt{\frac{3}{\pi k}}\frac{\varepsilon^{1/6}}{(\eta x_\eta)^{1/4}}\right\}\left\{C\cos\left(\frac{2}{3}k\frac{(\eta x_\eta)^{3/2}}{\varepsilon} - \frac{\pi}{12}\right)\right.$$
$$\left. + D\cos\left(\frac{2}{3}k\frac{(\eta x_\eta)^{3/2}}{\varepsilon} - \frac{5\pi}{12}\right)\right\} + \cdots.$$

TWO-VARIABLE

$$y(x;\varepsilon) = \frac{a_0 \cos\left(\frac{2}{3}\sqrt{\alpha/\beta}\,(\eta x_\eta)^{3/2}/\varepsilon\right) + b_0 \sin\left(\frac{2}{3}\sqrt{\alpha/\beta}\,(\eta x_\eta)^{3/2}/\varepsilon\right)}{(\beta\alpha)^{1/4}(\eta x_\eta)^{1/4}} + \cdots \varepsilon F_1 + \cdots.$$

Since $k = \sqrt{\alpha/\beta}$, it is seen that the dominant terms in these two expansions are matched if

$$\sigma(\varepsilon) = \varepsilon^{-1/6} \tag{3.7.36}$$

and, further, if

$$\sqrt{\frac{3}{\pi}}\,\beta^{1/4}\left\{C \cos\frac{\pi}{12} + D \cos\frac{5\pi}{12}\right\} = \frac{a_0}{\beta^{1/4}}, \tag{3.7.37}$$

$$\sqrt{\frac{3}{\pi}}\,\beta^{1/4}\left\{C \sin\frac{\pi}{12} + D \sin\frac{5\pi}{12}\right\} = \frac{b_0}{\beta^{1/4}}. \tag{3.7.38}$$

Equations (3.7.37) and (3.7.38) provide the basic relations for the constants in the solution. A uniformly valid first approximation including the transition point could be written down by adding Equation (3.7.31) and (3.7.22) and subtracting the common part. Further, the same procedure can be applied as $\tilde{x} \to -\infty$, so that ultimately the relationships between c_0, d_0 of Equation (3.7.23) and a_0, b_0, which provide the analytic continuation, are found.

When an eigenvalue problem is being considered, the asymptotic formulas are used, and the set of ε is determined by consideration of the homogeneous boundary conditions.

REFERENCES

3.7.1 A. Erdelyi, *Asymptotic Expansions*, New York: Dover Publications, 1956.

3.8 Nonlinear oscillations with slowly varying coefficients

This section presents an extension of the ideas of fast and slow variables to a class of problems that remain essentially nonlinear. Although the method is in principle fairly general, the particular nonlinear oscillations which can be treated explicitly in a fairly simple way are described by elliptic functions. The asymptotic expansion is of the general type used in this chapter; successive terms depend both implicitly and explicitly on the small parameter ε. Consideration of the second approximation is necessary in order to complete the first approximation. The condition which in the nearly linear cases was the nonoccurrence of secular terms becomes now an integral condition guaranteeing periodicity.

The method and results in this Section were worked out originally in a series of papers by G. Kuzmak. The work in Reference 3.8.1 gives more details, and some extension of the work presented here.

A class of differential equations with small and slowly varying damping and slowly variable "spring" force is considered:

$$\frac{d^2y}{dt^2} + \varepsilon H(\tilde{t}, y)\frac{dy}{dt} + G(\tilde{t}, y) = 0, \qquad \text{where} \quad \tilde{t} = \varepsilon t. \tag{3.8.1}$$

Here G is $O(1)$, so that t is of the order of a fast time scale, while $\tilde{t}$ represents slow variations. A suitable fast time for carrying out the perturbations is necessary. Let t^* be defined by

$$\frac{dt^*}{dt} = \psi(\tilde{t}), \qquad \psi = O(1). \tag{3.8.2}$$

The function $\psi(\tilde{t})$ is to be found later. Then, using

$$\frac{dy}{dt} = \psi(\tilde{t})\frac{\partial y}{\partial t^*} + \varepsilon\frac{\partial y}{\partial \tilde{t}},$$

$$\frac{d^2y}{dt^2} = \psi^2(\tilde{t})\frac{\partial^2 y}{\partial t^{*2}} + 2\varepsilon\psi(\tilde{t})\frac{\partial^2 y}{\partial t^*\,\partial \tilde{t}} + \varepsilon\frac{d\psi}{d\tilde{t}}\frac{\partial y}{\partial t^*} + \varepsilon^2\frac{\partial^2 y}{\partial \tilde{t}^2},$$

we can rewrite Equation (3.8.1) as

$$\left\{\psi^2(\tilde{t})\frac{\partial^2 y}{\partial t^{*2}} + G(\tilde{t}, y)\right\} + \varepsilon\left\{2\psi(\tilde{t})\frac{\partial^2 y}{\partial t^*\,\partial \tilde{t}} + \frac{d\psi}{d\tilde{t}}\frac{\partial y}{\partial t^*} + \psi(\tilde{t})H(\tilde{t}, y)\frac{\partial y}{\partial t^*}\right\}$$
$$+\varepsilon^2\left\{\frac{\partial^2 y}{\partial \tilde{t}^2} + H(\tilde{t}, y)\frac{\partial y}{\partial \tilde{t}}\right\} = 0. \tag{3.8.3}$$

Now, assuming that it is possible to construct a uniformly valid solution, we write a two-variable expansion:

$$y = F_0(t^*, \tilde{t}) + \varepsilon F_1(t^*, \tilde{t}) + O(\varepsilon^2). \tag{3.8.4}$$

In approximating Equation (3.8.3), it is necessary to expand $G(\tilde{t}, y)$ as follows:

$$G(\tilde{t}, y) = G(\tilde{t}, F_0 + \varepsilon F_1 + \cdots) = G(\tilde{t}, F_0) + \varepsilon F_1 G_y(\tilde{t}, F_0) + O(\varepsilon^2). \tag{3.8.5}$$

Similarly, for H we have

$$H(\tilde{t}, y) = H(\tilde{t}, F_0) + O(\varepsilon). \tag{3.8.6}$$

Thus, the first- and second-approximation equations are

$$\psi^2(\tilde{t})\frac{\partial^2 F_0}{\partial t^{*2}} + G(\tilde{t}, F_0) = 0, \tag{3.8.7}$$

$$\psi^2(\tilde{t})\frac{\partial^2 F_1}{\partial t^{*2}} + G_y(\tilde{t}, F_0)F_1 = -2\psi(\tilde{t})\frac{\partial^2 F_0}{\partial t^* \partial \tilde{t}} - \frac{d\psi}{d\tilde{t}}\frac{\partial F_0}{\partial t^*} - \psi(\tilde{t})H(\tilde{t}, F_0)\frac{\partial F_0}{\partial t^*}. \tag{3.8.8}$$

Now, Kuzmak proves a theorem that if F_0 and F_1 can be found as periodic solutions of Equations (3.8.7 and 3.8.8) with period in t^* independent of $\tilde{t}$, and if G and H are sufficiently smooth, then the $O(\varepsilon^2)$ error term from Equation (3.8.3) is uniformly bounded. We proceed directly to the problem of calculating the periodic solutions, F_0, F_1, assuming that G is such that a periodic solution can be found. Here $\tilde{t}$ is a parameter of Equation (3.8.7). Its solutions correspond to paths in the phase plane of

$$\left(W = \frac{\partial F_0}{\partial t^*}, \qquad F_0\right),$$

$$\frac{dW}{dF_0} = -\frac{1}{\psi^2(\tilde{t})}\frac{G(\tilde{t}, F_0)}{W}, \qquad dt^* = \frac{dF_0}{W}. \tag{3.8.9}$$

A periodic solution corresponds to a closed path, as shown in Figure 3.2.

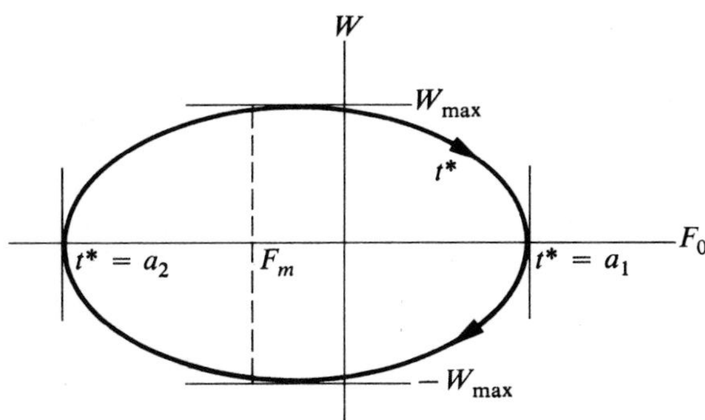

FIGURE 3.2 Phase plane of F_0.

The symmetry with respect to the F_0 axis shows that the velocity $W = \partial F_0/\partial t^*$ is the same at equal time intervals before and after zero velocity. If $t^* = a_1$ is the first zero of W in a cycle, we note that

$$F_0(a_1 - \rho, \tilde{t}) = F_0(a_1 + \rho, \tilde{t}) \tag{3.8.10}$$

and

$$\left(\frac{\partial F_0}{\partial t^*}\right)^2_{a_1+\rho} = \left(\frac{\partial F_0}{\partial t^*}\right)^2_{a_1-\rho}, \qquad \left(\frac{\partial^2 F_0}{\partial t^* \partial \tilde{t}}\frac{\partial F_0}{\partial t^*}\right)_{a_1+\rho} = \left(\frac{\partial^2 F_0}{\partial t^* \partial \tilde{t}}\frac{\partial F_0}{\partial t^*}\right)_{a_1-\rho}.$$

The same applies to successive zeroes of W, $a_2, a_3, \ldots$.

Now consider the construction of $F_1(t^*, \tilde{t})$, using the fact that $W = \partial F_0/\partial t^*$ is a solution of the linear homogeneous part of Equation (3.8.8). Let

$$F_1(t^*, \tilde{t}) = f(t^*, \tilde{t})\frac{\partial F_0}{\partial t^*}. \tag{3.8.11}$$

Then, Equation (3.8.8) becomes

$$\psi^2(\tilde{t})\left\{\frac{\partial^2 f}{\partial t^{*2}}\frac{\partial F_0}{\partial t^*} + 2\frac{\partial f}{\partial t^*}\frac{\partial^2 F_0}{\partial t^{*2}} + f\frac{\partial^3 F_0}{\partial t^{*3}}\right\} + f\frac{\partial F_0}{\partial t^*}G_y(\tilde{t}, F_0)$$
$$= -2\psi(\tilde{t})\frac{\partial^2 F_0}{\partial t^* \partial \tilde{t}} - \left\{\frac{d\psi}{d\tilde{t}} + \psi H(\tilde{t}, F_0)\right\}\frac{\partial F_0}{\partial t^*}. \tag{3.8.12}$$

Using the fact that F_0 satisfies Equation (3.8.7), we obtain a first-order equation for $\partial f/\partial t^*$. After multiplication by $\partial F_0/\partial t^*$, Equation (3.8.12) can be written

$$\psi^2(\tilde{t})\frac{\partial}{\partial t^*}\left\{\left(\frac{\partial F_0}{\partial t^*}\right)^2\frac{\partial f}{\partial t^*}\right\} = -2\psi(\tilde{t})\frac{\partial^2 F_0}{\partial t^* \partial \tilde{t}}\frac{\partial F_0}{\partial t^*} - \left\{\frac{d\psi}{d\tilde{t}} + \psi H(\tilde{t}, F_0)\right\}\left(\frac{\partial F_0}{\partial t^*}\right)^2, \tag{3.8.13}$$

so that

$$\frac{\partial f}{\partial t^*} = -\frac{1}{\psi^2(\tilde{t})(\partial F_0/\partial t^*)^2}\int_{a_1}^{t^*}\left\{2\psi(\tilde{t})\frac{\partial^2 F_0}{\partial t^* \partial \tilde{t}}\frac{\partial F_0}{\partial t^*}\right.$$
$$\left. + \left[\frac{d\psi}{d\tilde{t}} + \psi H(\tilde{t}, F_0)\right]\left(\frac{\partial F_0}{\partial t^*}\right)^2\right\} dt^*. \tag{3.8.14}$$

Now, assuming that F_0 has a period T in t^* independent of $\tilde{t}$, it is necessary to construct f to have a period T. First, we must show that $\partial f/\partial t^*$ is periodic with period T. Since T is the period produced by going once around the path of Figure 3.2, we have

$$T = \oint\frac{dF_0}{W} = 2\underbrace{\int\frac{dF_0}{W}}_{\text{lower branch}} = 2\underbrace{\int\frac{dF_0}{W}}_{\text{upper branch}}. \tag{3.8.15}$$

In order for $\partial f/\partial t^*$ to be periodic, we must have $\int_{a_1}^{t^*} = \int_{a_1}^{t^*+T}$ or $\oint = 0$. Because of the symmetry of the integrand in Equation (3.8.14) with respect to the F_0-axis (cf. Equation 3.8.10), periodicity for $\partial f/\partial t^*$ occurs only if the integral vanishes over one-half cycle. We need

$$\int_{a_1}^{a_2}\left\{2\psi(\tilde{t})\frac{\partial^2 F_0}{\partial t^* \partial \tilde{t}}\frac{\partial F_0}{\partial t^*} + \left[\frac{d\psi}{d\tilde{t}} + \psi H(\tilde{t}, F_0)\right]\left(\frac{\partial F_0}{\partial t^*}\right)^2\right\} dt^* = 0. \tag{3.8.16}$$

Thus, it is easy to show that $\partial f/\partial t^*$ is not only bounded but vanishes as $t^* \to a_1, a_2, \ldots$. Let

$$f(t^*, \tilde{t}) = \int_{a_1 - T/2}^{t^*} \frac{\partial f}{\partial t^*}(t^*, \tilde{t})\, dt^*. \tag{3.8.17}$$

Then f is periodic if

$$\oint \frac{\partial f}{\partial t^*}\, dt^* = \int_{a_1 - T/2}^{a_1 + T/2} \frac{\partial f}{\partial t^*}(t^*, \tilde{t})\, dt^* = 0. \tag{3.8.18}$$

But Equation (3.8.14) shows that $\partial f/\partial t^*$ is antisymmetric with respect to the F_0 axis or that

$$\frac{\partial f}{\partial t^*}(a_1 + \rho, \tilde{t}) = -\frac{\partial f}{\partial t^*}(a_1 - \rho, \tilde{t}). \tag{3.8.19}$$

Thus, Equation (3.8.18) is satisfied by Equation (3.8.14) when the periodicity condition of Equation (3.8.16) is enforced.

The periodicity condition (Equation 3.8.16), is the generalization of the requirement of no secular terms on a fast time scale, which was used in previous Sections. In general, the conditions can be written

$$\frac{d}{d\tilde{t}}\left\{ \psi(\tilde{t}) \int_{a_1}^{a_2} \left(\frac{\partial F_0}{\partial t^*}\right)^2 dt^* \right\} + \psi(\tilde{t}) \int_{a_1}^{a_2} H(\tilde{t}, F_0)\left(\frac{\partial F_0}{\partial t^*}\right)^2 dt^* = 0. \tag{3.8.20}$$

For the special case where the damping coefficient is independent of the amplitude $H = H(\tilde{t})$, Equation (3.8.20) is a simple differential equation:

$$\frac{d}{d\tilde{t}}\left[\psi(\tilde{t}) \int_{a_1}^{a_2} \left(\frac{\partial F_0}{\partial t^*}\right)^2 dt^* \right] + H(\tilde{t})\left[\psi(\tilde{t}) \int_{a_1}^{a_2} \left(\frac{\partial F_0}{\partial t^*}\right)^2 dt^* \right] = 0$$

with the solution

$$\psi(\tilde{t}) = C \frac{\exp\left[-\int_{\tilde{t}_0}^{\tilde{t}} H(\tilde{t})\, d\tilde{t}\right]}{\int_{a_1}^{a_2} (\partial F_0/\partial t^*)^2\, dt^*}. \tag{3.8.21}$$

For the special case of no damping, $H \equiv 0$, $\psi(\tilde{t})$ is simply

$$C\psi(\tilde{t})^{-1} = \int_{a_1}^{a_2} \left(\frac{\partial F_0}{\partial t^*}\right)^2 dt^*. \tag{3.8.22}$$

Special case: Undamped oscillations. The method just outlined can be applied to obtain explicit answers for the special equation

$$\frac{d^2 y}{dt^2} + a(\tilde{t})y + b(\tilde{t})y^3 = 0. \tag{3.8.23}$$

The equation of the first approximation, corresponding to Equation (3.8.7), is

$$\psi^2(\tilde{t})\frac{\partial^2 F_0}{\partial t^{*2}} + a(\tilde{t})F_0 + b(\tilde{t})F_0^3 = 0, \tag{3.8.24}$$

and the first integral which yields closed paths in the phase plane is

$$\psi^2(t)\left(\frac{\partial F_0}{\partial t^*}\right)^2 + a(\tilde{t})F_0^2 + \frac{b}{2}(\tilde{t})F_0^4 = C(\tilde{t}). \tag{3.8.25}$$

The oscillating solutions of Equation (3.8.24) can be expressed in terms of various elliptic functions with slowly varying amplitude and "phase." Suitable equations must be derived for the slowly varying amplitude and phase, and the periodicity conditions (Equation 3.8.22) must be used to find $\psi(\tilde{t})$. For one class of problems, let

$$F_0(t^*, \tilde{t}) = A_0(\tilde{t})sn[K(v(\tilde{t}))t^*, v(\tilde{t})], \tag{3.8.26}$$

where K is the complete elliptic integral of the second kind with module $\sqrt{v}$. (The solution of Equation 3.8.26 can be made general by replacing t^* by $t^* - \varphi(\tilde{t})$, where it can be shown that $\varphi(\tilde{t}) = \text{const}$; $A_{0_{\max}}$, φ are the constants of integration.)
Thus, we have

$$K(v) = \int_0^1 d\lambda/\sqrt{(1-\lambda^2)(1-v\lambda^2)}. \tag{3.8.27}$$

For small v, the oscillation is sinusoidal, while the representation above is good for $v < 1$. Note that

$$\frac{\partial F_0}{\partial t^*} = A_0(\tilde{t})K(v(\tilde{t}))\frac{\partial}{\partial u}sn(u, v), \qquad \text{where} \quad u = Kt^*;$$

$$\frac{\partial F_0}{\partial t^*} = A_0(\tilde{t})K(v(\tilde{t}))cn(u, v)\, dn(u, v).$$

Hence, Equation (3.8.24) is

$$\psi^2(\tilde{t})K^2(v)A_0\frac{\partial^2}{\partial u^2}sn(u, v) + a(\tilde{t})A_0 sn(u, v) + b(\tilde{t})A_0^3 sn^3 u = 0. \tag{3.8.28}$$

The usual differential equation for $sn(u, v)$,

$$\left[\frac{\partial}{\partial u}sn(u, v)\right]^2 = (1 - sn^2 u)(1 - v\,sn^2 u),$$

has the derivative

$$\frac{\partial^2}{\partial u^2} sn(u, v) = -(1 + v) snu + 2v sn^3 u. \tag{3.8.29}$$

Using Equation (3.8.29), we find that

$$\psi^2(\tilde{t})K^2(v(\tilde{t}))[-(1 + v)sn(u, v) + 2vsn^3u] + a(\tilde{t})sn(u, v) + b(\tilde{t})A_0^2(\tilde{t})sn^3u = 0. \tag{3.8.30}$$

Thus, for the differential equation of the first approximation (Equation 3.8.30) to be satisfied by the $sn(u, v)$ function, the amplitude A_0 and "phase" v must be chosen so that the coefficients of snu and sn^3u vanish identically. Thus, we have

$$-(1 + v)\psi^2 K^2(v) + a = 0, \tag{3.8.31}$$

$$2\psi^2 v K^2(v) + bA_0^2 = 0. \tag{3.8.32}$$

Equations (3.8.31) and (3.8.32) provide two relations for the three quantities (ψ, v, A_0), and the periodicity condition (Equation 3.8.22) provides the third:

$$2B = \psi(\tilde{t}) \int_{a_1}^{a_2} A_0^2(\tilde{t}) K^2(v(\tilde{t})) cn^2(Kt^*, v)\, dn^2(Kt^*, v)\, dt^*, \tag{3.8.33}$$

where B is the constant of integration. Equation (3.8.33) can be written

$$2B = \psi K A_0^2 \int_K^{3K} cn^2u\, dn^2u\, du = 2\psi K A_0^2 \int_0^K cn^2u\, dn^2u\, du.$$

Thus, the third relation can be written

$$(K\psi)A_0^2(\tilde{t})L(v) = B, \tag{3.8.34}$$

where

$$L(v) = \int_0^K cn^2(u, v)\, dn^2(u, v)\, du = \int_0^{\pi/2} \cos^2\varphi \sqrt{1 - v\sin^2\varphi}\, d\varphi$$

$$= \frac{1}{3v}[(1 + v)E(v) - (1 - v)K(v)];$$

$$E = \int_0^1 \sqrt{\frac{1 - v\lambda^2}{1 - \lambda^2}}\, d\lambda = \text{complete elliptic integral of second kind.}$$

This last result is easily worked out from identities involving hypergeometric functions. The three relations, Equations (3.8.31), (3.8.32), and (3.8.34), can be solved numerically for the three functions at any $\tilde{t}$, depending on the values of

$a(\tilde{t})$, $b(\tilde{t})$. The results can be expressed as

$$\frac{4L^2(\nu)\nu^2}{(1+\nu)^3} = p(\tilde{t})\text{ (say)} = \frac{B^2b^2(\tilde{t})}{a^3(\tilde{t})}, \tag{3.8.35}$$

$$\psi(\tilde{t}) = 1/[K(\nu(\tilde{t}))]\sqrt{a(\tilde{t})/[1+\nu(\tilde{t})]}, \tag{3.8.36}$$

$$A_0(\tilde{t}) = \sqrt{-2[a(\tilde{t})/b(\tilde{t})]\,[\nu(\tilde{t})/1+\nu(\tilde{t})]}. \tag{3.8.37}$$

A graph of the solution (from Kuzmak) for ν in this case is given in Figure 3.3. Various combinations for the signs of a, b can occur.

(1) $a(\tilde{t}) > 0$, $b(\tilde{t}) < 0$.

The curve for ν lies in the first quadrant, since Equation (3.8.32) shows that $\nu > 0$. The solution exists for $0 < p(\tilde{t}) < \frac{2}{9}$. If $p \geq \frac{2}{9}$, there are no oscillatory periodic solutions (also if $a < 0, b < 0$).

(2) $a(\tilde{t}) > 0$, $b(\tilde{t}) > 0$.

The curve for ν lies in the fourth quadrant, and the solution exists $0 < p < \infty$.

(3) $a(\tilde{t}) < 0$, $b(\tilde{t}) > 0$.

The curve for ν lies in the third quadrant, since $\nu < 0$, and the solution exists for $-\infty < p < -\frac{4}{9}$.

For Cases (2) and (3), the solution can also be expressed in terms of standard functions ($0 < \nu < 1$) by using $cn(u, \nu)$. There are also solutions for $a < 0$, $b > 0$ that oscillate not about zero (as sn, cn), but about $y = \pm\sqrt{-a/b}$, and these can be expressed in terms of $dn(u, \nu)$. The calculations are essentially the same as have been given above, and details are given in Kuzmak's paper (Reference 3.8.1).

For the cases where a small damping term appears in the equation, the solution can still be expressed in elliptic functions since F_0 satisfies the same equations. But now the slowly varying modulus $\nu(\tilde{t})$ is found as the solution of an ordinary differential equation, as is usual in the two-variable method.

It should be noted that the results here include both the results for adiabatic invariance (Section 3.6) and for the effect of a weak nonlinear spring in the period (Section 3.1) as special cases. In particular, the results for adiabatic invariance are approached as $b, \nu \to 0$. The differential equation (3.8.20) is the equation for the slowly varying amplitude.

REFERENCES

3.8.1 G. E. KUZMAK, "Asymptotic Solutions of Nonlinear Second Order Differential Equations with Variable Coefficients," *P.M.M.*, 23, *3* (1959), 515–526. (Appears in the English translation.)

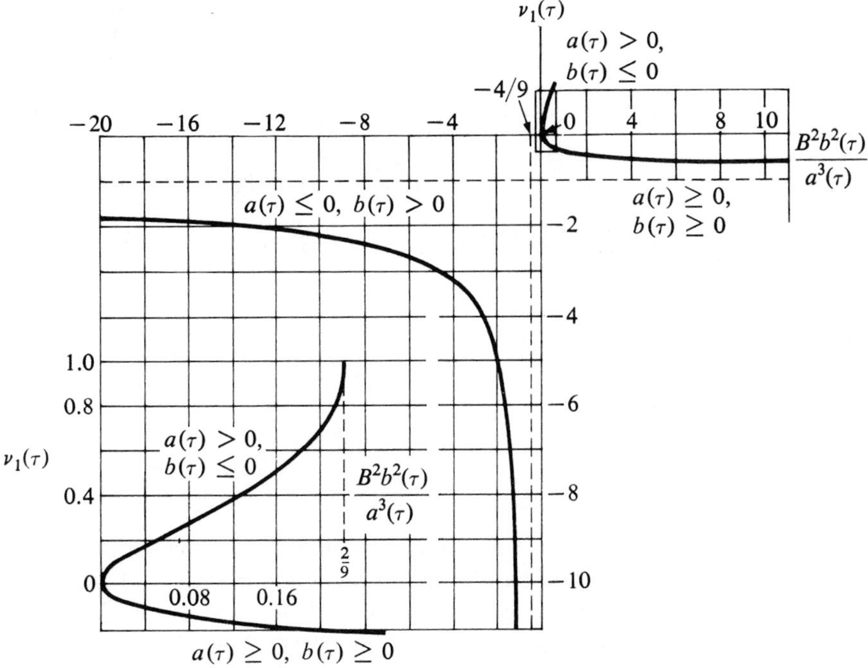

FIGURE 3.3 Numerical results of Kuzmak.

CHAPTER **4**

Applications to Partial Differential Equations

In this Section, the methods developed previously are applied to partial differential equations. The plan is the same as for the cases of ordinary differential equations discussed earlier. First, the very simplest case is discussed, in which a singular perturbation problem arises. This is a second-order equation which becomes a first-order one in the limit $\varepsilon = 0$. Following this, various more complicated physical examples of singular perturbations and boundary-layer theory are discussed. Next, the ideas of matching and inner and outer expansions are applied in some problems that are analogous to the singular boundary problems of Section 2.7.

4.1 Singular perturbation problems for second-order partial differential equations

In this Section, a study is made of the simplest problems for partial differential equations that lead to boundary layers; that is, which are singular in the sense of Sections 2.2 and 2.7. The aim is to base the discussion as much as possible on the mathematical situation. The simplest nontrivial case is that of a second-order equation which drops to a first-order equation as the small parameter $\varepsilon \to 0$. It is clear that some of the boundary data cannot be satisfied by the limit equation, so that boundary layers (in general) occur. The analogous case of a first-order partial differential equation reducing to a zero-order equation as $\varepsilon \to 0$ is, by the theory of characteristics for first-order equations, equivalent to a problem in ordinary differential equations.

Consider

$$\varepsilon\left\{\alpha_{11}\frac{\partial^2 u}{\partial x^2} + 2\alpha_{12}\frac{\partial^2 u}{\partial x\,\partial y} + \alpha_{22}\frac{\partial^2 u}{\partial y^2}\right\} = a\frac{\partial u}{\partial x} + b\frac{\partial u}{\partial y} \tag{4.1.1}$$

with constant coefficients. In the linear case, where the coefficients are functions of (x, y), the solutions can be expected to behave locally in the same way as the constant coefficient equation. However, nonlinearities especially in the lower-order operator usually introduce new effects which are not discussed here.

A boundary or initial-value problem for Equation (4.1.1) which leads to a unique solution $u(x, y; \varepsilon)$ is considered. The kind of boundary-value problem that makes sense for Equation (4.1.1) depends on the type of the equation, which is a property only of the highest-order differential operator appearing in that equation:

$$L_2 u = \alpha_{11}\frac{\partial^2 u}{\partial x^2} + 2\alpha_{12}\frac{\partial^2 u}{\partial x\,\partial y} + \alpha_{22}\frac{\partial^2 u}{\partial y^2}. \tag{4.1.2}$$

The main type classifications of the operator L_2 and some significant properties are as follows.

I. Elliptic type. No real characteristics. A point-disturbance solution of $L_2 u = 0$ influences the entire space. Thus, one boundary condition u, or a normal derivative, or combination is prescribed on a closed boundary. The simplest case and canonical form is the Laplace equation, $u_{xx} + u_{yy} = 0$.

II. Hyperbolic type. Real characteristic curves exist in the xy-plane and form a coordinate system. A point disturbance solution of $L_2 u = 0$ influences a restricted portion, bounded by the characteristic curves, of the (x, y) space. The direction of propagation (future) is not in the equation but must be assigned. Two initial conditions on a space-like arc define a solution in a domain bounded by characteristics. One boundary condition is assigned on a time-like arc. A characteristic value problem assigns a compatible boundary condition on a characteristic curve. The simplest case is the wave equation $u_{xx} - u_{yy} = 0$.

III. Parabolic type. A dividing case between I and II, in which the real characteristics coalesce. Half the space is influenced by a point disturbance. One initial condition on a characteristic arc or one boundary condition is prescribed. The simplest case is $u_{xx} = u_y$.

If $\phi(x, y) = \text{const}$ is the equation of a family of characteristic curves for L_2, the equation of these curves is

$$\alpha_{11}\left(\frac{\partial \phi}{\partial x}\right)^2 + 2\alpha_{12}\left(\frac{\partial \phi}{\partial x}\right)\left(\frac{\partial \phi}{\partial y}\right) + \alpha_{22}\left(\frac{\partial \phi}{\partial y}\right)^2 = 0 \tag{4.1.3}$$

or, if the slope of a characteristic $\zeta = dy/dx$ on $(\phi = \text{const}) = -\phi_x/\phi_y$,

$$\alpha_{11}\xi^2 - 2\alpha_{12}\xi + \alpha_{22} = 0. \tag{4.1.4}$$

The type of classification of Equation (4.1.1) thus depends only on the discriminant.

I. Elliptic: $\alpha_{12}^2 - \alpha_{11}\alpha_{22} < 0$, no real roots.
II. Hyperbolic: $\alpha_{12}^2 - \alpha_{11}\alpha_{22} > 0$, two real directions $\zeta_\pm$ assigned at each point.
III. Parabolic: $\alpha_{12}^2 - \alpha_{11}\alpha_{22} = 0$, double root $\zeta = \pm\alpha_{12}$.

A separate discussion is given for each type of equation.

Elliptic type. Since α_{11}, α_{22} must be of the same algebraic sign, let $\alpha_{11} > 0$, $\alpha_{22} > 0$, and note that

$$|\alpha_{12}| < \sqrt{\alpha_{11}\alpha_{22}}, \qquad \alpha_{11}, \alpha_{22} > 0. \tag{4.1.5}$$

Consider, at first, an interior boundary-value problem with $u = u_B(P_B)$ a prescribed function of position on a closed smooth boundary curve (Figure 4.1). Here u_B is independent of ε.

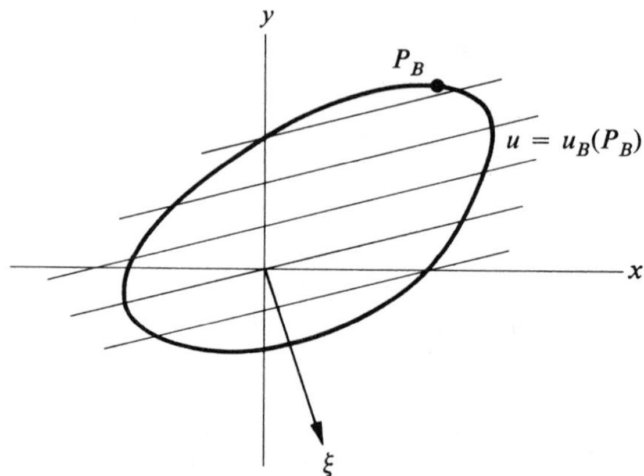

FIGURE 4.1 Boundary-value problem.

This set of boundary conditions defines a unique regular solution $u(x, y: \varepsilon)$ at all points interior to and on the boundary. As $\varepsilon \to 0$ with (x, y) fixed in the interior of the domain, the exact solution approaches the outer solution, which can be thought of as the first term of an outer expansion (valid off the boundary):

$$\lim_{\substack{\varepsilon \to 0,\\ x, y \text{ fixed}}} u(x, y; \varepsilon) = u_0(x, y). \tag{4.1.6}$$

Here $u_0(x, y)$ satisfies the limit equation of first-order,

$$a\frac{\partial u_0}{\partial x} + b\frac{\partial u_0}{\partial y} = 0. \tag{4.1.7}$$

Solutions of Equation (4.1.7) are expressed in terms of the characteristic curves†:

$$\xi = bx - ay = \text{const.}$$

These are called subcharacteristics of the original equation (4.1.1). The main underlying structure of the solution is given by these subcharacteristics, since $u_0 = u_0(\xi)$. The subcharacteristic curves are sketched in Figure 4.1. It is clear that the boundary condition on one side of the domain is sufficient to define $u_0(x, y) = u_0(\xi)$ in the whole domain. Also, $u_0(\xi)$, in general, does not satisfy the boundary condition on the other side of the domain, so that a boundary layer is needed.

In order to study this boundary layer and its matching to $u_0(\xi)$, it is convenient to introduce an orthogonal coordinate system (ξ, η) based on the subcharacteristics ξ. The coordinate η is chosen here arbitrarily, for convenience. (Different choices of η do not affect the essential boundary-layer character but may influence the form of higher-order corrections.)

$$\xi = bx - ay, \qquad \eta = ax + by. \tag{4.1.8}$$

The transformation formulas are

$$\begin{gathered}
\frac{\partial u}{\partial x} = b\frac{\partial u}{\partial \xi} + a\frac{\partial u}{\partial \eta}, \qquad \frac{\partial u}{\partial y} = -a\frac{\partial u}{\partial \xi} + b\frac{\partial u}{\partial \eta}, \\
\frac{\partial^2 u}{\partial x^2} = b^2\frac{\partial^2 u}{\partial \xi^2} + 2ab\frac{\partial^2 u}{\partial \xi\,\partial \eta} + a^2\frac{\partial^2 u}{\partial \eta^2}, \\
\frac{\partial^2 u}{\partial x\,\partial y} = -ab\frac{\partial^2 u}{\partial \xi^2} + (b^2 - a^2)\frac{\partial^2 u}{\partial \xi\,\partial \eta} + ab\frac{\partial^2 u}{\partial \eta^2} \\
\frac{\partial^2 u}{\partial y^2} = a^2\frac{\partial^2 u}{\partial \xi^2} - 2ab\frac{\partial^2 u}{\partial \xi\,\partial \eta} + b^2\frac{\partial^2 u}{\partial \eta^2}.
\end{gathered} \tag{4.1.9}$$

The original equation (4.1.1) now reads

$$\varepsilon\left\{A_{11}\frac{\partial^2 u}{\partial \xi^2} + 2A_{12}\frac{\partial^2 u}{\partial \xi\,\partial \eta} + A_{22}\frac{\partial^2 u}{\partial \eta^2}\right\} = \frac{\partial u}{\partial \eta}, \tag{4.1.10}$$

† These are defined parametrically by $dx/ds = a$, $dy/ds = b$ in accord with the familiar interpretation of Equation (4.1.7) as a derivative in the direction whose slope is b/a.

where the coefficients A_{ij} are given by

$$
\begin{aligned}
(a^2 + b^2)A_{11} &= \alpha_{11}b^2 - 2\alpha_{12}ab + \alpha_{22}a^2, \\
(a^2 + b^2)A_{12} &= \alpha_{11}ab + \alpha_{12}(b^2 - a^2) - \alpha_{22}ab, \\
(a^2 + b^2)A_{22} &= \alpha_{11}a^2 + 2\alpha_{12}ab + \alpha_{22}b^2.
\end{aligned}
\tag{4.1.11}
$$

Since the equation is still elliptic, we know that the discriminant

$$A_{12}^2 - A_{11}A_{22} < 0 \tag{4.1.12}$$

and, further, that

$$(a^2 + b^2)A_{22} = (\sqrt{\alpha_{11}}a \pm \sqrt{\alpha_{22}}b)^2 \mp 2ab(\sqrt{\alpha_{11}\alpha_{22}} \mp \alpha_{12}) > 0 \tag{4.1.13}$$

if we choose the upper sign for $ab < 0$, and the lower for $ab > 0$. The original domain has an image denoted by $\eta = \eta_B(\xi)$ in the $\xi\eta$-plane (Figure 4.2).

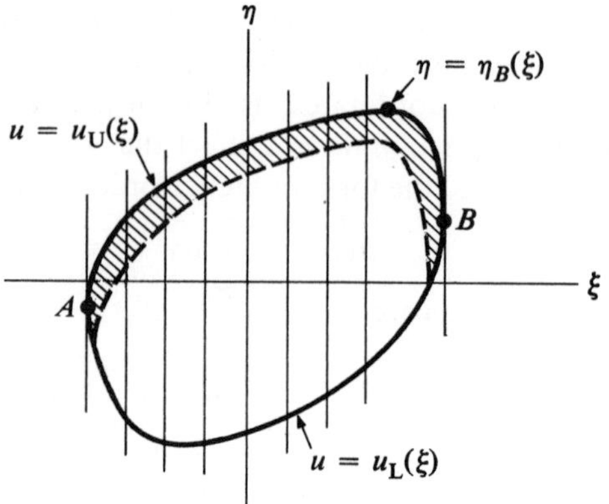

FIGURE 4.2 Subcharacteristic coordinates.

Let the assigned boundary values be denoted $u = u_U(\xi)$ on the upper part of the domain between A and B, and $u = u_L(\xi)$ on the lower part.

In the region of the boundary layer, we expect $\partial/\partial\eta$ to be large, so that a boundary-layer coordinate

$$\eta^* = \frac{\eta - \eta_B(\xi)}{\delta(\varepsilon)} \tag{4.1.14}$$

and an associated limit process can be introduced ($\varepsilon \to 0$, η^*, ξ fixed). The largest-order terms on the left-hand side of Equation (4.1.10) are, then, $O(\varepsilon/\delta^2)$, and the term on the right is $O(1/\delta)$. Thus, the boundary layer has thickness ε, and it follows that

$$\eta^* = \frac{\eta - \eta_B(\xi)}{\varepsilon}. \tag{4.1.15}$$

The boundary-layer solution is represented as the first term of an asymptotic expansion

$$u(x, y; \varepsilon) = u_{\mathrm{BL}}(\xi, \eta^*) + \cdots. \tag{4.1.16}$$

Note that, under the transformation from (ξ, η) to (ξ, η^*), we have

$$\frac{\partial u}{\partial \eta} \to \frac{1}{\varepsilon}\frac{\partial u}{\partial \eta^*}, \qquad \frac{\partial u}{\partial \xi} \to -\frac{1}{\varepsilon}\left(\frac{d\eta_B}{d\xi}\right)\frac{\partial u}{\partial \eta^*} + \cdots, \ldots,$$

so that the boundary-layer equation derived from Equation (4.1.10) is

$$K(\xi)\frac{\partial^2 u_{\mathrm{BL}}}{\partial \eta^{*2}} = \frac{\partial u_{\mathrm{BL}}}{\partial \eta^*}, \tag{4.1.17}$$

where

$$K(\xi) = A_{11}\left(\frac{d\eta_B}{d\xi}\right)^2 - 2A_{12}\left(\frac{d\eta_B}{d\xi}\right) + A_{22}. \tag{4.1.18}$$

Notice that the boundary-layer equation is an ordinary differential equation in this case. The assumed orders of magnitude are certainly all right, unless $d\eta_B/d\xi \to \infty$. The important case where $d\eta_B/d\xi = \infty$ along an arc, that is, the case of a subcharacteristic boundary, will be discussed later. The location of the boundary layer is now decided by the criterion that it must match with the outer solution $u_0(\xi)$.

This means (exponential) decay of the boundary-layer dependence on η^* in this case. The solution of Equation (4.1.17) is

$$u_{\mathrm{BL}}(\xi, \eta^*) = A(\xi) + B(\xi)\, e^{\eta^*/K(\xi)}. \tag{4.1.19}$$

Everything depends on the sign of $K(\xi)$. Since the equation is elliptic, there are no real roots $d\eta_B/d\xi$ of Equation (4.1.18), which is nothing but the characteristic form (Equation 4.1.4) expressed in A_{ij}. Thus, $K(\xi)$ does not vanish, and sign K = sign $A_{22} > 0$ from Equation (4.1.13).

Exponential decay occurs as $\eta^* \to -\infty$; the boundary layer appears on the upper boundary in Figure 4.2. With matching, the solution is thus

$$u_{\mathrm{BL}}(\xi) = u_{\mathrm{L}}(\xi) + \{u_{\mathrm{U}}(\xi) - u_{\mathrm{L}}(\xi)\}\, e^{\eta^*/K(\xi)}, \qquad u_0(\xi) = u_{\mathrm{L}}(\xi). \tag{4.1.20}$$

The boundary-layer solution in this case is also the first term of a uniformly valid composite expansion. The location of the boundary layer in the original figure (Figure 4.1) depends on the orientation of the coordinates (ξ, η); that is, only on the signs of (a, b). A qualitative sketch of the possibilities is given in Figure 4.3 below.

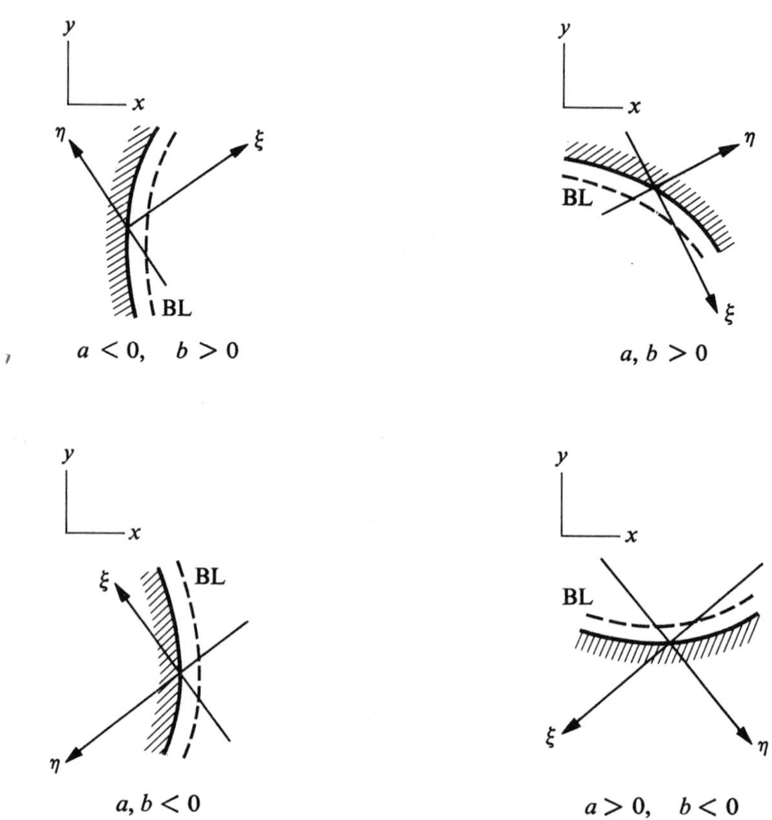

FIGURE 4.3 Various possibilities of boundary layers.

We still have to discuss the case where a segment of the boundary is subcharacteristic, say $\xi = \xi_S = \text{const}$ as in Figure 4.4. The outer solution carries the constant $u_L(\xi_S)$ as the boundary is approached, so that the boundary condition $u = u_S(\eta)$ is violated. In this case, it can be expected that $\partial/\partial\xi$ is large in the layer, so that the suitable boundary-layer coordinate (balancing $\partial^2/\partial\xi^2$ and $\partial/\partial\eta$) is

$$\xi^* = \frac{\xi - \xi_S}{\sqrt{\varepsilon}}, \tag{4.1.21}$$

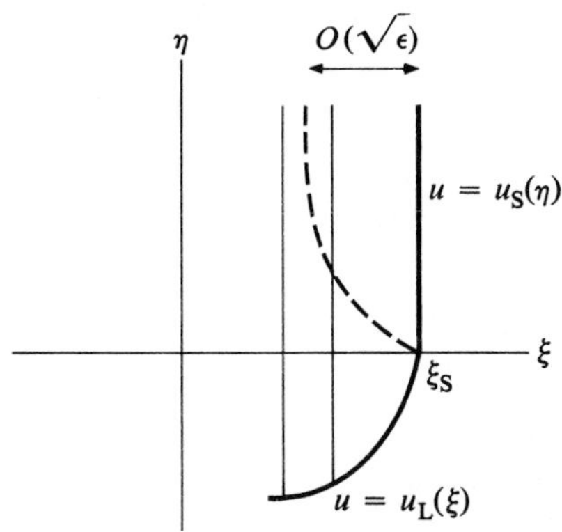

FIGURE 4.4 Boundary layer on a subcharacteristic.

and the boundary-layer thickness is $O(\sqrt{\varepsilon})$. The boundary-layer solution is the first term of an asymptotic expansion

$$u(\xi, \eta; \varepsilon) = u_{\mathrm{BL}}(\xi^*, \eta) + \cdots \tag{4.1.22}$$

associated with the limit ($\varepsilon \to 0$, ξ^*, η fixed). Thus, Equation (4.1.10) yields the boundary-layer equation

$$A_{11}\frac{\partial^2 u_{\mathrm{BL}}}{\partial \xi^{*2}} = \frac{\partial u_{\mathrm{BL}}}{\partial \eta}. \tag{4.1.23}$$

Here $A_{11} = \text{const}$, so that the boundary-layer equation is the heat equation, a partial differential equation in this case. Also $A_{11} > 0$, just as A_{22} (cf. Equation 4.1.13), so that $+\eta$ is the timelike coordinate. The solution of Equation (4.1.23) is to be found satisfying the boundary conditions at $u = u_{\mathrm{S}}(\eta)$ on $\xi = \xi_{\mathrm{S}}$ and matching to $u_0(\xi)$. The matching as usual can be carried out by an intermediate limit and results in

$$u_{\mathrm{BL}}(-\infty, \eta) = u_{\mathrm{L}}(\xi_{\mathrm{S}}). \tag{4.1.24}$$

Various representations can be used for the solution of the heat equation. For example, if a source representation is used on $\xi^* = 0$, we have

$$u_{\mathrm{BL}}(\xi^*, \eta) = u_{\mathrm{L}}(\xi_{\mathrm{S}}) + \frac{1}{2\sqrt{\pi A_{11}}}\int_0^{\eta} \exp\left[-\frac{\xi^{*2}}{4A_{11}(\eta - \bar{\eta})}\right]\frac{Q(\bar{\eta})\, d\bar{\eta}}{\sqrt{\eta - \bar{\eta}}}. \tag{4.1.25}$$

This matches u_0 as $\xi^* \to -\infty$, and the source strength $Q(\eta)$ is found from the solution of Abel's integral equation on the boundary $\xi^* = 0$,

$$u_S(\eta) - u_L(\xi_S) = \frac{1}{2\sqrt{\pi A_{11}}} \int_0^\eta \frac{Q(\bar\eta)}{\sqrt{\eta - \bar\eta}}\, d\bar\eta. \tag{4.1.26}$$

The solution of the integral equation is

$$Q(\eta) = \frac{1}{\pi}\frac{d}{d\eta}\int_0^\eta \frac{2[u_S(\bar\eta) - u_L(\xi_S)]\sqrt{\pi A_{11}}}{\sqrt{\eta - \bar\eta}}\, d\bar\eta. \tag{4.1.27}$$

Alternatively, a doublet representation could be used directly. In any case, the boundary layer spreads upwards in Figure 4.4 from its origin at ($\eta = 0$, $\xi = \xi_S$). For example, if $u_S = \text{const}$, the boundary-layer solution is

$$u_{BL}(\xi^*, \eta) = u_S + (u_L(\xi_S) - u_S)\,\text{erf}\,\frac{\xi^*}{2\sqrt{\eta}} = u_S + \{u_L(\xi_S) - u_S\}\,\text{erf}\,\frac{\xi - \xi_S}{2\sqrt{\varepsilon\eta}}. \tag{4.1.28}$$

It has been tacitly assumed here that the initial condition ($\eta = 0$) for the boundary-layer equation is the same as the condition at the edge of the boundary layer [$u_{BL} \to u_L(\xi_S)$ either as ($\xi^* \to -\infty$, η fixed) or as ($\eta \to 0$, ξ^* fixed].

It can be expected that more general elliptic cases have a similar structure. For example, for strictly linear equations where

$$a = a(x, y) \qquad \text{and} \qquad b = b(x, y), \tag{4.1.29}$$

the subcharacteristics are not straight but form a family of curves defined by the differential equation

$$\left(\frac{dy}{dx}\right) = \frac{b(x, y)}{a(x, y)}. \tag{4.1.30}$$

If no singular points of this equation occur in the domain of interest, then the behavior is qualitatively the same as before. If singular points do occur, then certain local expansions valid near such points may have to be constructed.

When the lower-order operator is quasi-linear, that is, when

$$a = a(x, y, u), \qquad b = b(x, y, u),$$

the solution of the limit equation $\varepsilon = 0$ (Equation 4.1.7) can become many-valued (steepening of fronts), and jumps in u (shock waves) may have to be inserted in order to obtain a one-valued solution. The structure of these jumps is then found from suitable boundary-layer equations.

On the other hand, if the higher-order operator is quasi-linear, that is,

$$\alpha_{ij} = \alpha_{ij}(x, y, u), \tag{4.1.31}$$

then the type of the equation is not known in advance in a given (x, y) domain but depends on the solution u. It is clear that various complications can arise, although a knowledge of the outer expansion should enable the overall-type structure to be sketched.

We return now to a simpler case and consider the features typical when the higher-order operator L_2 of Equation (4.1.1) is hyperbolic, and the coefficients are constant.

Hyperbolic case. $\alpha_{12}^2 - \alpha_{11}\alpha_{22} > 0$

All the essential features are illustrated by considering L_2 to be the simple wave operator, and t a coordinate corresponding to time. Assuming a suitable length scale, and normalizing the time by (length/signal speed), a dimensionless equation can be written

$$\varepsilon\left\{\frac{\partial^2 u}{\partial x^2} - \frac{\partial^2 u}{\partial t^2}\right\} = a\frac{\partial u}{\partial x} + b\frac{\partial u}{\partial t}. \tag{4.1.32}$$

Equation (4.1.32) has real characteristics (r, s)

$$r = t - x, \qquad s = t + x. \tag{4.1.33}$$

The characteristics serve to define the region of influence, propagating into the future, of a disturbance at a point Q (Figure 4.5). For the specification of

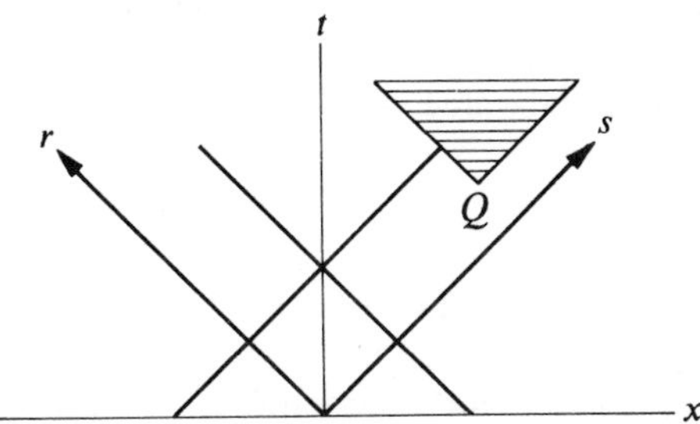

FIGURE 4.5 Characteristic coordinate system.

a boundary-value problem for Equation (4.1.32), the number of boundary conditions to be specified on an arc depends on the nature of the arc with respect to the characteristic directions of propagation. For example, on $t = 0$ typical initial conditions (u, u_t) must be given in order to find the solution for $t > 0$. For $x = 0$, one boundary condition (for example, u) must be given to define the solution (signal propagating from the boundary) for $x > 0$. Along $t = 0$, two characteristics lead from the boundary into the region of interest, but for $x = 0$, only one does. Generalizing this idea, the directions of an arc, with respect to the characteristic directions and the future direction, can be classified as timelike, spacelike, or characteristic. (See Figure 4.6, where the characteristics have arrows pointing to the future.)

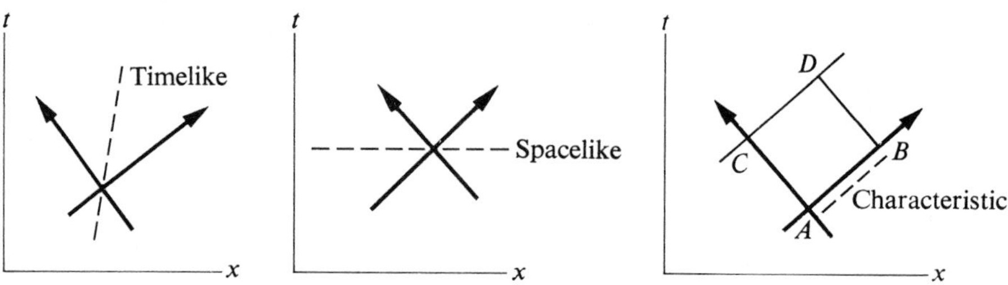

FIGURE 4.6 Directions of arcs.

One boundary condition is specified on the timelike arc corresponding to one characteristic leading into the adjacent region in which the solution is defined. Two boundary conditions are given on the spacelike arc corresponding to the two characteristics leading into the adjacent domain. When the boundary curves are characteristic, only one condition can be prescribed, and the characteristic relations must hold. The characteristic initial-value problem prescribes one condition on AB and on AC to define the solution in $ABCD$.

Now consider the initial-value problem in $-\infty < x < \infty$ for Equation (4.1.32):

$$u(x, 0) = F(x), \tag{4.1.34}$$

$$u_t(x, 0) = G(x). \tag{4.1.35}$$

(See Figure 4.7.)

According to the general theory, the solutions at a point $P(x, t)$ can depend only on that part of the initial data which can send a signal to P, the part cut out of the initial line by the backward running characteristics through P, $(x_1 < x < x_2)$. Now consider what happens as $\varepsilon \to 0$. In particular, consider the behavior of the limit equation

$$a\frac{\partial u}{\partial x} + b\frac{\partial u}{\partial t} = 0. \tag{4.1.36}$$

The solution in this case depends only on the data connected to P along a

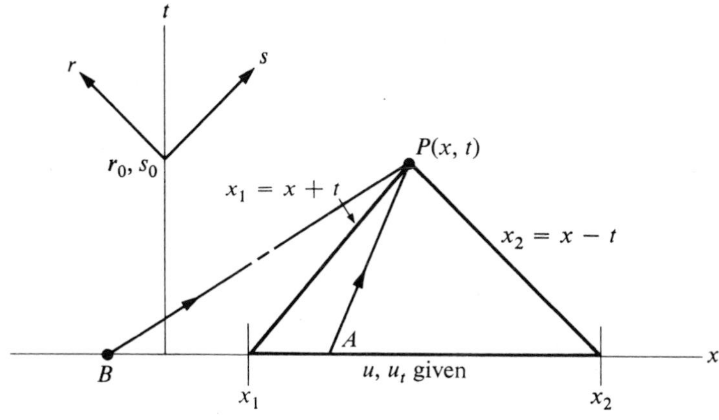

FIGURE 4.7 Initial-value problem.

subcharacteristic of the original equation

$$bx - at = \text{const} \tag{4.1.37}$$

The general solution of Equation (4.1.36) has the form

$$u(x, t) = f\left(x - \frac{a}{b}t\right). \tag{4.1.38}$$

Now if the subcharacteristic originates at point A between x_1 and x_2, that is if

$$\left|\frac{b}{a}\right| > 1, \tag{4.1.39}$$

it is reasonable to conceive of Equation (4.1.38) as a limiting form of the exact solution. In this case, as $\varepsilon \to 0$, it is only the data at point A which affects the solution in the limit. However, if

$$\left|\frac{a}{b}\right| > 1, \tag{4.1.40}$$

the subcharacteristic to P lies outside the usual domain of influence and originates at B. The speed of the disturbances associated with the sub-characteristics is greater than that of the characteristics. In this case, one can not expect the solution (Equation 4.1.38) to the limit problem to be a limit of the exact solution of Equation (4.1.32). This strange behavior is connected with the fact that condition (4.1.40) makes the solutions $u(x, t; \varepsilon)$ unstable; and this does not occur in the usual physical systems which are studied. For stability, it is necessary that the subcharacteristics be timelike. These points about stability are easily demonstrated from the characteristic form of Equation (4.1.32), and the rules for the propagation of jumps. If the characteristic coordinates (r, s) of Equation (4.1.33) are introduced, then Equation (4.1.32) becomes (see Figure 4.7)

$$-4\varepsilon\frac{\partial^2 u}{\partial r\,\partial s} = (b - a)\frac{\partial u}{\partial r} + (b + a)\frac{\partial u}{\partial s}, \tag{4.1.41}$$

and

$$\frac{\partial u}{\partial x} = -\frac{\partial u}{\partial r} + \frac{\partial u}{\partial s}, \qquad \frac{\partial u}{\partial t} = \frac{\partial u}{\partial r} + \frac{\partial u}{\partial s}.$$

Consider now the propagation along $(r = r_0 = \text{const})$ of a jump in the derivative $(\partial u/\partial r)$. Let

$$\kappa = \left[\frac{\partial u}{\partial r}\right]_{r=r_0} \equiv \frac{\partial u}{\partial r}(r_0+, s) - \frac{\partial u}{\partial r}(r_0-, s). \tag{4.1.42}$$

Assuming that u itself is continuous across $r = r_0$, we can evaluate Equation (4.1.41) at r_0+ and r_0- and form the difference to obtain

$$-4\varepsilon\frac{\partial \kappa}{\partial s} = (b - a)\kappa. \tag{4.1.43}$$

The solution has the form

$$\kappa = \kappa_0 \exp\left[-\frac{b - a}{4s}(s - s_0)\right]. \tag{4.1.44}$$

A jump across a characteristic propagates to infinity along that characteristic. If

$b - a > 0$, we have exponential decay and stability;

if

$b - a < 0$, we have exponential growth and instability.

A parallel discussion for jumps in $\partial u/\partial s$ across a characteristic $s = s_0$ gives the following results:

$b + a > 0$ implies exponential decay and stability;

$b + a < 0$ implies exponential growth and instability.

Combining these relations, we see that for stability we must have

$$b > 0 \quad \text{and} \quad \frac{b}{|a|} > 1. \tag{4.1.45}$$

Thus, we restrict the further discussion to the stable case in which Equation (4.1.45) is satisfied and study first the initial-value problem specified by Equations (4.1.34) and (4.1.35) as $\varepsilon \to 0$.

Initial-Value Problem. Since the limit solution (4.1.38) can only satisfy one initial condition, the existence of an initial boundary layer, analogous to that discussed in Section 2.2, can be expected. An initially valid expansion can be expressed in the coordinates $(\tilde{t}, x)$, where

$$\tilde{t} = \frac{t}{\delta(\varepsilon)}, \qquad \delta \to 0. \tag{4.1.46}$$

The associated limit process has ($x, \tilde{t}$ fixed) and consists in a "vertical" approach to the initial line. The expansion has the form

$$u(x, t; \varepsilon) = U_0(x, \tilde{t}) + \beta_1(\varepsilon)U_1(x, \tilde{t}) + \cdots. \tag{4.1.47}$$

In order to satisfy the initial conditions independent of ε, we need

$$\beta_1(\varepsilon) = \delta,$$

and then we obtain

$$\frac{\partial u}{\partial t}(x, t; \varepsilon) = \frac{1}{\delta}\frac{\partial U_0}{\partial \tilde{t}} + \frac{\partial U_1}{\partial \tilde{t}} + \cdots. \tag{4.1.48}$$

Thus, to take care of the initial conditions (Equations 4.1.34, 4.1.35), we need

$$U_0(x, 0) = F(x), \qquad U_1(x, 0) = U_2(x, 0) = \cdots = 0, \tag{4.1.49}$$

$$\frac{\partial U_0}{\partial \tilde{t}}(x, 0) = 0, \qquad \frac{\partial U_1}{\partial \tilde{t}}(x, 0) = G(x), \qquad \frac{\partial U_2}{\partial \tilde{t}}(x, 0) = \cdots = 0. \tag{4.1.50}$$

Using the inner expansion in Equation (4.1.32), we have

$$\varepsilon\left\{\frac{\partial^2 U_0}{\partial x^2} + \delta\frac{\partial^2 U_1}{\partial x^2} + \cdots - \frac{1}{\delta^2}\frac{\partial^2 U_0}{\partial \tilde{t}^2} - \frac{\partial^2 U_1}{\partial \tilde{t}^2} + \cdots\right\}$$
$$= a\frac{\partial U_0}{\partial x} + \cdots + \frac{b}{\delta}\frac{\partial U_0}{\partial \tilde{t}} + b\frac{\partial U_1}{\partial \tilde{t}} + \cdots.$$

A second-order equation results for U_0 only if

$$\delta = \varepsilon$$

and, with this choice, the following sequence of approximate equations is obtained:

$$\frac{\partial^2 U_0}{\partial \tilde{t}^2} + b\frac{\partial U_0}{\partial \tilde{t}} = 0, \tag{4.1.51}$$

$$\frac{\partial^2 U_1}{\partial \tilde{t}^2} + b\frac{\partial U_1}{\partial \tilde{t}} = -a\frac{\partial U_0}{\partial x}, \tag{4.1.52}$$

$$\vdots$$

In accordance with the general ideas of the first part of this Section, the boundary-layer equations are ordinary differential equations, since the boundary layer does not occur on a subcharacteristic. This must be true for any hyperbolic initial-value problem, since a spacelike arc can never be subcharacteristic. Equations (4.1.49) and (4.1.50) provide the initial conditions for the initial-layer equations, and the solutions are easily found:

$$U_0(x, \tilde{t}) = F(x), \tag{4.1.53}$$

$$U_1(x, \tilde{t}) = \left[G(x) + \frac{a}{b}F'(x)\right][1 - e^{-\tilde{t}}] - \frac{a}{b}\tilde{t}F'(x). \tag{4.1.54}$$

Thus, finally, we have the initially valid expansion (Equation 4.1.47)

$$u(x, t; \varepsilon) = F(x) + \varepsilon\left\{\left[G(x) + \frac{a}{b}F'(x)\right][1 - e^{-\tilde{t}}] - \frac{a}{b}\tilde{t}F'(x)\right\} + \cdots. \tag{4.1.55}$$

These solutions contain persistent terms as well as typical boundary-layer decay terms with a time scale $t = \varepsilon$. The behavior of Equation (4.1.55) provides initial conditions for an outer expansion. First, we construct the outer expansion, based on the limit process ($\varepsilon \to 0$, x, t fixed), the first term of which is the limit solution (4.1.38). The orders of the various terms are evident from the orders in Equation (4.1.55). Thus, we have

$$u(x, t; \varepsilon) = u_0(x, t) + \varepsilon u_1(x, t) + \varepsilon^2 u_2(x, t) + \cdots. \tag{4.1.56}$$

In the outer expansion, the higher-order derivatives are small and the lower-order operator dominates. The sequence of equations which approximates Equation (4.1.32) is

$$a\frac{\partial u_0}{\partial x} + b\frac{\partial u_0}{\partial t} = 0, \tag{4.1.57}$$

$$a\frac{\partial u_1}{\partial x} + b\frac{\partial u_1}{\partial t} = \left(\frac{\partial^2 u_0}{\partial x^2} - \frac{\partial^2 u_0}{\partial t^2}\right), \tag{4.1.58}$$

$$\vdots$$

The general solutions can all be expressed in terms of arbitrary functions:

$$u_0 = f(\xi), \qquad \xi = x - \frac{a}{b}t. \tag{4.1.59}$$

The equation for u_1 becomes

$$a\frac{\partial u_1}{\partial x} + b\frac{\partial u_1}{\partial t} = \left(1 - \frac{a^2}{b^2}\right)f''(\xi). \tag{4.1.60}$$

This is easily solved by introducing ($\tau = t$, ξ) as coordinates, and the result is

$$u_1(x, t) = \frac{a}{b^2}\frac{b^2 - a^2}{b^2 + a^2}\left(x + \frac{b}{a}t\right)f''(\xi) + f_1(\xi). \tag{4.1.61}$$

Thus, the outer expansion is

$$u(x, t) = f(\xi) + \varepsilon\left\{f_1(\xi) + \frac{a}{b^2}\frac{b^2 - a^2}{b^2 + a^2}\left(x + \frac{b}{a}t\right)f''(\xi)\right\} + \cdots. \tag{4.1.62}$$

The arbitrary functions, f, f_1, etc., in the outer expansion (Equation 4.1.62) must be determined by matching Equation (4.1.55). A limit intermediate to the two already considered has (x, t_η fixed) as $\varepsilon \to 0$:

$$t_\eta = \frac{t}{\eta(\varepsilon)}, \qquad \varepsilon \ll \eta \ll 1. \tag{4.1.63}$$

Thus, we have

$$t = \eta t_\eta \to 0, \qquad \tilde{t} = \frac{\eta}{\varepsilon}t_\eta \to \infty.$$

Under this limit, the initially valid expansion (Equation 4.1.55) becomes

$$u(x, t; \varepsilon) = F(x) + \varepsilon\left\{G(x) + \frac{a}{b}F'(x) - \frac{a}{b}\frac{\eta}{\varepsilon}t_\eta F'(x)\right\} + \cdots. \tag{4.1.64}$$

In the outer expansion, we have

$$f(\xi) = f\left(x - \frac{a}{b}t\right), \qquad f\left(x - \frac{a}{b}\eta t_\eta\right) = f(x) - \frac{a}{b}\eta t_\eta f'(x) + \cdots.$$

The outer expansion approaches

$$u(x, t; \varepsilon) = f(x) - \frac{a}{b}\eta t_\eta f'(x) + \cdots + \varepsilon f_1(x) - \frac{a}{b^2}\frac{b^2 - a^2}{b^2 + a^2}f''(x) + \cdots. \tag{4.1.65}$$

The terms of order one in Equations (4.1.64) and (4.1.65) can be matched, and then the terms of order η are matched identically; terms of order ε can also be matched. Thus, we have

$$f(x) = F(x), \tag{4.1.66}$$

$$f_1(x) + \frac{a}{b^2}\frac{b^2 - a^2}{b^2 + a^2} f''(x) = G(x) + \frac{a}{b}F'(x). \tag{4.1.67}$$

The final result expresses the outer expansion in terms of the given initial values,

$$u(x, t; \varepsilon) = F\left(x - \frac{a}{b}t\right)$$
$$+\varepsilon\left\{\frac{b^2 - a^2}{b^3} tF''\left(x - \frac{a}{b}t\right) + \frac{a}{b}F'\left(x - \frac{a}{b}t\right) + G\left(x - \frac{a}{b}t\right)\right\}. \tag{4.1.68}$$

We can see that after a little while, the solution is dominated by the given initial value of u which propagates along the subcharacteristic.

Radiation Problems. We next consider a signaling or radiation problem in which boundary conditions are prescribed on a timelike arc and propagate into the quiescent medium in $x > 0$. For the first problem, the boundary condition is prescribed at $x = 0$, and we have to distinguish two cases according to the slope of the subcharacteristics, that is, whether they run into or out of the boundary $x = 0$. (See Figure 4.8.) The subcharacteristics are given by

$$\xi = x - \frac{a}{b}t = \text{const}, \tag{4.1.69}$$

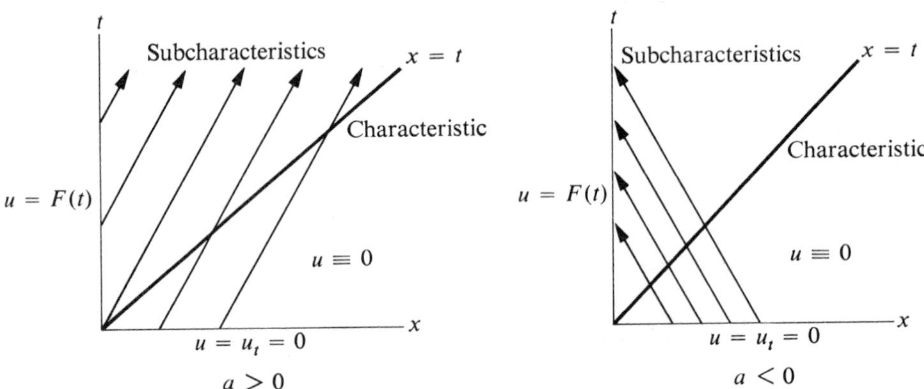

FIGURE 4.8 Radiation problems.

and for $a > 0$, outgoing, and $a < 0$, incoming, the boundary condition is

$$u(0, t) = F(t), \qquad t > 0. \tag{4.1.70}$$

There is a real discontinuity in the function and for its derivative along the characteristic curve $x = t$, but the intensity of the jump decays exponentially ($b > |a|$) according to the considerations of Equation (4.1.44). The solution is identically zero for $x > t$.

$a > 0$. *Outgoing subcharacteristics.* The "outer" solution is an asymptotic expansion of the same form as before:

$$u(x, t; \varepsilon) = u_0(x, t) + \varepsilon u_1(x, t) + \cdots. \tag{4.1.71}$$

The sequence of equations satisfied by u_i is the same as before. Equations (4.1.57) and (4.1.58) and the solution u_0 can be written

$$u_0 = f(\zeta), \qquad \text{where} \quad \zeta = t - \frac{b}{a}x. \tag{4.1.72}$$

The boundary condition (Equation 4.1.70) can be satisfied by identifying $f = F$, so that the first-approximation outer solution is

$$u_0 = \begin{cases} 0, & t < \dfrac{b}{a}x, \\ F\left(t - \dfrac{b}{a}x\right), & t > \dfrac{b}{a}x. \end{cases} \tag{4.1.73}$$

This solution, however, has a discontinuity on the particular subcharacteristic through the origin. Such a discontinuity is not permitted in the solution to the exact equation (4.1.32) with $\varepsilon > 0$, since any discontinuities can appear only on characteristics. Thus, to obtain a uniformly valid solution, a suitable boundary layer must be introduced on the particular subcharacteristic $\zeta = 0$ which supports the discontinuity in the outer solution. In order to derive the boundary-layer equations, we consider a limit process in which $(\tilde{x}, \tilde{t})$ are fixed, where

$$\tilde{x} = \frac{x - (a/b)t}{\delta(\varepsilon)}, \qquad \delta(\varepsilon) \to 0\,; \tag{4.1.74}$$

$$\tilde{t} = t, \tag{4.1.75}$$

and try to choose $\delta(\varepsilon)$ so that a meaningful problem results. Here $\delta(\varepsilon)$ is the measure of thickness of the boundary layer. The expansion has the form

$$u(x, t; \varepsilon) = U_0(\tilde{x}, \tilde{t}) + \mu(\varepsilon)U_1(\tilde{x}, \tilde{t}) + \cdots. \tag{4.1.76}$$

The first term is of order one, so that it can match to Equation (4.1.73).

The derivatives of Equation (4.1.76) have the form

$$\frac{\partial u}{\partial x}(x, t; \varepsilon) = \frac{1}{\delta}\frac{\partial U_0}{\partial \tilde{x}} + \frac{\mu}{\delta}\frac{\partial U_1}{\partial \tilde{x}} + \cdots,$$

$$\frac{\partial u}{\partial t}(x, t; \varepsilon) = \frac{-a/b}{\delta(\varepsilon)}\frac{\partial U_0}{\partial \tilde{x}} + \frac{\partial U_0}{\partial \tilde{t}} - \frac{a/b}{\delta}\frac{\partial U_1}{\partial \tilde{x}} + \cdots.$$

The operator on the right-hand side of Equation (4.1.32) now has the form

$$a\frac{\partial u}{\partial x} + b\frac{\partial u}{\partial t} = b\left[\frac{\partial U_0}{\partial \tilde{t}} + \mu(\varepsilon)\frac{\partial U_1}{\partial \tilde{t}} + \cdots\right]. \tag{4.1.77}$$

The dominant terms of the wave operator are $U_{0\tilde{x}\tilde{x}}$, so that Equation (4.1.32) becomes

$$\frac{\varepsilon}{\delta^2}\left\{\frac{\partial^2 U_0}{\partial \tilde{x}^2} + \cdots - \frac{a^2}{b^2}\frac{\partial^2 U_0}{\partial \tilde{x}^2} + \cdots\right\} = b\frac{\partial U_0}{\partial \tilde{t}} + \cdots. \tag{4.1.78}$$

The distinguished limiting case, which results in a nontrivial equation, has

$$\delta = \sqrt{\varepsilon}. \tag{4.1.79}$$

The boundary-layer thickness here is an order of magnitude larger than in the initial boundary layer. The boundary-layer equation is, then, a partial differential equation; the boundary layer is on a subcharacteristic. From Equation (4.1.78), we obtain

$$\kappa\frac{\partial^2 U_0}{\partial \tilde{x}^2} = \frac{\partial U_0}{\partial \tilde{t}}, \tag{4.1.80}$$

where $\kappa = (1 - a^2/b^2)/b > 0$. Here $\kappa > 0$ assures that $\tilde{t} = t$ is a positive timelike direction and that Equation (4.1.80) is an ordinary heat or diffusion equation which describes the resolution of the discontinuity of the outer expansion on $\zeta = 0$. The boundary conditions for Equation (4.1.80) have to come from matching with the outer expansion. Matching for this problem is carried out with a class of intermediate limits (x_η, t fixed), where

$$x_\eta = \frac{x - (a/b)t}{\eta(\varepsilon)}, \qquad \sqrt{\varepsilon} \ll \eta \ll 1. \tag{4.1.81}$$

In the limit, then, we have

$$x - \frac{a}{b}t = \eta x_\eta \to 0, \qquad \tilde{x} = \frac{x - (a/b)t}{\sqrt{\varepsilon}} = \frac{\eta}{\sqrt{\varepsilon}}x_\eta \to \pm\infty.$$

Under this limit, the outer and boundary-layer expansions behave as follows:

OUTER

$$u(x, t; \varepsilon) = u_0 + \cdots \quad \begin{cases} \to 0, & t < \dfrac{b}{a}x, \\[2ex] \to F(0+), & t > \dfrac{b}{a}x; \end{cases} \tag{4.1.82}$$

BOUNDARY LAYER

$$u(x, t; \varepsilon) = U_0(\tilde{x}, t) + \cdots \to U_0(\pm\infty, t) + \cdots. \tag{4.1.83}$$

For matching, the terms in Equations (4.1.82) and (4.1.83) must be the same, and this provides the boundary conditions illustrated in Figure 4.9 for the

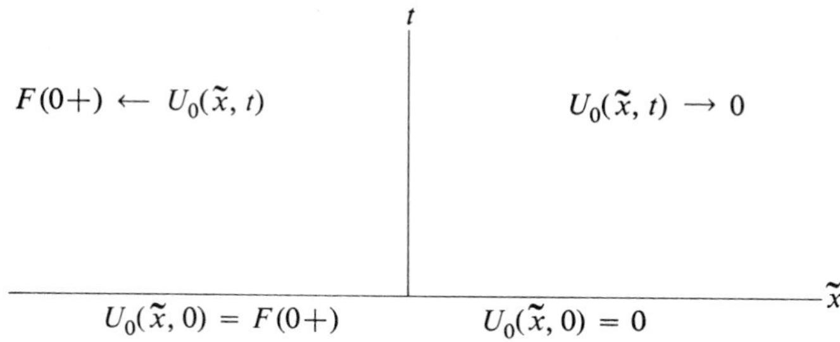

FIGURE 4.9 Wave-front problem.

boundary-layer equations (Equation 4.1.80). Initial conditions are chosen here consistent with the boundary and in such a way that the physical process represents the resolution of the discontinuity at $\zeta = 0$. A rigorous treatment of the initial conditions demands a discussion of initially valid expansions, which is not given here. The main point here is the nature of the boundary-layer equation. The solution corresponding to the conditions stated is

$$U_0(\tilde{x}, t) = \frac{F(0+)}{2} \operatorname{erfc}\left(\frac{\tilde{x}}{2\sqrt{t}}\right). \tag{4.1.84}$$

The discontinuity of the outer solution is replaced here by the diffusive solution of the heat equation.

$a < 0$ *Incoming subcharacteristics.* The qualitative difference of this case and the case just discussed is striking. If an outer expansion is contemplated of the form of Equation (4.1.71), the only reasonable solution of the form

$f(t - (b/a)x)$ is zero, since now disturbances propagate along the subcharacteristics from the quiescent region to the boundary. Thus, we have

$$u_0 \equiv 0. \tag{4.1.85}$$

The discontinuity occurs at the boundary $x = 0$, and the boundary layer occurs at $x = 0$. The boundary-layer equations should be ordinary differential equations, since again in this case the boundary layer is not on a subcharacteristic. To derive these equations, consider ($\tilde{x}$, $\tilde{t}$ fixed), where

$$\tilde{x} = \frac{x}{\delta(\varepsilon)}, \qquad \tilde{t} = t \qquad \text{as} \quad \varepsilon \to 0. \tag{4.1.86}$$

The expansion is of the usual form,

$$u(x, t; \varepsilon) = U_0(\tilde{x}, \tilde{t}) + \nu_1(\varepsilon)U_1(\tilde{x}, \tilde{t}) + \cdots. \tag{4.1.87}$$

The basic equation (Equation 4.1.32) takes the form

$$\frac{\varepsilon}{\delta^2}\frac{\partial^2 U_0}{\partial x^2} + \cdots = \frac{a}{\delta}\frac{\partial U_0}{\partial \tilde{x}} + b\frac{\partial U_0}{\partial \tilde{t}} + \cdots. \tag{4.1.88}$$

Again, $\delta = \varepsilon$ is a distinguished case for the boundary layer not on a subcharacteristic and

$$\frac{\partial^2 U_0}{\partial \tilde{x}^2} = a\frac{\partial U_0}{\partial \tilde{x}}. \tag{4.1.89}$$

The solution satisfying the boundary condition of Equation (4.1.70) is

$$U_0(\tilde{x}, \tilde{t}) = F(\tilde{t})\, e^{a\tilde{x}}, \qquad a < 0. \tag{4.1.90}$$

The boundary layer here is just a region of exponential decay adjacent to the boundary.

Problems

4.1.1 Consider the boundary-layer problem for $u(x, t; \varepsilon)$ in $x > (a/b)t > 0$, as $\varepsilon \to 0$ for Equation (4.1.32), with the boundary conditions

$$u = \frac{\partial u}{\partial t} = 0, \qquad t = 0; \qquad u\left(\frac{a}{b}t, t\right) = F(t), \qquad t > 0.$$

Construct an integral representation of the solution to the first-approximation boundary-layer equation.

4.1.2 An incompressible fluid (density ρ, specific heat c, thermal conductivity k) flows through a circular grid of radius L located at $x = 0$. The velocity of the fluid is assumed always to be U in the $+x$-direction. The temperature of the grid is maintained at $T = T_B = \text{const}$, and the temperature of the fluid at upstream infinity is T_∞. Thus, the differential equation for the temperature field is

$$\kappa\left\{\frac{\partial^2 T}{\partial x^2} + \frac{\partial^2 T}{\partial r^2} + \frac{1}{r}\frac{\partial T}{\partial r}\right\} = U\frac{\partial T}{\partial x},$$

where

$$\kappa = k/\rho c.$$

Write the problem in suitable dimensionless coordinates. [Use

$$x^* = x/L, \qquad r^* = r/L, \qquad T(x, r) = T_\infty + (T_B - T_\infty)\theta(x^*, r^*).]$$

Study the behavior of the solution for ε small, where

$$\varepsilon = \kappa/UL.$$

Find the "outer" solution and the necessary boundary layers. In particular show that the rate of heat transfer to the fluid is independent of k as $\varepsilon \to 0$.

Discuss the validity of these solutions for the regions where $x^* \to \infty$.

4.1.3 Consider heat transfer to a viscous incompressible fluid flowing steadily in a circular pipe of radius R. The equation for the temperature distribution is

$$\rho c u(r)\frac{\partial T}{\partial x} = k\left\{\frac{\partial^2 T}{\partial r^2} + \frac{1}{r}\frac{\partial T}{\partial r} + \frac{\partial^2 T}{\partial x^2}\right\},$$

where ρ = fluid density. c = fluid specific heat = const, k = thermal conductivity = const. For laminar flow, the velocity distribution in the pipe is parabolic:

$$\frac{u(r)}{U} = 1 - \left(\frac{r}{R}\right)^2.$$

Let the temperature be raised at the wall from the constant value T_0 for $x < 0$ to T_1 for $x > 0$. (See Figure 4.10.)

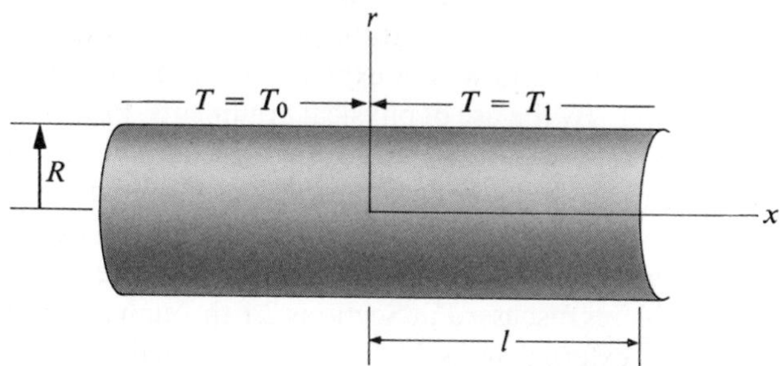

FIGURE 4.10 Heat transfer in pipe flow.

For

$$\varepsilon = \frac{k/\rho c}{UR} \ll 1 \qquad \left(\text{note that } \varepsilon = \frac{1}{RePr}\right),$$

construct a suitable boundary-layer theory. Thus, show that the heat transferred to the fluid $Q(l)$ in the length l is approximately

$$\frac{Q}{([k(T_i - T_0)]/R)(2\pi Rl)} = K^*\left(\frac{R}{l}\right)^{1/3},$$

and evaluate the constant K^*.

[*Hint*: Use similarity methods or Laplace transform on the boundary-layer equation.]

Indicate the mathematical problem to be solved for the next higher-order approximation. Is there a singularity of heat transfer at $x = 0$ in the higher approximations?

4.1.4 Construct the Riemann function R for

$$\varepsilon(u_{xx} - u_{tt}) = au_x + bu_t,$$

so that the solution of the initial value with

$$u(x, 0) = 0, \qquad u_t(x, 0) = V(x)$$

is represented as

$$u(x, t; \varepsilon) = \int_{x-t}^{x+t} R(x - \xi, t; \varepsilon)V(\xi)\, d\xi.$$

Show how inner and outer expansions as $\varepsilon \to 0$ can be obtained from the exact solution.

4.2 Boundary-layer theory in viscous incompressible flow

The original physical problem from which the ideas of mathematical boundary-layer theory originated was the problem of viscous, incompressible flow past an object. The aim was to explain the origin of the resistance in a slightly viscous fluid. By the use of physical arguments, Prandtl deduced that for small values of the viscosity, a thin region near the solid boundary (where the fluid is brought to rest) is described by approximate boundary-layer equations, and the flow outside this region is essentially inviscid. These ideas find a natural mathematical expression in terms of the ideas of singular perturbation problems discussed in Sections 2.1 through 2.6. In this Section, we show how the external inviscid flow is associated with an outer-limit process and the boundary layer with an inner-limit process. The boundary condition of no slip is lost, and the order of the equations is lowered in the outer limit, so that the problem is indeed singular in the terminology used previously.

In order to illustrate these ideas explicitly, the entire discussion should be carried out in dimensionless variables. Consider uniform flow with velocity U past an object with characteristic length L (Figure 4.11). Given the fluid

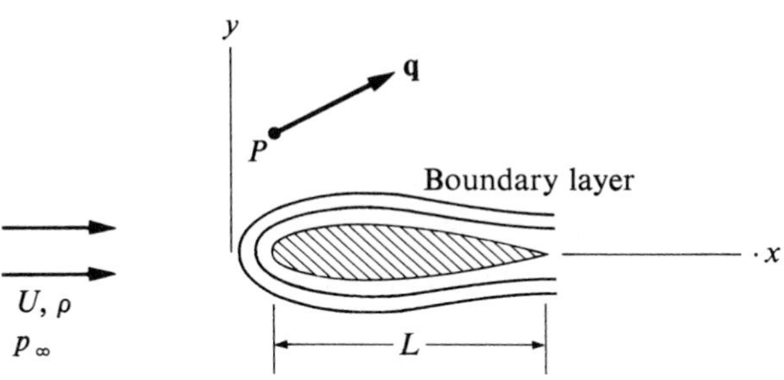

FIGURE 4.11 Flow past a body.

density ρ and viscosity coefficient μ, there is one overall dimensionless number, the Reynolds number, Re:

$$\mathrm{Re} = UL\rho/\mu = UL/\nu. \tag{4.2.1}$$

Pressure does not enter a dimensionless parameter since the level of pressure has no effect on the flow.† The limit processes are all concerned with $\mathrm{Re} \to \infty$ or

$$\varepsilon = 1/\mathrm{Re} \to 0. \tag{4.2.2}$$

Now, make all velocities dimensionless with U, all lengths with L, and the pressure with ρU^2. The full problem is expressed in the continuity and momentum equations, written in an invariant vector form:

NAVIER–STOKES EQUATIONS:

$$\operatorname{div} \mathbf{q} = 0, \tag{4.2.3a}$$

$$\underbrace{\mathbf{q} \cdot \nabla \mathbf{q} \equiv \nabla\left(\frac{q^2}{2}\right) - (\mathbf{q} \times \boldsymbol{\omega})}_{\text{transport or inertia}} = \underbrace{-\nabla p}_{\text{pressure}} - \underbrace{\varepsilon \operatorname{curl} \boldsymbol{\omega}}_{\text{viscous body force}}, \tag{4.2.3b}$$

† That is, the Mach number is always zero.

where

$$\boldsymbol{\omega} = \text{vorticity} = \operatorname{curl} \mathbf{q}. \tag{4.2.3c}$$

Vorticity represents the angular velocity of a fluid element. Also it can be shown that the viscous force per area on a surface is

$$\boldsymbol{\tau}_v = -\varepsilon(\boldsymbol{\omega} \times \mathbf{n}), \qquad \mathbf{n} = \text{outward normal (dimensionless)}, \tag{4.2.4}$$

$$\mathbf{q}(\infty) = \mathbf{i}, \qquad \text{uniform flow}, \tag{4.2.5}$$

$$\mathbf{q} = \mathbf{q}_b = 0 \qquad \text{on the body} \qquad \text{(no slip condition)}. \tag{4.2.6}$$

The outer expansion is carried out, keeping the representative point P fixed and letting $\varepsilon \to 0$. The expansion has the form of an asymptotic expansion in terms of a suitable sequence $\alpha_i(\varepsilon)$:

$$\begin{aligned} \mathbf{q}(P;\varepsilon) &= \mathbf{q}_0(P) + \alpha_1(\varepsilon)\mathbf{q}_1(P) + \cdots, \qquad && \varepsilon \to 0; \\ p(P;\varepsilon) &= p_0(P) + \alpha_1(\varepsilon)p_1(P) + \cdots, && P \text{ fixed}. \end{aligned} \tag{4.2.7}$$

Here $(\mathbf{q}_0, p_0)$ represents an inviscid flow. In many cases of interest, this flow is irrotational. This fact can be demonstrated by considering the equation for vorticity propagation obtained from curl (4.2.3b),

$$\operatorname{curl}(\mathbf{q} \times \boldsymbol{\omega}) = \varepsilon \operatorname{curl} \operatorname{curl} \boldsymbol{\omega}. \tag{4.2.8}$$

For plane flow, the vorticity vector is normal to the xy-plane and can be written

$$\boldsymbol{\omega} = \mathbf{k}\omega(P), \qquad \text{plane flow}. \tag{4.2.9}$$

Thus, Equation (4.2.8) can be written

$$\mathbf{q} \cdot \nabla\omega = \varepsilon\nabla^2\omega. \tag{4.2.10}$$

The physical interpretation of Equation (4.2.10) is that the vorticity is transported along the streamlines but diffuses (like heat) due to the action of viscosity. The solid boundary is the only source of vorticity; as $\varepsilon \to 0$, the diffusion is small and is confined to a narrow boundary layer close to the body (except if the flow separates). Under the outer limit, Equation (4.2.10) becomes

$$\mathbf{q} \cdot \nabla\omega = 0, \tag{4.2.11}$$

so that vorticity is constant along a streamline.† For uniform flow, $\omega = 0$ at ∞, and hence $\omega = 0$ throughout. We obtain, in terms of the outer expansion,

$$\boldsymbol{\omega}_0 = \operatorname{curl} \mathbf{q}_0 = 0. \tag{4.2.12}$$

† $\mathbf{q} \cdot \nabla$ is the operator of differentiation along a streamline.

Thus, the basic outer flow $(\mathbf{q}_0, p_0)$ is a potential flow. For example, in cartesian components, $\mathbf{q}_0 = u_0\mathbf{i} + v_0\mathbf{j}$, and the components can be expressed by an analytic function,

$$u_0 - iv_0 = F'(z), \qquad z = x + iy. \tag{4.2.13}$$

The problem is thus purely kinematic. Integration of the limit form of Equations (4.2.3) along a streamline yields Bernoulli's law:

$$p_0 = \tfrac{1}{2}(1 - q_0^2), \qquad p_0(\infty) = 0, \tag{4.2.14}$$

and accounts for all the dynamics of potential flow. In addition, stream (ψ) and potential (ϕ) functions exist

$$\phi + i\psi = F(z), \qquad u_0 = \phi_x = \psi_y, \qquad v_0 = \phi_y = -\psi_x. \tag{4.2.15}$$

An important question, which can not be answered by the present approach, is what potential flow $F(z)$ to choose for the problem of high Re flow past a given body. Real flows tend to separate toward the rear of a closed body and to generate a viscous wake. This implies that the correct limiting potential flow separates from the body. Furthermore, if Re is sufficiently high, turbulence sets in, so that a description under the steady Navier–Stokes equations is not valid. Thus, for our purposes we consider the simplest potential flow, for example, that which closes around the body. The approximation is understood to be valid only in a region of limited extent near the nose of the body.

Now, with respect to the higher terms of the outer expansion, the following observation can be made. Every (q_i, p_i) is a potential flow. This follows by induction from the fact that the viscous body force is zero in a potential flow:

$$\operatorname{curl} \boldsymbol{\omega}_0 = 0 \qquad \text{or} \qquad \nabla^2_{(x,y)}\mathbf{q}_0 = 0. \tag{4.2.16}$$

The inner expansion is derived from a limit process in which a representative point $\tilde{P}$ approaches the boundary as $\varepsilon \to 0$. The boundary layer in this problem is along a streamline of the inviscid flow, a subcharacteristic of the full problem. Characteristic surfaces in general are the locus of possible discontinuities, and streamlines of an inviscid flow can support a discontinuity in vorticity. In the inviscid limit in which the external flow is potential flow, this discontinuity is only at the solid surface where the tangential velocity jumps (if the boundary condition of zero velocity on the surface is enforced). Now the vorticity equation (Equation 4.2.10) has the same structure as the general partial differential equation discussed in Section 4.1. The boundary layer resolving the vorticity occurs on a subcharacteristic and, hence, should be of $O(\sqrt{\varepsilon})$ in thickness. Thus, symbolically,

$$\tilde{P} = \frac{P - P_b}{\sqrt{\varepsilon}}, \qquad P_b = \text{point of the boundary,} \tag{4.2.17}$$

is held fixed as $\varepsilon \to 0$. This order of magnitude can also be checked explicitly as below.

Before considering flow past a body, however, it is worthwhile to outline the simpler problem of purely radial flow in a wedge-shaped sector. (Figure 4.12). For this simple geometry, the Navier–Stokes equations simplify

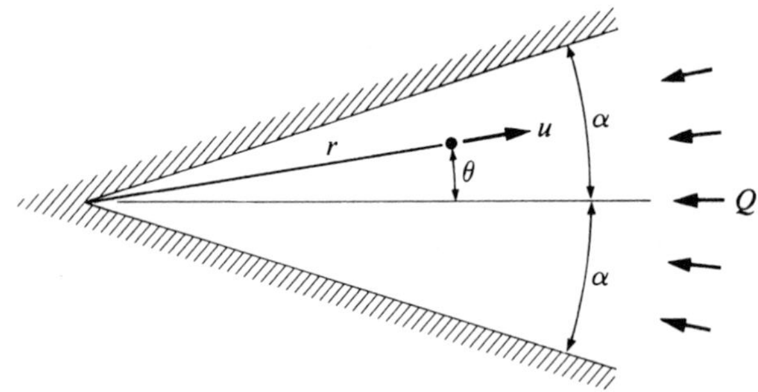

FIGURE 4.12 Viscous sink flow in a sector.

sufficiently to allow an exact solution to be constructed. For inflow, there is a sink at the origin, and the solutions are well behaved as $\mathrm{Re} \to \infty$ in the sense that boundary layers form near the walls. For outflow, however, the solutions can exhibit a much more complicated structure, including regions of back-flow. The limit solutions for this case as $\mathrm{Re} \to \infty$ may have vortex sheets in the interior of the channel. Only the case of inflow is considered here.

4.2.1 Radial viscous inflow

The mass flux, per unit width of channel, Q = mass/sec-length, is prescribed. The overall Reynolds number is, thus,

$$\mathrm{Re} = \frac{Q}{\mu} = \frac{1}{\varepsilon}. \tag{4.2.18}$$

By dimensional reasoning, the radial velocity and pressure must be of the form

$$\text{outward radial velocity} = \frac{Q}{\mu r} f(\theta), \tag{4.2.19}$$

$$\text{pressure} = \rho \frac{Q^2}{\mu^2 r^2} g(\theta). \tag{4.2.20}$$

Thus, the full Navier–Stokes equations become ordinary differential equations:

$$\text{radial momentum,} \qquad -f^2(\theta) = 2g(\theta) + \varepsilon \frac{d^2 f}{d\theta^2}; \tag{4.2.21}$$

$$\text{tangential momentum,} \qquad 0 = -\frac{dg}{d\theta} + 2\varepsilon \frac{df}{d\theta}. \tag{4.2.22}$$

Mass conservation leads to the normalization

$$-\int_{-\alpha}^{\alpha} f(\theta)\, d\theta = 1, \tag{4.2.23}$$

while the condition of no slip at the walls is

$$f(\pm\alpha) = 0. \tag{4.2.24}$$

In order to study the solution as $\varepsilon \to 0$, outer and inner expansions, as indicated above, are constructed. The outer expansion, associated with the limit $\varepsilon \to 0$, θ fixed, represents a sequence of potential flows.

OUTER EXPANSION

$$\begin{aligned} f(\theta; \varepsilon) &= F_0(\theta) + \gamma_1(\varepsilon)F_1(\theta) + \gamma_2(\varepsilon)F_2(\theta) + \cdots, \\ g(\theta; \varepsilon) &= G_0(\theta) + \gamma_1(\varepsilon)G_1(\theta) + \gamma_2(\varepsilon)G_2(\theta) + \cdots. \end{aligned} \tag{4.2.25}$$

The limit ($\varepsilon = 0$) form of Equations (4.2.21) and (4.2.22) yields

$$-F_0^2 = 2G_0, \tag{4.2.26}$$

$$0 = -\frac{dG_0}{d\theta}. \tag{4.2.27}$$

The no-slip condition is given up so that $F_0 = G_0 = \text{const}$, and the normalization (Equation 4.2.23) yields

$$F_0 = -\frac{1}{2\alpha}, \qquad G_0 = -\frac{1}{8\alpha^2}. \tag{4.2.28}$$

Now, in order to have a balance of viscous forces and inertia near the walls ($\theta = \pm\alpha$), it is necessary that the viscous layer have a thickness $O(\sqrt{\varepsilon})$. An inner limit $\varepsilon \to 0$, $\tilde{\theta} = (\theta \pm \alpha)/\sqrt{\varepsilon}$ fixed, is considered. It follows that the inner expansion is of the form (valid near each wall)

INNER EXPANSION

$$f(\theta;\varepsilon) = f_0(\tilde{\theta}) + \beta(\varepsilon)f_1(\tilde{\theta}) + \cdots, \qquad g(\theta;\varepsilon) = g_0(\tilde{\theta}) + \beta(\varepsilon)g_1(\tilde{\theta}) + \cdots,$$

$$\tilde{\theta} = (\theta \pm \alpha)/\sqrt{\varepsilon}. \tag{4.2.29}$$

The equations of motion reduce to

$$O(1): \qquad -f_0^2 = 2g_0 + \frac{d^2f_0}{d\tilde{\theta}^2}; \tag{4.2.30}$$

$$O\left(\frac{1}{\sqrt{\varepsilon}}\right): \qquad 0 = -\frac{dg_0}{d\tilde{\theta}}. \tag{4.2.31}$$

The solutions to these boundary-layer equations should satisfy the no-slip condition, so that

$$f_0(0) = 0. \tag{4.2.32}$$

The other boundary conditions for Equations (4.2.30) and (4.2.31) are found by matching with the outer solution. Equation (4.2.31) states that, to this order, there is no pressure gradient across the thin viscous layer adjacent to the wall. The matching, thus, fixes the level of pressure in the boundary layer. An intermediate limit is

$$\lim_{\eta}\,(\varepsilon \to 0), \qquad \theta_\eta = \frac{(\theta \pm \alpha)}{\eta(\varepsilon)}, \qquad \varepsilon \ll \eta \ll 1. \tag{4.2.33}$$

In this limit, we have

$$\theta = \mp\alpha + \eta\theta_\eta \to \mp\alpha, \tag{4.2.34}$$

$$\tilde{\theta} = \frac{\eta}{\varepsilon}\theta_\eta \to \pm\infty. \tag{4.2.35}$$

It is assumed that the inner and outer expansions are matched by an intermediate limit. Consider now only the lower wall $\theta = -\alpha$; the solution at the upper wall is found by symmetry. The matching of pressures to first order is

$$\lim_{\eta}\,\{G_0(\theta) + \cdots - g_0(\tilde{\theta}) + \cdots\} = 0. \tag{4.2.36}$$

In this case, we know that

$$G_0 = g_0 = \text{const} = -\frac{1}{4\alpha^2}. \tag{4.2.37}$$

Thus, Equation (4.2.30) becomes

$$\frac{d^2f_0}{d\tilde{\theta}^2} + f_0^2(\tilde{\theta}) = \frac{1}{4\alpha^2}. \tag{4.2.38}$$

Matching of the velocities now gives

$$\lim_{\eta} \{F_0(\theta) + \cdots - f_0(\tilde{\theta}) - \cdots\} = 0$$

or

$$\lim_{\eta} \left\{ F_0(-\alpha + \eta\theta_\eta) - f_0\left(\frac{\eta}{\sqrt{\varepsilon}}\theta_\eta\right)\right\} = 0. \tag{4.2.39}$$

The velocity of the potential flow at the wall is matched to the velocity of the boundary-layer flow at infinity in this case:

$$f_0(\infty) \to F_0(-\alpha) = -1/2\alpha. \tag{4.2.40}$$

Thus, the solution of Equation (4.2.38) for $0 \leq \tilde{\theta} < \infty$ must be found satisfying the conditions of Equations (4.2.32) and (4.2.40). It is clear that the boundary condition (Equation 4.2.40) is consistent with Equation (4.2.38). The existence of the solution to Equation (4.2.38), as well as the form near infinity, is easily seen from the phase plane of Equation (4.2.38). Let

$$w_0 = df_0/d\tilde{\theta}. \tag{4.2.41}$$

Then Equation (4.2.38) becomes

$$\frac{dw_0}{df_0} = \frac{(1/4\alpha^2) - f_0^2}{w_0}. \tag{4.2.42}$$

The paths of the integral curves are indicated in Figure 4.13. The arrows

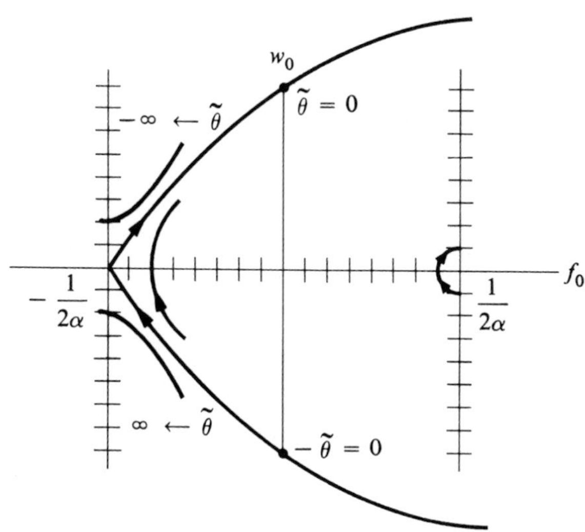

FIGURE 4.13 Phase plane (Equation 4.2.42).

indicate the direction of increasing $\tilde{\theta}$ according to Equation (4.2.41). The singularity at $w_0 = 0, f_0 = -1/2\alpha$ is a saddle point whose paths are

$$w_0^2 - \frac{1}{\alpha}\left(f_0 + \frac{1}{2\alpha}\right)^2 = \text{const.} \tag{4.2.43}$$

Two exceptional paths,

$$w_0 = \pm\frac{1}{\sqrt{\alpha}}\left(f_0 + \frac{1}{2\alpha}\right), \tag{4.2.44}$$

enter the saddle points, the ($-$) sign corresponding to the boundary layer at the lower wall. The value of $\tilde{\theta}$ along the path is found by integration of Equation (4.2.42) along the path from ($f_0 = 0, \tilde{\theta} = 0$). Near the singular point, integration of Equation (4.2.41) shows that

$$f_0 = -\frac{1}{2\alpha} + k_0 e^{-\tilde{\theta}/\sqrt{\alpha}} + \cdots, \tag{4.2.45}$$

where k_0 is known from integration along the path. Equation (4.2.45) shows that the boundary layer approaches its limiting value with an error which is transcendentally small for intermediate limits.

The need for higher-order terms arises because of the mass-flow defect in the boundary layer. The first term of a uniformly valid ($-\alpha \le \theta \le \alpha$) composite expansion of the form

$$f(\theta;\varepsilon) = \mathscr{F}_0(\theta;\varepsilon) + \gamma_1(\varepsilon)\mathscr{F}_1(\theta;\varepsilon) + \cdots \tag{4.2.46}$$

can be found by adding f_0 for both walls to F_0 and subtracting the common part $-1/2\alpha$:

$$\mathscr{F}_0(\theta;\varepsilon) = f_0\left(\frac{\theta+\alpha}{\sqrt{\varepsilon}}\right) + f_0\left(\frac{\theta-\alpha}{\sqrt{\varepsilon}}\right) + \frac{1}{2\alpha}. \tag{4.2.47}$$

The mass-flow integral (Equation 4.2.23) is

$$-\int_{-\alpha}^{\alpha}\left[f_0\left(\frac{\theta+\alpha}{\sqrt{\varepsilon}}\right) + f_0\left(\frac{\theta-\alpha}{\sqrt{\varepsilon}}\right) + \frac{1}{2\alpha}\right]d\theta$$

$$\to 1 - 2\sqrt{\varepsilon}\int_0^{\infty}\left[\frac{1}{2\alpha} + f_0(\tilde{\theta})\right]d\tilde{\theta} + \cdots.$$

The error is thus $O(\sqrt{\varepsilon})$, and this has to be made up by the next term in the outer expansion. Hence, we have $\gamma_1(\varepsilon) = \sqrt{\varepsilon}$ and

$$\int_{-\alpha}^{\alpha} F_1(\theta)\,d\theta = -2\int_0^{\infty}\left[\frac{1}{2\alpha} + f_0(\tilde{\theta})\right]d\tilde{\theta}. \tag{4.2.48}$$

Once the (F_1, G_1) are found, the next boundary-layer terms (f_1, g_1) can be constructed and the procedure repeated.

We next apply these ideas to flow past a body.

4.2.2 *Flow past a body*

Consider steady plane flow past a body of the general form indicated in Figure 4.14. In order to carry out the boundary-layer and outer expansions, it

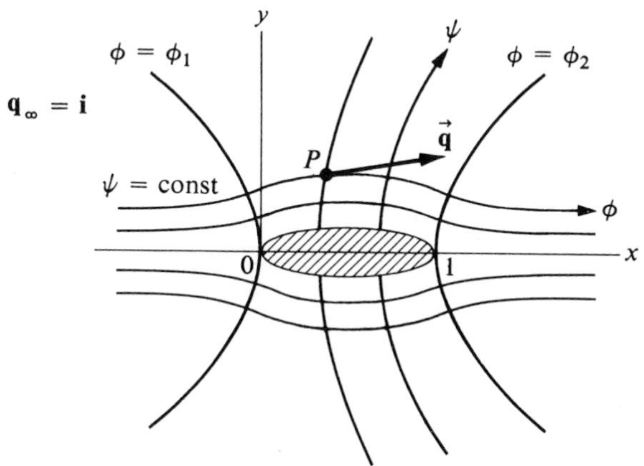

FIGURE 4.14 Streamline coordinates.

is convenient to choose a special coordinate system. In a very interesting paper (Reference 4.2.1), Saul Kaplun discussed the choice of "optimal" coordinates. He shows that it is possible to find certain coordinates in which the boundary-layer equations and solutions are uniformly valid first approximations in the entire flow field, including the so-called flow due to displacement thickness. However, the construction of such coordinates is, in general, just as difficult as it is to proceed directly in any convenient system. The first approximation to the skin-friction is independent of the coordinates. Here we express the Navier–Stokes equations in terms of a network of potential lines (ϕ = const) and streamlines (ψ = const), which represent the idealized inviscid flow around the object.

This choice of coordinates at least has the advantage of allowing the ideas of boundary-layer theory to be expressed independent of the body shape and of having a simple representation of the first-order outer flow. Thus, $\psi = 0$ is always the bounding streamline along which the boundary layer appears. In addition to the basic definitions (Equations 4.2.13, 4.2.14, and 4.2.15), we note the following expressions for the velocity components, (q_ϕ, q_ψ), vorticity, etc., in the *viscous* flow. The results follow from general vector formulas in orthogonal curvilinear coordinates. (See Figure 4.15.)

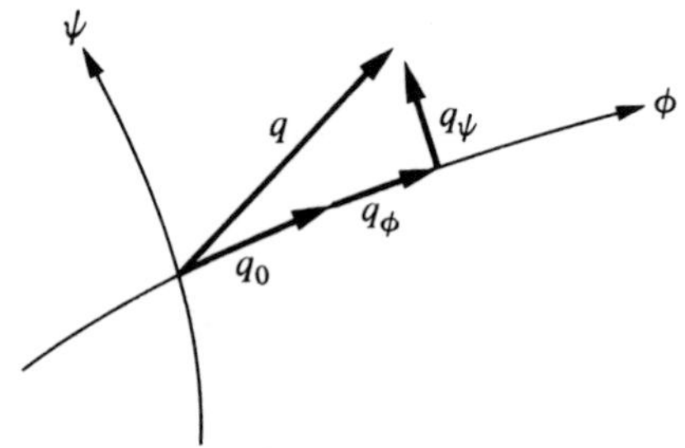

FIGURE 4.15 Detail of velocity components.

$$dz = \frac{dF}{F'}, \qquad (dx)^2 + (dy)^2 = \frac{(d\phi)^2 + (d\psi)^2}{|F'|^2} = \frac{(d\phi)^2 + (d\psi)^2}{q_0^2}, \tag{4.2.49}$$

$$\omega = q_0^2\left\{\frac{\partial}{\partial\phi}\left(\frac{q_\psi}{q_0}\right) - \frac{\partial}{\partial\psi}\left(\frac{q_\phi}{q_0}\right)\right\}, \qquad \boldsymbol{\omega} = \mathbf{k}\omega, \tag{4.2.50}$$

$$\mathbf{q} \times \boldsymbol{\omega} = (q_\phi \mathbf{i}_\phi + q_\psi \mathbf{i}_\psi) \times (\omega\mathbf{k}) = \omega q_\psi \mathbf{i}_\phi - \omega q_\phi \mathbf{i}_\psi, \tag{4.2.51}$$

$$\nabla = \left(q_0\frac{\partial}{\partial\phi},\ q_0\frac{\partial}{\partial\psi}\right), \tag{4.2.52}$$

$$\text{curl}\,\boldsymbol{\omega} = \mathbf{i}_\phi q_0\frac{\partial\omega}{\partial\psi} - \mathbf{i}_\psi q_0\frac{\partial\omega}{\partial\phi}. \tag{4.2.53}$$

Thus, the basic Navier–Stokes equations (4.2.3a, b) become

continuity,
$$\frac{\partial}{\partial\phi}\left(\frac{q_\phi}{q_0}\right) + \frac{\partial}{\partial\psi}\left(\frac{q_\psi}{q_0}\right) = 0; \tag{4.2.54}$$

ϕ-momentum,
$$q_0\frac{\partial}{\partial\phi}\left(\frac{q_\phi^2 + q_\psi^2}{2}\right) - q_\psi\omega = -q_0\frac{\partial p}{\partial\phi} - \varepsilon q_0\frac{\partial\omega}{\partial\psi}; \tag{4.2.55}$$

ψ-momentum,
$$q_0\frac{\partial}{\partial\psi}\left(\frac{q_\phi^2 + q_\psi^2}{2}\right) + q_\phi\omega = -q_0\frac{\partial p}{\partial\psi} + \varepsilon q_0\frac{\partial\omega}{\partial\phi}. \tag{4.2.56}$$

The viscous stress is now $\tau_v = \varepsilon q_0^2(\partial/\partial\psi)(q_\phi/q_0)$. From the form of these equations, it seems clear that a small simplification can be achieved by measuring the velocities at a point P relative to the inviscid velocity q_0 at that point. Let

$$w_\phi = \frac{q_\phi}{q_0}, \qquad w_\psi = \frac{q_\psi}{q_0}. \tag{4.2.57}$$

It follows that, for the vorticity, we have

$$\omega = q_0^2\left\{\frac{\partial w_\psi}{\partial \phi} - \frac{\partial w_\phi}{\partial \psi}\right\}, \tag{4.2.58}$$

and Equations (4.2.54), (4.2.55), and (4.2.56) become

$$\frac{\partial w_\phi}{\partial \phi} + \frac{\partial w_\psi}{\partial \psi} = 0,$$

$$w_\phi \frac{\partial w_\phi}{\partial \phi} + w_\psi \frac{\partial w_\phi}{\partial \psi} + (w_\phi^2 + w_\psi^2)\frac{\partial}{\partial \phi}(\log q_0)$$
$$= -\frac{1}{q_0^2}\frac{\partial p}{\partial \phi} + \varepsilon\left\{\frac{\partial^2 w_\phi}{\partial \phi^2} + \frac{\partial^2 w_\phi}{\partial \psi^2} - 2\frac{\partial \log q_0}{\partial \psi}\left(\frac{\partial w_\psi}{\partial \phi} - \frac{\partial w_\phi}{\partial \psi}\right)\right\}, \tag{4.2.59}$$

$$w_\phi \frac{\partial w_\psi}{\partial \phi} + w_\psi \frac{\partial w_\psi}{\partial \psi} + (w_\phi^2 + w_\psi^2)\frac{\partial}{\partial \psi}(\log q_0)$$
$$= -\frac{1}{q_0^2}\frac{\partial p}{\partial \psi} + \varepsilon\left\{\frac{\partial^2 w_\psi}{\partial \phi^2} + \frac{\partial^2 w_\psi}{\partial \psi^2} + 2\frac{\partial \log q_0}{\partial \phi}\left(\frac{\partial w_\psi}{\partial \phi} - \frac{\partial w_\phi}{\partial \psi}\right)\right\}. \tag{4.2.60}$$

The viscous surface stress, correspondingly, is $\tau_v = \varepsilon q_0^2(\partial w_\phi/\partial \psi)$. The domain of the problem is sketched in Figure 4.16. The body occupies the slit $\psi = 0$, $\phi_1 < \phi < \phi_2$.

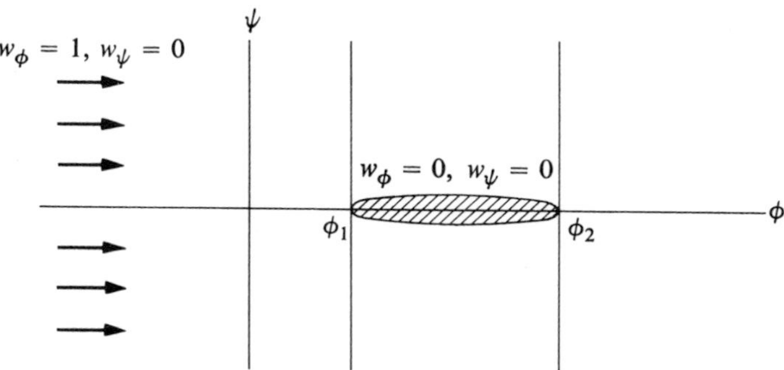

FIGURE 4.16 Boundary-value problem in the (ϕ, ψ)-plane.

The boundary conditions are as follows:

uniform flow at infinity upstream, $w_\psi \to 0, \quad w_\phi \to 1, \quad \phi \to -\infty;$ (4.2.61)

no-slip at the body surface, $w_\phi = w_\psi = 0, \quad \psi = 0, \quad \phi_1 < \phi < \phi_2.$ (4.2.62)

Now, in order to construct the expansions, we consider first the outer or Euler limit ($\varepsilon \to \infty$, ϕ, ψ fixed). This represents inviscid and, in this case, irrotational, flow around the object. The limit flow is, thus,

$$w_\phi \to 1, \qquad w_\psi \to 0, \qquad p = \tfrac{1}{2}(1 - q_0^2) \qquad \text{(Bernoulli equation).} \tag{4.2.63}$$

As an outer expansion, we have the limit flow as the first term, and corrections due to the inner solution appearing as higher terms. The general form of the outer expansion is, thus,

$$w_\phi(\phi, \psi; \varepsilon) = 1 + \beta(\varepsilon)w_\phi^{(1)}(\phi, \psi) + \cdots, \tag{4.2.64}$$

$$w_\psi(\phi, \psi; \varepsilon) = \beta(\varepsilon)w_\psi^{(1)}(\phi, \psi) + \cdots, \tag{4.2.65}$$

$$p(\phi, \psi; \varepsilon) = \tfrac{1}{2}(1 - q_0^2) + \beta(\varepsilon)p^{(1)}(\phi, \psi) + \cdots. \tag{4.2.66}$$

All corrections with superscript (1) vanish at upstream infinity. However, other boundary conditions for these correction terms can not be found without discussing the inner viscous boundary layer. To construct the boundary layer and correction equations, we consider an inner-limit process and associated expansion where

$$\tilde{\psi} = \frac{\psi}{\delta(\varepsilon)}, \qquad \phi \text{ fixed} \quad \text{as} \quad \varepsilon \to 0. \tag{4.2.67}$$

The expansion has the following form:

$$w_\phi(\phi, \psi; \varepsilon) = W_\phi(\phi, \tilde{\psi}) + \cdots, \tag{4.2.68}$$

$$w_\psi(\phi, \psi; \varepsilon) = \delta(\varepsilon)W_\psi(\phi, \tilde{\psi}) + \cdots, \tag{4.2.69}$$

$$p(\phi, \psi; \varepsilon) = P(\phi, \tilde{\psi}) + \cdots. \tag{4.2.70}$$

The form is deduced from the following considerations, in addition to those which indicated that the boundary layer occupies a thin region close to $\psi = 0$. The first term of the expression for the velocity component w_ϕ along the streamline is of order one, so that it can be matched to the outer expansion (Equation 4.2.64). The first term in the expansion for w_ψ must, then, be of the order $\delta(\varepsilon)$, so that a nontrivial continuity equation results:

$$\frac{\partial W_\phi}{\partial \phi} + \frac{\partial W_\psi}{\partial \psi} = 0. \tag{4.2.71}$$

The first term in the pressure is also $O(1)$ in order to match to Equation (4.2.66). Under the boundary-layer limit, the inviscid velocity field which occurs in the coefficient approaches the surface distribution of inviscid velocity according to

$$q_0(\phi, \psi) = q_0(\phi, \delta(\varepsilon)\tilde{\psi}) = q_0(\phi, 0) + \delta(\varepsilon)\tilde{\psi}\frac{\partial q_0}{\partial \psi}(\phi, 0) + \cdots \tag{4.2.72}$$

or

$$q_0(\phi, \psi) = q_B(\phi) + O(\delta(\varepsilon)),$$

where $q_B(\phi)$ = inviscid surface-velocity distribution. The inertia and pressure terms in Equation (4.2.59) are both of $O(1)$, while $\varepsilon(\partial^2 W_\phi/\partial\psi^2)$ is of the order ε/δ^2. The distinguished limiting case has

$$\delta = \sqrt{\varepsilon}. \tag{4.2.73}$$

It is only this case that allows a nontrivial system of boundary-layer equations capable of satisfying the boundary conditions and being matched to the outer flow. With this assumption, the first-approximation momentum equations are

$$W_\phi \frac{\partial W_\phi}{\partial \phi} + W_\psi \frac{\partial W_\phi}{\partial \tilde{\psi}} + \frac{W_\phi^2}{q_B(\phi)}\frac{dq_B}{d\phi} = -\frac{1}{q_B^2}\frac{\partial P}{\partial \phi} + \frac{\partial^2 W_\phi}{\partial \tilde{\psi}^2}, \tag{4.2.74}$$

$$0 = -\frac{1}{q_B^2}\frac{\partial P}{\partial \tilde{\psi}}. \tag{4.2.75}$$

Equation (4.2.75) tells us that the layer is so thin that the pressure does not vary across the layer and, rather, that

$$P = P(\phi). \tag{4.2.76}$$

Hence, the pressure is easily matched to the pressure in the outer solution. All the matching is carried out with the help of an intermediate limit in which the representative point approaches the wall but not as fast as it does in the distinguished limit. In the intermediate limit, we have

$$\psi_\eta = \frac{\psi}{\eta(\varepsilon)}, \qquad \phi \text{ fixed}, \tag{4.2.77}$$

where

$$\sqrt{\varepsilon} \ll \eta \ll 1.$$

Thus, in the intermediate limit, we see that

$$\psi = \eta\psi_\eta \to 0, \qquad \tilde{\psi} = \frac{\eta}{\sqrt{\varepsilon}}\psi_\eta \to \infty. \tag{4.2.78}$$

It is sufficient to consider only positive ψ to illustrate the ideas. Matching of pressure (cf. Equations 4.2.66, 4.2.70) takes the form

$$\lim_{\varepsilon\to 0} \{\tfrac{1}{2}(1 - q_0^2(\phi, \eta\psi_\eta)) + \beta(\varepsilon)p^{(1)}(\phi, \eta\psi_\eta) + \cdots - P(\phi) - \cdots\} = 0.$$

Hence, to first order, we have

$$P(\phi) = \tfrac{1}{2}(1 - q_B^2(\phi)) = P_B(\phi) \quad \text{(say)}. \tag{4.2.79}$$

The pressure distribution on the body is that of the inviscid flow, if we neglect the boundary layer. Thus, the system of boundary-layer equations (Equations 4.2.71, 4.2.74) is

$$\begin{aligned} \frac{\partial W_\phi}{\partial \phi} + \frac{\partial W_\psi}{\partial \tilde{\psi}} &= 0, \\ W_\phi \frac{\partial W_\phi}{\partial \phi} + W_\psi \frac{\partial W_\phi}{\partial \tilde{\psi}} &= \frac{1 - W_\phi^2}{q_B}\frac{dq_B}{d\phi} + \frac{\partial^2 W_\phi}{\partial \tilde{\psi}^2}, \end{aligned} \tag{4.2.80}$$

a system for (W_ϕ, W_ψ). The boundary conditions to be satisfied are no-slip,

$$W_\phi(\phi, 0) = W_\psi(\phi, 0) = 0, \qquad \phi_1 < \phi < \phi_2, \tag{4.2.81}$$

and matching. The system (Equation 4.2.80) is parabolic, so that only the interval $\phi_1 < \phi < \phi_2$ need be considered at first. The next quantity to be matched is the velocity component along a streamline, which also contains an order-one term. Inner and outer expansions (Equations 4.2.68 and 4.2.64) must read the same in intermediate variables, so that

$$\lim_{\varepsilon\to 0} \{1 + \alpha(\varepsilon)w_\phi^{(1)}(\phi, \eta\psi_\eta) + \cdots - W_\phi(\phi, (\eta/\sqrt{\varepsilon})\psi_\eta) - \cdots\} = 0. \tag{4.2.82}$$

Thus, the boundary condition is obtained:

$$\lim_{\tilde{\psi}\to\infty} W_\phi(\phi, \tilde{\psi}) = 1. \tag{4.2.83}$$

This is usually interpreted by saying that the velocity at the outer edge of the boundary layer is that of the inviscid flow adjacent to the body. Since the system (Equation 4.2.80) is parabolic, there is no upstream influence, so that the solution again must match the undisturbed flow:

$$W_\phi(0, \tilde{\psi}) = 1. \tag{4.2.84}$$

The conditions of Equations (4.2.84), (4.2.83), and (4.2.81) serve to define a unique solution in the strip $\phi_1 < \phi < \phi_2$. The solution downstream of the body, $\phi > \phi_2$, should really be discussed also. The boundary-layer equations and expansion are the same, but the boundary conditions corresponding to the wake are different. Now the upstream boundary-layer solution just calculated provides initial conditions on $\phi = \phi_2$ for $-\infty < \tilde{\psi} < \infty$; and the initial-value problem can be solved to find the flow downstream.

Assume now that the solution of Equation (4.2.80) has been found for all $\phi > \phi_1$, so that W_ϕ, W_ψ are known functions. The matching of the normal component of velocity along the potential lines W_ψ can be discussed next, and this provides a boundary condition which defines the correction in the outer flow due to the presence of the boundary layer. The intermediate limit of inner and outer expansions is

$$\lim_{\varepsilon \to 0} \left\{ \beta(\varepsilon) w_\psi^{(1)}(\phi, \eta\psi_\eta) + \cdots - \sqrt{\varepsilon}\, W_\psi\left(\phi, \frac{\eta\psi_\eta}{\sqrt{\varepsilon}}\right) - \cdots \right\} = 0. \tag{4.2.85}$$

Matching is achieved to first order, provided the limits exist, if first of all

$$\beta(\varepsilon) = \sqrt{\varepsilon} \tag{4.2.86}$$

and

$$w_\psi^{(1)}(\phi, 0) = W_\psi(\phi, \infty), \qquad \phi > \phi_1. \tag{4.2.87}$$

Equation (4.2.87) has the form of a boundary condition for $w^{(1)}$, which can be interpreted as an effective thin body added to the original body; it defines the flow due to displacement thickness. The limit in Equation (4.2.87) exists since the solutions for $[1 - W_\phi]$ can be shown to decay exponentially as $\psi \to \infty$ and

$$W_\psi(\phi, \psi) = \int_0^\psi \left[-\frac{\partial W}{\partial \phi}(\phi, \lambda) \right] d\lambda. \tag{4.2.88}$$

Thus, the outer flow $w_\phi^{(1)}$, $w_\psi^{(1)}$, $p^{(1)}$ can, in principle, be computed, and further matching of p, w_ϕ can be used to define the second-order boundary layer. Various local nonuniformities can develop, such as near sharp, leading, or trailing edges, corners, etc., which make it unwise to attempt to carry the procedure very far. Analogous procedures can be carried out for compressible flow where the energy balance of the flow must also be considered. The subject is discussed with a point of view similar to that given here by

P. A. Lagerstrom in Reference 4.2.2. Further complications occur when different types of interaction with shock waves in the outer flow have to be considered, but the ideas behind these methods seem capable of handling all cases that arise.

The quantity of most physical interest from the boundary-layer theory is the skin-friction on the surface, which now is represented by

$$\tau_v = \sqrt{\varepsilon}\, q_B^2(\phi)(\partial W_\phi/\partial\tilde{\psi})(\phi, 0). \tag{4.2.89}$$

When the boundary-layer solution is found, $(\partial W_\phi/\partial\tilde{\psi})(\phi, 0)$ can be calculated, and the estimate of the skin friction is obtained. The classical result is given here—the skin-friction coefficient is proportional to $1/\sqrt{\mathrm{Re}}$.

Unfortunately, no elementary solutions of the boundary-layer system (Equation 4.2.80) under boundary conditions (Equations 4.2.81, 4.2.84) exist. The only cases in which substantial simplifications can be achieved are cases of similarity when the problem can be reduced to ordinary differential equations. Otherwise, numerical integration of the system must be relied on, although some rough approximate methods can also be derived.

The cases of similarity can either be interpreted as local approximations or as solutions which are really asymptotic to solutions of the Navier–Stokes equations in a sense different from having $\varepsilon \to 0$. That is, the characteristic length L used to define ε really drops out of the problem, and the expansion is really in terms of the coordinates (x, y) or (φ, ψ). For example, consider the flow past a semi-infinite body generated by a source at $z = 1$ in a free stream (see Figure 4.17). The inviscid flow and coordinates are given by

$$\phi + i\psi = z + \log(z - 1) - i\pi = -\frac{z^2}{2} + \cdots, \qquad z \to 0. \tag{4.2.90}$$

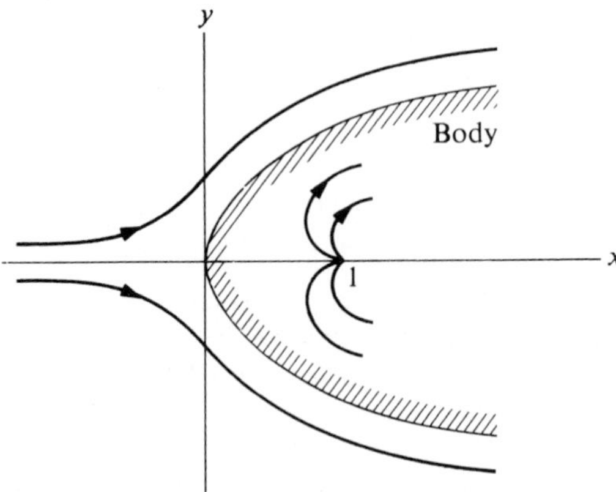

FIGURE 4.17 Source half-body.

Thus, near the origin we have the stagnation-point flow

$$\phi = \frac{y^2 - x^2}{2}, \qquad \psi = -xy. \tag{4.2.91}$$

The body is, at $x = 0$,

$$q_B = \frac{\partial \phi}{\partial y} = y = \sqrt{2\phi}. \tag{4.2.92}$$

The boundary-layer equations (Equation 4.2.80) are, for this case,

$$\frac{\partial W_\phi}{\partial \phi} + \frac{\partial W_\psi}{\partial \tilde{\psi}} = 0, \tag{4.2.93}$$

$$W_\phi \frac{\partial W_\phi}{\partial \phi} + W_\psi \frac{\partial W_\phi}{\partial \tilde{\psi}} = \frac{1 - W_\phi^2}{2\phi} + \frac{\partial^2 W_\phi}{\partial \tilde{\psi}^2} \tag{4.2.94}$$

with boundary conditions

$$W_\phi(\phi, 0) = W_\psi(\psi, 0) = 0, \qquad W_\phi(\phi, \infty) = 1. \tag{4.2.95}$$

The system (Equations 4.2.93, 4.2.94, 4.2.95) has similarity, which enables the problem to be reduced to ordinary differential equations. The form is

$$W_\phi = F(\eta), \tag{4.2.96}$$

where

$$\eta = \frac{\tilde{\psi}}{2\sqrt{\phi}},$$

$$W_\psi = \frac{1}{\sqrt{\phi}} G(\eta), \tag{4.2.97}$$

$$\frac{dG}{d\eta} - \eta \frac{dF}{d\eta} = 0, \qquad G(0) = F(0) = 0, \tag{4.2.98}$$

$$\frac{d^2F}{d\eta^2} + 2(\eta F - G)\frac{dF}{d\eta} + 2(1 - F^2) = 0, \qquad F(\infty) = 1. \tag{4.2.99}$$

According to Equation (4.2.89), the skin-friction is obtained once this system is solved from

$$\tau_v = \sqrt{\phi/\varepsilon}\, F'(0). \tag{4.2.100}$$

The existence of the solution to the problem posed in Equations (4.2.98) and (4.2.99) as well as to the more general class of similar problems in which

$q_B = c\phi^m$ (the form 4.2.96, 4.2.97 is the same) is proved by H. Weyl in Reference 4.2.3. For the special case of the stagnation-point flow, the similar solution can be interpreted as the local solution near the origin. It turns out that in this case the solution to the boundary-layer equation (Equations 4.2.98, 4.2.99) is also a solution to the full Navier–Stokes equations. The parameter ε really drops out of the local solution, since the local solution cannot depend on the length L. The length L drops out of the similarity variable $\tilde{\psi}/\sqrt{\phi}$ when dimensional coordinates are re-introduced as follows:

$$\tilde{\psi} = \rho UL\sqrt{\varepsilon}\,\Psi, \qquad \phi = UL\Phi \qquad \text{when } \Phi, \Psi \text{ are dimensional,} \tag{4.2.101}$$

$$\frac{\tilde{\psi}}{\sqrt{\phi}} = \frac{\rho UL}{\sqrt{UL}}\sqrt{\frac{\mu}{\rho UL}}\frac{\Psi}{\sqrt{\Phi}} = \Psi\sqrt{\frac{\rho\mu}{\Phi}}. \tag{4.2.102}$$

Similar considerations apply to the velocity components to show that expansion is really in terms of Φ or (x^*) and is valid near the origin.

The same remarks apply to another classical case that is usually discussed, namely the flow past a semi-infinite flat plate, in which case we have

$$\phi = x, \qquad \psi = y, \tag{4.2.103}$$

$$q_B(\phi) = 1. \tag{4.2.104}$$

The similarity form is the same (Equations 4.2.96, 4.2.97), and the equations are a simplified version of Equations (4.2.98) and (4.2.99) with the $(1 - F^2)$ term missing. There is no characteristic length L in the problem, so that the parameter ε is artificial. If an arbitrary length is used for L (and this can be done), it must drop out of the answer. When similarity is combined with the artificial expansion in terms of ε, the expansion corresponding to boundary-layer theory becomes an expansion in terms of the space coordinates. For example, in dimensional coordinates (x^*, y^*), the boundary-layer expansion (Equations 4.2.68, 4.2.69, 4.2.70) and outer expansions (Equations 4.2.64, 4.2.65, 4.2.66) take the form

$$\frac{q_x}{U} = U_0(\zeta) + \sqrt{\frac{\nu}{Ux^*}}\,U_1(\zeta) + \cdots \qquad \text{(boundary layer),}$$

$$\frac{q_y}{U} = \sqrt{\frac{\nu}{Ux^*}}\,V_0(\zeta) + \cdots, \qquad \text{where} \qquad \zeta = \frac{y^*}{\sqrt{x^*}}\sqrt{\frac{U}{\nu}}, \tag{4.2.105}$$

$$\frac{p - p_\infty}{\rho U^2} = \sqrt{\frac{\nu}{Ux^*}}\,P_1(\zeta) + \cdots,$$

$$\frac{q_x}{U} = 1 + \sqrt{\frac{\nu}{Ux^*}}\,u_1(\zeta) + \cdots,$$

$$\frac{q_y}{U} = \sqrt{\frac{\nu}{Ux^*}}\,v_1(\zeta) + \cdots \qquad \text{(outer expansion)}, \qquad (4.2.106)$$

$$\frac{p - p_\infty}{\rho U^2} = \sqrt{\frac{\nu}{Ux^*}}\,p_1(\zeta) + \cdots.$$

These expansions are seen to be valid for small ν/Ux^* and are thus non-uniform near the nose, where a more complete treatment of the Navier–Stokes equations is needed. However, the skin-friction has a singularity only like $1/\sqrt{x}$ which is integrable at the nose. This indicates that probably a first approximation to the total drag can be found as $\varepsilon \to 0$.

A general result can be proved: If a problem with a parameter has similarity, then the approximate solution in terms of this parameter can not be uniformly valid, unless the approximate solution turns out to be the exact solution (as in the stagnation-point case). By similarity, here we mean the fact, for example, that if a solution depends on coordinates and a parameter $(x, y; \varepsilon)$, the solution must depend on two combinations of these due to invariance. In the case of the semi-infinite flat plate, the Navier–Stokes solution $u(x, y; \varepsilon) = fn(x/\varepsilon, y/\varepsilon)$ and the boundary-layer solution is not uniformly valid. The proof of this theorem, as well as much detailed discussion of expansions for both ε small and ε large in special problems for the Navier–Stokes equations, is given in Reference 4.2.4.

Problem

Consider the unsteady version of the Navier–Stokes equations in suitable dimensionless units for describing the flow produced above an infinite porous plate set in motion parallel to itself. The equations and boundary conditions are

$$\frac{\partial u}{\partial t} + v(t)\frac{\partial u}{\partial y} = \varepsilon\frac{\partial^2 u}{\partial y^2},$$

$$u(y, 0) = 0 \qquad \text{(initial conditions)},$$

$$u(0, t) = 1 \qquad \text{(boundary conditions)}.$$

Discuss the approximate solutions as $\varepsilon \to 0$ for the case when $v > 0$ (blowing) and when $v < 0$ (suction).

REFERENCES

4.2.1 S. Kaplun, "The Role of Coordinate Systems in Boundary Layer Theory," *Z.A.M.P.* V, *2*, (1954) 111–135.

4.2.2 P. A. Lagerstrom, "Laminar Flow Theory," *High Speed Aerodynamics and Jet Propulsion*, IV, Princeton Univ. Press, 1964, 20–282.

4.2.3 H. Weyl, "On the Simplest Differential Equations of Boundary Layer Theory." *Annals of Math.*, 43, *2*, 381–407.

4.2.4 P. A. Lagerstrom, and J. D. Cole, "Examples Illustrating Expansion Procedures for the Navier–Stokes Equations," *Journal of Rational Mechanics and Analysis*, 4, *6* (Nov. 1955), 817–882.

4.3 Magnetohydrodynamic pipe flow

In the magnetohydrodynamics of an electrically conducting viscous incompressible fluid, the motion is described by the Navier–Stokes equations with the added effect of body forces ($\mathbf{j} \times \mathbf{B}$) due to the action of the magnetic field ($\mathbf{B}$) on electric currents ($\mathbf{j}$) in the fluid. The electric current density is calculated from Ohm's law, and the Maxwell equations describe the magnetic problem. For a large class of problems, it can be shown that displacement currents can be neglected, and the induced electric field is $\mathbf{q} \times \mathbf{B}$. The full system of partial differential equations describing this is thus of rather high order. For the simple geometries of this section, interesting boundary-layer problems arise that have a relatively simple physical interpretation. The example shows how some general ideas apply to a higher-order system.

For steady flow, the versions of the Maxwell equations needed are

$$\mathbf{j} = \frac{1}{\mu_0} \operatorname{curl} \mathbf{B} = \sigma(\mathbf{E} + \mathbf{q} \times \mathbf{B}), \qquad \mathbf{j} = \text{current/area}, \tag{4.3.1}$$

$$0 = \operatorname{curl} \mathbf{E}, \tag{4.3.2}$$

$$0 = \operatorname{div} \mathbf{B}, \tag{4.3.3}$$

where

$$\sigma = \text{electric conductivity (mho/meter)} = \text{const},$$

$$\mu_0 = \text{magnetic permeability (MKSQ units)}.$$

The electric field can be eliminated, and the induction equation can be written as follows.

INDUCTION

$$\operatorname{curl}(\mathbf{q} \times \mathbf{B}) = \mathbf{B} \cdot \nabla \mathbf{q} - \mathbf{q} \cdot \nabla \mathbf{B} = \frac{1}{\mu_0 \sigma} \operatorname{curl} \operatorname{curl} \mathbf{B} = -\frac{1}{\mu_0 \sigma} \nabla^2 \mathbf{B} \tag{4.3.4}$$

in cartesian coordinates. For a complete system, the induction equation for **B** (Equation 4.3.4) has to be added to the Navier–Stokes system, and a body-force per volume $\mathbf{j} \times \mathbf{B}$ appears in the right-hand side of the momentum equation:

MOMENTUM

$$\rho \mathbf{q} \cdot \nabla \mathbf{q} = -\nabla p + \mathbf{j} \times \mathbf{B} - \mu \operatorname{curl} \operatorname{curl} \mathbf{q}. \tag{4.3.5}$$

4.3.1 Insulating pipe

The problem considered is analogous to fully developed laminar pipe flow (Poiseuille flow) in ordinary fluid mechanics. Incompressible conducting fluid flows in the x_1-direction inside an infinitely long pipe in the presence of an externally applied uniform magnetic field B_0 in the x_2-direction. (See Figure 4.18.) Introduce ( )* for dimensional quantities. The cross

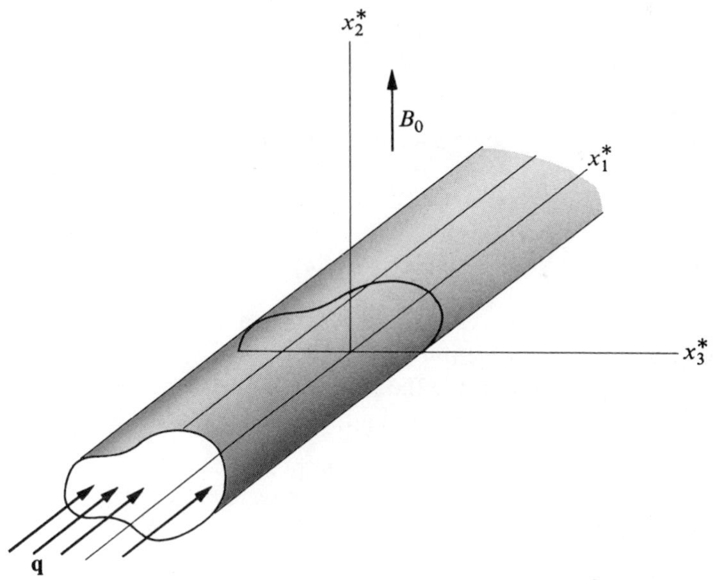

FIGURE 4.18 Insulating pipe flow.

section of the pipe is an arbitrary (convex) curve given by, for example,

$$x_2^* = Lg(x_3^*/L), \qquad x_2^* > 0 \quad \text{(say)}, \tag{4.3.6}$$

when L = characteristic length of pipe cross section. Nothing depends on

x_1^* except the pressure p^*, but the pressure gradient $\partial p^*/\partial x_1$ is constant, negative to drive the flow through the pipe.

Under these circumstances, it can be shown† that the magnetic-field components in the (x_2^*, x_3^*)-plane are constants, such that

$$B_2^* = B_0, \qquad B_3^* = 0. \tag{4.3.7}$$

The transverse velocity components $q_2^* = q_3^* = 0$, and the pressure is represented as

$$p^*(x_1^*, x_2^*, x_3^*) = -kx_1^* - \frac{B_1^{*2}(x_2^*, x_3^*)}{\mu_0} k = \text{const.} \tag{4.3.8}$$

The resulting equations of motion which need to be considered are the x_1-components of the momentum and induction equations. The momentum equation contains only the terms representing the pressure gradient, Lorentz force, and viscous force. Thus, we have

$$0 = k - j_3^* B_0 + \rho\nu\nabla^{*2} q_1^*, \tag{4.3.9}$$

$$0 = B_0 \frac{\partial q_1^*}{\partial x_2^*} - \frac{1}{\mu_0 \sigma} \nabla^{*2} B_1^*. \tag{4.3.10}$$

For the current-density components, from Equation (4.3.1) we have

$$j_3^* = -\frac{1}{\mu_0} \frac{\partial B_1^*}{\partial x_2^*} = \sigma\{E_3^* + q_1^* B_0\}, \tag{4.3.11}$$

$$j_2^* = \frac{1}{\mu_0} \frac{\partial B_1^*}{\partial x_3^*}. \tag{4.3.12}$$

The boundary-value problem for $q_1^*(x_2^*, x_3^*)$, $B_1^*(x_2^*, x_3^*)$ of Equations (4.3.9) and (4.3.10) to be solved inside the pipe is completed by the addition of the boundary conditions of no-slip and no-normal current at the boundary:

$$q_1^* = B_1^* = 0, \qquad \text{on the boundary.} \tag{4.3.13}$$

The condition on B_1^* follows from

$$0 = j_3^*\, dx_2^* - j_2^*\, dx_3^* = -\frac{1}{\mu_0}\left(\frac{\partial B_1^*}{\partial x_2^*} dx_2^* - \frac{\partial B_1^*}{\partial x_3^*} dx_3^*\right) = -\frac{dB_1^*}{\mu_0} \tag{4.3.14}$$

along the boundary curve. The constant value of B_1^* could be put to zero, for example, by conditions of symmetry of the cross section. Currents and forces are unaffected by a constant B_1^*.

† These results follow from the Maxwell equations and Ohms law with the assumption that $E_1^* = 0$ and $j_1^* = 0$. In this Section, ( )* is used for dimensional quantities.

It is convenient to express the problem in dimensionless variables, remembering that in the main part of the flow viscosity effects are small. Thus, currents are made dimensionless with k/B_0, lengths with L, and the induced field B_1 with $\mu Lk/B_0$. It follows that q_1^* should be dimensionless with $k/\sigma B_0^2$. Thus, let the dimensionless variables be

$$\begin{aligned} u(x_2, x_3) &= \frac{\sigma B_0^2}{k} q_1^*(x_2^*, x_3^*), & b(x_2, x_3) &= \frac{B_0}{\mu Lk} B_1^*(x_2^*, x_3^*), \\ j_3(x_2, x_3) &= \frac{B_0}{k} j_3^* = -\frac{\partial b}{\partial x_2}, & j_2(x_2, x_3) &= \frac{B_0}{k} j_2^* = \frac{\partial b}{\partial x_3}. \end{aligned} \tag{4.3.15}$$

In these variables, Equations (4.3.9) and (4.3.10) read

$$0 = 1 - \frac{\partial b}{\partial x_2} + \varepsilon\left\{\frac{\partial^2 u}{\partial x_2^2} + \frac{\partial^2 u}{\partial x_3^2}\right\}, \tag{4.3.16}$$

$$0 = \frac{\partial u}{\partial x_2} + \left\{\frac{\partial^2 b}{\partial x_2^2} + \frac{\partial^2 b}{\partial x_3^2}\right\} \tag{4.3.17}$$

with boundary conditions $u = b = 0$ on the pipe surface, that is, $x_2 = g(x_3) > 0$. In these units, the whole problem depends on a single parameter ε:

$$\varepsilon = \frac{\rho\nu}{\sigma B_0^2 L^2}. \tag{4.3.18}$$

The parameter was introduced by Hartmann, in his study of pipe flow, in the form of the Hartmann number Ha,

$$\mathrm{Ha} = B_0 L\sqrt{\sigma/\rho\nu} = 1/\sqrt{\varepsilon}.$$

Here ε measures the relative size of viscous body forces and Lorentz forces. For example, in pipe flows of liquid metals, $\varepsilon \ll 1$. A fairly complete treatment of this problem has been given by Chang and Lundgren (Reference 4.3.1) for cases of various wall properties. Eigenfunction expansions are constructed for the rectangular channel, and some ideas of boundary-layer theory are used. Here we proceed completely on the basis of boundary-layer theory ($\varepsilon \ll 1$)', and we construct the details of the flow inside as well as outside the boundary layer.

For $\varepsilon = 0$, we have inviscid equations, and the momentum balance becomes a balance between pressure gradient and Lorentz body forces. This kind of flow exists in the center of the pipe outside of the viscous boundary layer, and we call it the core flow. These facts can be represented by an asymptotic expansion of the solution to Equations (4.3.16) and (4.3.17) in terms of functions of ε (actually powers) with the points (x_2, x_3) fixed, that is, off the boundary.

CORE FLOW

$$b(x_2, x_3; \varepsilon) = b_0(x_2, x_3) + \alpha_1(\varepsilon)b_1(x_2, x_3) + \cdots, \tag{4.3.19}$$

$$u(x_2, x_3; \varepsilon) = \beta_0(\varepsilon)u_0(x_2, x_3) + \beta_1(\varepsilon)u_1(x_2, x_3) + \cdots. \tag{4.3.20}$$

The dominant term for velocity in the core depends on ε in an, as yet, unknown fashion. The unit of velocity is $k/\sigma B_0^2$, so that if viscosity decreases ($\varepsilon \to 0$), it can be expected that u will increase. Thus, we expect $\beta_0 \to \infty$ as $\varepsilon \to 0$, and, of course, $\beta_1/\beta_0 \to 0$, $\alpha_1 \to 0$. From Equations (4.3.16) and (4.3.17), we obtain the dominant equations for the core flow:

$$0 = 1 + \frac{\partial b_0}{\partial x_2}, \tag{4.3.21}$$

$$0 = \frac{\partial u_0}{\partial x_2}. \tag{4.3.22}$$

Equation (4.3.22) says that the current density $j_3 = 1$ in the core, and Equation (4.3.22) states that the velocity profile is cylindrical:

$$b_0 = -x_2 + F(x_3) \quad \{\text{for symmetry in } x_2, F \equiv 0\}, \tag{4.3.23}$$

$$u_0 = G(x_3). \tag{4.3.24}$$

The uniform current flowing across the pipe must return in the boundary layer. The function $G(x_3)$ which gives the x_3-profiles, as well as $\beta_0(\varepsilon)$, must be found by matching the core-flow solution with the boundary layer.

BOUNDARY LAYER

Consider the upper half of the pipe, and for the boundary layer, introduce the boundary-layer coordinates, using the x_2-distance from boundary,

$$\tilde{x}_2 = \frac{x_2 - g(x_3)}{\tau(\varepsilon)}, \qquad \tilde{x}_3 = x_3, \tag{4.3.25}$$

which are convenient for matching. Similar considerations apply to the lower half in case the pipe is not symmetric about the x_3-axis. But here we consider the case of symmetry. This implies that $F(x_3) \equiv 0$, $\tau(\varepsilon)$ measures the thickness of the boundary layer, and $\tilde{x}_2 = 0$ is the boundary. Again, an expansion in ε is assumed, but now we keep the boundary-layer coordinates $\tilde{x}_2, \tilde{x}_3$ fixed:

$$b(x_2, x_3; \varepsilon) = \tilde{b}(\tilde{x}_2, \tilde{x}_3) + \cdots, \tag{4.3.26}$$

$$u(x_2, x_3; \varepsilon) = \delta(\varepsilon)\tilde{u}(\tilde{x}_2, \tilde{x}_3) + \cdots. \tag{4.3.27}$$

The order of $\tilde{b}$ in Equation (4.3.26) was chosen with the idea of matching to the core flow. Note that

$$\frac{\partial}{\partial x_2} = \frac{1}{\tau}\frac{\partial}{\partial \tilde{x}_2}, \qquad \frac{\partial}{\partial x_3} = -g'(x_3)\frac{1}{\tau}\frac{\partial}{\partial \tilde{x}_2} + \frac{\partial}{\partial \tilde{x}_3},$$

so that the dominant terms of ∇^2 are

$$\frac{\partial^2}{\partial x_2^2} + \frac{\partial^2}{\partial x_3^2} = \frac{[1 + g'^2(x_3)]}{\tau^2}\frac{\partial^2}{\partial \tilde{x}_2^2} + \cdots = \frac{\sec^2\theta(x_3)}{\tau^2}\frac{\partial^2}{\partial \tilde{x}_2^2} + \cdots, \tag{4.3.28}$$

where $\tan\theta = g'(x_3)$. Equations (4.3.16) and (4.3.17) now become

$$0 = 1 + \frac{1}{\tau}\frac{\partial \tilde{b}}{\partial \tilde{x}_2} + \frac{\varepsilon\delta}{\tau^2}\sec^2\theta\frac{\partial^2 \tilde{u}}{\partial \tilde{x}_2^2}, \tag{4.3.29}$$

$$0 = \frac{\delta}{\tau}\frac{\partial \tilde{u}}{\partial \tilde{x}_2} + \frac{\sec^2\theta}{\tau^2}\frac{\partial^2 \tilde{b}}{\partial \tilde{x}_2^2}. \tag{4.3.30}$$

The solutions of these equations must satisfy $\tilde{u} = \tilde{b} = 0$ at $\tilde{x}_2 = 0$ and must match to the core flow. The core flow and the boundary layer are to be matched as usual by an intermediate limit in which x_3 and x_η are fixed as $\varepsilon \to 0$,

$$x_\eta = \frac{x_2 - g(x_3)}{\eta(\varepsilon)}, \tag{4.3.31}$$

where $\tau \ll \eta \ll 1$. Thus, under the intermediate limit, we have

$$x_2 = g(x_3) + \eta x_\eta \to g(x_3), \tag{4.3.32}$$

$$\tilde{x}_2 = \frac{\eta}{\tau}x_\eta \to -\infty, \qquad (x_\eta < 0). \tag{4.3.33}$$

According to the appearance of the limit system (Equations 4.3.21, 4.3.22), there are subcharacteristics of the full system, namely the lines ($x_3 = $ const). Arbitrary functions of x_3 appear in the outer solutions. Thus we can expect the boundary-layer equations to be ordinary differential equations, since the boundary layer does not occur along the subcharacteristic. Thus, second-order equations are needed, and the consistent set is given by

$$\frac{1}{\tau} = \frac{\varepsilon\delta}{\tau^2}, \qquad \frac{\delta}{\tau} = \frac{1}{\tau^2}.$$

The conclusion is that

$$\tau = \sqrt{\varepsilon}, \qquad \delta = 1/\sqrt{\varepsilon}, \tag{4.3.34}$$

and the resulting equations are

$$0 = \frac{\partial \tilde{b}}{\partial \tilde{x}_2} + \sec^2 \theta(x_3) \frac{\partial^2 \tilde{u}}{\partial \tilde{x}_2^2}, \tag{4.3.35}$$

$$0 = \frac{\partial \tilde{u}}{\partial \tilde{x}_2} + \sec^2 \theta \frac{\partial^2 \tilde{b}}{\partial \tilde{x}_2^2}. \tag{4.3.36}$$

The force balance in the boundary layer is between Lorentz body forces which drive the flow down the pipe and viscous forces which resist the motion.

Integration of Equations (4.3.35) and (4.3.36) gives

$$-g(x_3) = \tilde{b} + \sec^2 \theta \frac{\partial \tilde{u}}{\partial \tilde{x}_2}, \tag{4.3.37}$$

$$G(x_3) = \tilde{u} + \sec^2 \theta \frac{\partial \tilde{b}}{\partial \tilde{x}_2}. \tag{4.3.38}$$

In the integration, the matching conditions have been taken into account with the idea that $(\partial \tilde{u}/\partial \tilde{x}_2, \partial \tilde{b}/\partial \tilde{x}_2) \to 0$, $\tilde{x}_2 \to -\infty$. Furthermore, $\delta = \beta_0 = 1/\sqrt{\varepsilon}$, so that the velocity can match. All that remains is to satisfy the boundary condition at $\tilde{x}_2 = 0$. But $\tilde{u}$ satisfies

$$\frac{\partial^2 \tilde{u}}{\partial \tilde{x}_2} - \cos^4 \theta(x_3)\tilde{u} = -\cos^4 \theta G(x_3), \tag{4.3.39}$$

so that we have

$$\tilde{u}(\tilde{x}_2, x_3) = G(x_3)\{1 - \exp[\tilde{x}_2 \cos^2 \theta(x_3)]\}. \tag{4.3.40}$$

and, from Equation (4.3.37),

$$\tilde{b} = -g(x_3) + G(x_3) \exp[\tilde{x}_2 \cos^2 \theta]. \tag{4.3.41}$$

Taking into account the boundary condition at $\tilde{x}_2 = 0$ identifies

$$G(x_3) = g(x_3). \tag{4.3.42}$$

This curious result states that the velocity x_3-profile in the core flow of the pipe is the same as the shape of the cross section. Thus, the complete boundary-layer solution is

$$\tilde{u} = -\tilde{b} = g(x_3)\{1 - \exp[\tilde{x}_2 \cos^2 \theta(x_3)]\}. \tag{4.3.43}$$

It is clear that this approximation is not valid near the edges of the pipe where $\cos\theta = 0(x_3 = \pm 1, x_2 = 0)$, where the boundary has the subcharacteristic direction. In fact, a different type of boundary layer exists in a neighborhood $O(\varepsilon^{1/3})$ in x_3 around these points, but this boundary layer does not affect the flow crucially, and we skip details here.

A single, uniformly valid (except near $x_3 = \pm 1, x_2 = 0$) approximation can be written by adding the boundary layer and core flows and subtracting the part common to both. Thus, we obtain

$$b(x_2, x_3\,; \varepsilon) = -x_2 + g(x_3)\exp\left[\frac{x_2 - g(x_3)}{\sqrt{\varepsilon}}\cos^2\theta(x_3)\right] + \cdots, \tag{4.3.44a}$$

$$u(x_2, x_3\,; \varepsilon) = \frac{1}{\sqrt{\varepsilon}}g(x_3)\left\{1 - \exp\left[\frac{x_2 - g(x_3)}{\sqrt{\varepsilon}}\cos^2\theta(x_3)\right]\right\} + \cdots. \tag{4.3.44b}$$

Various overall relations involving mass flow, voltage drop, etc., can be worked out from Equations (4.3.44) and (4.3.45).

4.3.2 Rectangular pipe with electrodes

In this Section we extend the considerations of the preceding Section to the case of conducting walls. We assume here that the conductivity of the electrodes is much larger than that of the fluid; the walls are practically perfect conductors. This enables the interior boundary-value problem to be solved independent of external circuitry.

The geometry of the problem is the same as before, except that the cross section is rectangular (height $2H$, width $2L$). The top and bottom walls, $x_2^* = \pm H$, are insulators; the side walls, $x_3^* = \pm L$, are electrodes. The boundary condition on the insulators is $B_1 = \text{const}$, and symmetry can be used, so that

$$\begin{aligned} B_1 &= B_w, & x_2^* &= H\,; \\ B_1 &= -B_w, & x_2^* &= -H. \end{aligned} \tag{4.3.45}$$

We assume that the electric field E_2^* is zero in the electrodes; the potential is constant on an electrode. It follows from continuity of the tangential component E_2^* that $E_2^* = 0$ in the fluid at the wall. Hence, we see that $j_2^* = 0$ at the electrode or

$$\partial B_1/\partial x_3^* = 0, \qquad x_3^* = \pm L. \tag{4.3.46}$$

Next, we write the problem in dimensionless variables, measuring B_1 in terms of B_w.

$$b = \frac{B_1}{B_w}, \qquad u = \mu\sigma L\left(\frac{B_0}{B_w}\right)u_1,$$

$$j_3 = -\frac{\partial b}{\partial y} = \frac{\mu L}{B_w} j_3^*, \tag{4.3.47}$$

where

$$y = \frac{x_2^*}{L}, \qquad z = \frac{x_3^*}{L}.$$

Equations (4.3.9) and (4.3.10) become

$$-\kappa = \frac{\partial b}{\partial y} + \varepsilon\left\{\frac{\partial^2 u}{\partial y^2} + \frac{\partial^2 u}{\partial z^2}\right\}, \tag{4.3.48}$$

$$0 = \frac{\partial u}{\partial y} + \left\{\frac{\partial^2 b}{\partial y^2} + \frac{\partial^2 b}{\partial z^2}\right\}, \tag{4.3.49}$$

where

$$\kappa = \frac{(-\partial P/\partial x_1)\mu L}{B_w B_0}, \qquad \varepsilon = \frac{\rho\nu}{\sigma B_0^2 L^2}.$$

The channel and boundary conditions are shown in Figure 4.19, where $h = H/L$.

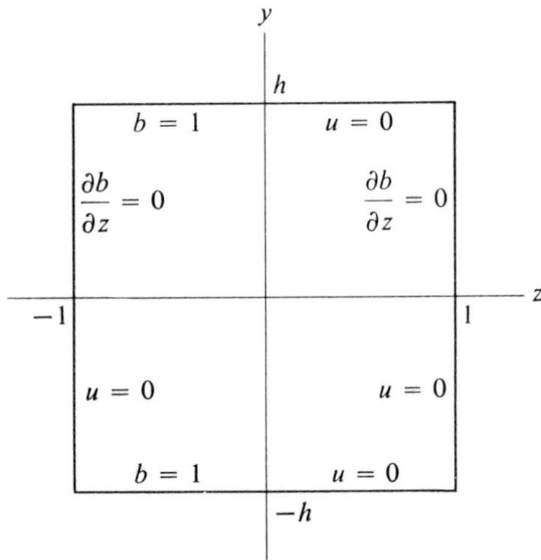

FIGURE 4.19 Rectangular pipe with electrodes.

Fixing B_w fixes the sign and magnitude of current in a given channel. The parameter κ expresses the pressure rise or drop and specifies the operation of the device. Also $\varepsilon \ll 1$ as before, and κ is independent of ε. In this case, there is a core flow and boundary layers both on the electrodes and insulating walls. We anticipate the orders of magnitude as before:

CORE FLOW

$$b(z, y; \varepsilon) = b_0(z, y) + \cdots, \tag{4.3.50}$$

$$u(z, y; \varepsilon) = (1/\sqrt{\varepsilon})u_0(z, y) + \cdots, \tag{4.3.51}$$

and now

$$-\kappa = \partial b_0/\partial y, \qquad 0 = \partial u_0/\partial y. \tag{4.3.52}$$

Symmetry considerations give the core solutions as before:

$$b_0 = -\kappa y, \qquad u_0 = u_0(z), \qquad j_{0_3} = +\kappa = \text{const}. \tag{4.3.53}$$

INSULATOR BOUNDARY LAYER

Let $\tilde{y} = (y - h)/\sqrt{\varepsilon}$, and

$$\tilde{b} = b(z, y) + \cdots, \qquad u = \frac{1}{\sqrt{\varepsilon}}\tilde{u}(z, \tilde{y}) + \cdots.$$

The integrals of the boundary-layer equation (Equations 4.3.37, 4.3.38) are obtained with $\theta = 0$ with the matching, now giving

$$-\kappa h = \tilde{b} + \frac{\partial \tilde{u}}{\partial \tilde{y}}, \tag{4.3.54}$$

$$u_0(z) = \tilde{u} + \frac{\partial \tilde{b}}{\partial \tilde{y}}. \tag{4.3.55}$$

If we take account of the boundary condition that $\tilde{b} = 1$, $\tilde{u} = 0$ at $\tilde{y} = 0$, the solution of Equations (4.3.54) and (4.3.55) is

$$\tilde{u} = (1 + \kappa h)(1 - e^{\tilde{y}}), \qquad \tilde{b} = -\kappa h + (1 + \kappa h)e^{\tilde{y}}. \tag{4.3.56}$$

Note that the core velocity $u_0(z)$ is constant and that

$$u_0 = 1 + \kappa h. \tag{4.3.57}$$

Note also that Equation (4.3.55) thus states that the tangential component of electric field (E_3) is constant across this boundary layer.

ELECTRODE BOUNDARY LAYERS

The electrode boundary layers have the different character expected along the subcharacteristic. In order to discover the nature of this boundary layer, a general form of expansion which can match to the core flow is assumed in terms of an arbitrary boundary-layer coordinate. Consider the left electrode. Let

$$\bar{z} = \frac{z+1}{\delta(\varepsilon)} \tag{4.3.58}$$

and (for matching)

$$b(z, y; \varepsilon) = \bar{b}(\bar{z}, y) + \cdots, \qquad u(z, y; \varepsilon) = (1/\sqrt{\varepsilon})\bar{u}(\bar{z}, y) + \cdots. \tag{4.3.59}$$

Then equations (4.3.48) and (4.3.49) become

$$-\kappa = \frac{\partial \bar{b}}{\partial y} + \sqrt{\varepsilon}\left\{\frac{1}{\delta^2}\frac{\partial^2 \bar{u}}{\partial \bar{z}^2} + \frac{\partial^2 \bar{u}}{\partial y^2}\right\}, \qquad 0 = \frac{1}{\sqrt{\varepsilon}}\frac{\partial \bar{u}}{\partial y} + \frac{1}{\delta^2}\left\{\frac{\partial^2 \bar{b}}{\partial \bar{z}^2} + \frac{\partial^2 \bar{b}}{\partial y^2}\right\}. \tag{4.3.60}$$

A nontrivial set of equations is obtained only for

$$\delta = \varepsilon^{1/4},$$

so that the electrode boundary layer is an order of magnitude thicker than that on the insulator. The boundary-layer equations are now partial differential equations. Thus, we have

$$-\kappa = \frac{\partial \bar{b}}{\partial y} + \frac{\partial^2 \bar{u}}{\partial \bar{z}^2}, \tag{4.3.61}$$

$$0 = \frac{\partial \bar{u}}{\partial y} + \frac{\partial^2 \bar{b}}{\partial \bar{z}^2}. \tag{4.3.62}$$

All the physical mechanisms are of equal importance in this boundary layer, but the diffusion terms are approximated in a way normal for viscous boundary layers. Matching to the core flow takes place as $\bar{z} \to \infty$, so that the problem for Equations (4.3.61) and (4.3.62) must be solved in a strip $[0 \le \bar{z} \le \infty, y \le 1]$ (see Figure 4.20):

$$\bar{u} \to 1 + \kappa h, \qquad \bar{b} \to -\kappa y, \qquad \bar{z} \to \infty. \tag{4.3.63}$$

We know that, at the electrode,

$$\bar{u} = \frac{\partial \bar{b}}{\partial \bar{z}} = 0, \qquad \bar{z} = 0. \tag{4.3.64}$$

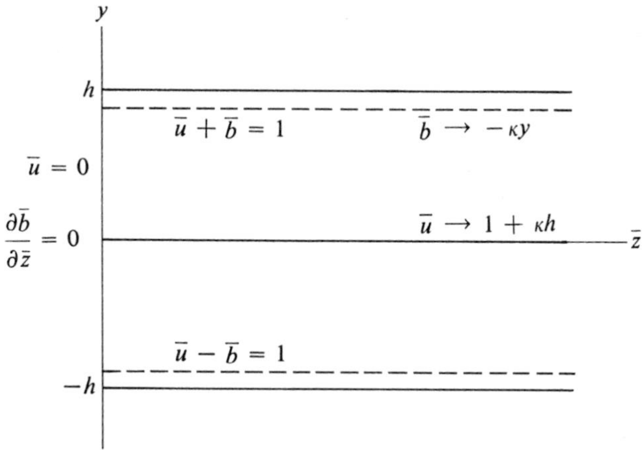

FIGURE 4.20 Electrode boundary layer.

The boundary conditions to be satisfied at the top and bottom walls are not immediately obvious, but the structure of Equations (4.3.61) and (4.3.62) shows that they are necessary. Since the insulator boundary layer (really the cross-field boundary layer) is much thinner than the electrode (parallel field) boundary layer, we consider matching the solutions of Equations (4.3.61) and (4.3.62) to some boundary layer as $y \to \pm h$. For this boundary layer, we can assume that

$$b(z, y; \varepsilon) = \tilde{\bar{b}}(\bar{z}, \tilde{y}) + \cdots, \qquad u(z, y; \varepsilon) = (1/\sqrt{\varepsilon})\tilde{\bar{u}}(z, \tilde{y}) + \cdots, \tag{4.3.65}$$

where

$$\bar{z} = \frac{z + 1}{\varepsilon^{1/4}}, \qquad \tilde{y} = \frac{y + h}{\sqrt{\varepsilon}}.$$

The $\bar{z}$ variation is still sufficiently slow so that the same insulator boundary-layer equations as before are obtained:

$$0 = \frac{\partial \tilde{\bar{b}}}{\partial \tilde{y}} + \frac{\partial^2 \tilde{\bar{u}}}{\partial \tilde{y}^2}, \tag{4.3.66}$$

$$0 = \frac{\partial \tilde{\bar{u}}}{\partial \tilde{y}} + \frac{\partial^2 \tilde{\bar{b}}}{\partial \tilde{y}^2}. \tag{4.3.67}$$

These equations should satisfy the real boundary conditions $\tilde{\bar{u}} = 0, \tilde{\bar{b}} = 1$ as

$\tilde{y} = 0$ and match the electrode boundary layer as $\tilde{y} \to -\infty$, $\bar{z}$ fixed. The solutions to Equations (4.3.66) and (4.3.67) can thus be written

$$\tilde{\bar{u}} = f(\bar{z})\{1 - e^{\tilde{y}}\}, \tag{4.3.68}$$

$$\tilde{\bar{b}} = 1 - f(\bar{z})\{1 - e^{\tilde{y}}\}. \tag{4.3.69}$$

Here we see that $f(\bar{z})$ is the unknown function to be found from matching. However, as $\tilde{y} \to -\infty$,

$$\tilde{\bar{u}} + \tilde{\bar{b}} \to 1,$$

so that, for the electrode boundary layer, we have

$$\bar{u} + \bar{b} \to 1 \qquad \text{as} \quad y \to h. \tag{4.3.70}$$

Since $\bar{u}$ is symmetric in y, and $\bar{b}$ is antisymmetric, it follows that

$$\bar{u} - \bar{b} \to 1 \qquad \text{as} \quad y \to -h. \tag{4.3.71}$$

The boundary conditions for Equations (4.3.61) and (4.3.62) are now complete. This can be demonstrated by considering the problem for (ϕ, ψ) defined by

$$\phi = \tfrac{1}{2}\{\bar{u} - (1 + \kappa h)\} + \tfrac{1}{2}\{\bar{b} + \kappa y\}, \tag{4.3.72}$$

$$\psi = \tfrac{1}{2}\{\bar{u} - (1 + \kappa h)\} - \tfrac{1}{2}\{\bar{b} + \kappa y\}. \tag{4.3.73}$$

Thus, we have

$$\bar{u} = 1 + \kappa h + \phi + \psi, \tag{4.3.74}$$

$$\bar{b} = -\kappa y + \phi - \psi. \tag{4.3.75}$$

Hence ϕ, ψ vanish as $\bar{z} \to \infty$, and the equations for ϕ, ψ uncouple. Equations (4.3.61) and (4.3.62) become

$$0 = \frac{\partial \phi}{\partial y} + \frac{\partial^2 \phi}{\partial \bar{z}^2}, \tag{4.3.76}$$

$$0 = \frac{\partial \psi}{\partial y} - \frac{\partial^2 \psi}{\partial \bar{z}^2}. \tag{4.3.77}$$

These are a backward and forward heat equation, respectively, with y the timelike variable. Equations (4.3.70) and (4.3.71) are, thus, initial conditions:

$$\phi = 0, \qquad y = h; \qquad \psi = 0, \qquad y = -h. \tag{4.3.78}$$

The solutions to Equations (4.3.76) and (4.3.77) are, however, coupled by the boundary conditions at $\bar{z} = 0$. Thus, we obtain

$$\phi + \psi = -(1 + \kappa h) \qquad \text{at} \quad \bar{z} = 0, \tag{4.3.79}$$

$$\frac{\partial\phi}{\partial\bar{z}} - \frac{\partial\psi}{\partial\bar{z}} = 0 \qquad \text{at} \quad \bar{z} = 0. \tag{4.3.80}$$

The solution can now be constructed by using a source representation. Equation (4.3.80) says that the local source strengths on the boundary are equal. Let

$$\psi(y, \bar{z}) = \frac{1}{2\sqrt{\pi}} \int_{-h}^{y} \left(\exp\left[-\frac{\bar{z}^2}{4(y-\eta)} \right] \Big/ \sqrt{y-\eta} \right) Q(\eta)\, d\eta\,, \tag{4.3.81}$$

$$\phi(y, \bar{z}) = \frac{1}{2\sqrt{\pi}} \int_{y}^{h} \left(\exp\left[-\frac{\bar{z}^2}{4(\eta-y)} \right] \Big/ \sqrt{(\eta-y)} \right) Q(\eta)\, d\eta\,, \tag{4.3.82}$$

and

$$(\partial\psi/\partial\bar{z})(y, 0) = (\partial\phi/\partial\bar{z})(y, 0) = -Q(y).$$

The boundary conditions at infinity are automatically satisfied, and the combination of Equations (4.3.81) and (4.3.82), according to the boundary condition (Equation 4.3.79), yields the basic integral equation of the problem:

$$\frac{1}{2\sqrt{\pi}} \int_{-h}^{h} \frac{Q(\eta)\, d\eta}{\sqrt{|y-\eta|}} = -(1 + \kappa h). \tag{4.3.83}$$

This is a special form of a class of integral equations solved by Carleman in Reference 4.3.2. The special solution corresponding to Equation (4.3.83) is

$$Q(\eta) = \sqrt{\frac{2}{\pi}} \frac{1 + \kappa h}{(h^2 - \eta^2)^{1/4}}. \tag{4.3.84}$$

The result is easily verified by direct substitution and the use of well-known identities of hypergeometric functions. Using this result, we can compute ϕ, ψ from Equations (4.3.81) and (4.3.82), and the field quantities from Equations (4.3.74) and (4.3.75). The same problem that we are considering here has been studied by Grinberg in Reference 4.3.3. His method relies on transformations of different representations of solutions of the exact equations (Equations 4.3.48, 4.3.49). However, by applying asymptotic approximations to his integral equations, he arrives at Equation (4.3.83) also.

REFERENCES

4.3.1 C. C. Chang, and T. S. Lundgren, "Duct Flow in Magnetohydrodynamics," *Z.A.M.P.* 12, *2* (1961), 100–114.

4.3.2 T. CARLEMAN, "Uber die Abel'sche Integralgleichung mit konstanten Integrationsgrenzen," *Math. Zeit. 15* (1922).
4.3.3 G. A. GRINBERG, "On Steady Flow of a Conducting Fluid in a Rectangular Tube with Two Nonconducting Walls, and Two Conducting Ones Parallel to an External Magnetic Field," *P.M.M.* 25, *6* (1961) 1024–1034.

4.4 Viscous boundary layer in a rotating fluid

As an example of boundary-layer theory, a brief discussion is given in this Section of the flow in a slightly viscous, incompressible fluid in which small disturbances are superimposed on solid-body rotation. Problems of this sort arise in practical oceanographic and meteorological examples, as well as in centrifuges and other devices.

The basic system of equations describing the motion is still the Navier–Stokes system of Section 4.2, but here it is sufficient to consider only the vorticity form (Equation 4.2.8):

$$-\text{curl}\,(\mathbf{q} \times \boldsymbol{\omega}) = \mathbf{q} \cdot \nabla\boldsymbol{\omega} - \boldsymbol{\omega} \cdot \nabla\mathbf{q} = -\nu\,\text{curl curl}\,\boldsymbol{\omega}. \qquad (4.4.1)$$

Consider a mass of fluid slightly disturbed from solid-body rotation around the z-axis. The velocity components in cylindrical coordinates (r, θ, z) can be represented, in the case of axial symmetry, as

$$q_r = u(r, z), \qquad q_\theta = \Omega r + v(r, z), \qquad q_z = w(r, z), \qquad (4.4.2)$$

where Ω = angular velocity of rotation around the z-axis (see Figure 4.21).

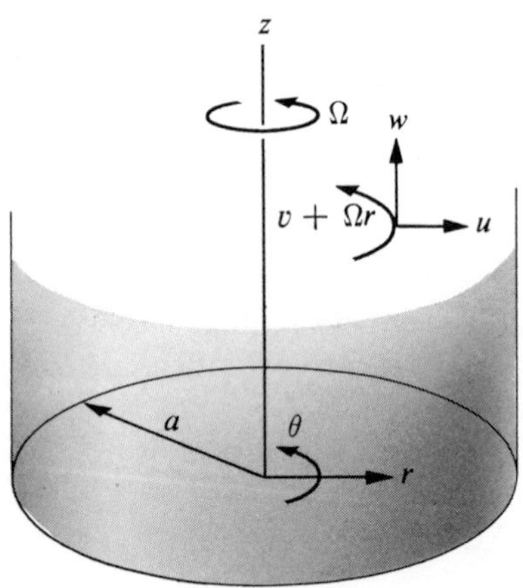

FIGURE 4.21 Flow in a rotating system.

For small disturbances, $(u, v, w) \ll \Omega r$, and this approximation is introduced explicitly below. According to the usual formulas, the components of vorticity $\boldsymbol{\omega}$ are

$$\omega_r = -\frac{\partial v}{\partial z}, \qquad \omega_\theta = \frac{\partial u}{\partial z} - \frac{\partial w}{\partial r}, \qquad \omega_z = 2\Omega + \frac{1}{r}\frac{\partial(rv)}{\partial r}. \tag{4.4.3}$$

There is a large constant component of vorticity (ω_z) due to the solid-body rotation and small perturbation components. Thus, as an approximation to the transport and stretching of vorticity in the left-hand side of Equation (4.4.1), we have the following:

$$\mathbf{q}\cdot\nabla\boldsymbol{\omega} - \boldsymbol{\omega}\cdot\nabla\mathbf{q} = -2\Omega\frac{\partial \mathbf{q}}{\partial z} + O(q^2). \tag{4.4.4}$$

Now, we can introduce a dimensionless version of the basic equation by using a characteristic length a, say the radius of a container for defining a length scale. Thus, we measure the variables in the following units: length $\sim a$, velocity $\sim \Omega a$, vorticity $\sim \Omega$. One dimensionless parameter, ε, enters the equations and is an inverse Reynolds number:

$$\varepsilon = \frac{\nu}{\Omega a^2}. \tag{4.4.5}$$

The basic equation (Equation 4.4.1) in these units becomes (using the same notation for dimensionless quantities)

$$\mathbf{q}\cdot\nabla\boldsymbol{\omega} - \boldsymbol{\omega}\cdot\nabla\mathbf{q} = -\varepsilon \operatorname{curl}\operatorname{curl}\boldsymbol{\omega}. \tag{4.4.6}$$

According to Equation (4.4.4), the linearized version of Equation (4.4.6), valid for small disturbances to solid-body rotation, is

$$2\frac{\partial \mathbf{q}}{\partial z} = \varepsilon \operatorname{curl}\operatorname{curl}\boldsymbol{\omega}. \tag{4.4.7}$$

We now consider expansions of the solutions to Equation (4.4.7), which includes $\operatorname{div}\mathbf{q} = 0$ for the case of $\varepsilon \to 0$. It is clear from Equation (4.4.7) that the cylinders $r = \text{const}$ are subcharacteristic surfaces and that an outer expansion would take the form

$$\mathbf{q}(r, z; \varepsilon) = \mathbf{q}_0(r) + \cdots. \tag{4.4.8}$$

It follows from considerations of mass conservation that the radial velocity is zero (no sources on the axis):

$$u_0(r) = 0. \tag{4.4.9}$$

The occurrence of (approximate) slip lines on $r = \text{const}$ was noted by G. I.

Taylor in the study of the slow motion of a sphere along the axis of a rotating fluid. The flow is undisturbed outside the diameter of the sphere. Here we consider an outer flow which is basically solid-body rotation, so that we have

$$u_0 = v_0 = w_0 = 0. \tag{4.4.10}$$

We concentrate on the viscous boundary layer formed near a surface $z = 0$, on which the condition of solid-body rotation (at speed Ω) is violated. For example, the rotation velocity of a solid surface at $z = 0$ is slightly different from the solid-body value:

$$u(r, 0) = 0\,; \qquad v(r, 0) = \kappa r, \qquad |\kappa| \ll \Omega\,; \qquad w(r, 0) = 0. \tag{4.4.11}$$

The boundary layer adjusts the velocity components from Equation (4.4.11) to zero. The components of the right-hand side of the basic equation (4.4.7) are

$$(\text{curl curl}\,\boldsymbol{\omega})_r = \frac{\partial^3 v}{\partial z^3} + \frac{\partial^2}{\partial z\,\partial r}\left\{\frac{1}{r}\frac{\partial(rv)}{\partial r}\right\}, \tag{4.4.12}$$

$$(\text{curl curl}\,\boldsymbol{\omega})_\theta = -\frac{\partial^2}{\partial z^2}\left(\frac{\partial u}{\partial z} - \frac{\partial w}{\partial r}\right) - \frac{\partial}{\partial r}\left[\frac{1}{r}\frac{\partial}{\partial r}\left(r\frac{\partial u}{\partial z} - r\frac{\partial v}{\partial r}\right)\right], \tag{4.4.13}$$

$$(\text{curl curl}\,\boldsymbol{\omega})_z = -\frac{1}{r}\frac{\partial}{\partial r}\left[r\frac{\partial^2 v}{\partial z^2} - r\frac{\partial}{\partial r}\left(\frac{1}{r}\frac{\partial}{\partial r}(rv)\right)\right]. \tag{4.4.14}$$

We expect changes with respect to z to be large, so that the boundary-layer expansion is derived from an inner limit in which $(r, \tilde{z})$ are held fixed, where

$$\tilde{z} = \frac{z}{\delta(\varepsilon)}, \qquad \delta \to 0. \tag{4.4.15}$$

The general form of the inner expansion is, thus,

$$\begin{gathered} u(r, z\,; \varepsilon) = \alpha(\varepsilon) U(r, \tilde{z}) + \cdots, \qquad v(r, z\,; \varepsilon) = V(r, \tilde{z}) + \cdots, \\ w(r, z\,; \varepsilon) = \alpha\delta W(r, \tilde{z}) + \cdots. \end{gathered} \tag{4.4.16}$$

The order of magnitude of the w velocity component has been chosen so that the structure of the continuity equation is preserved,

$$\frac{\partial}{\partial r}(rU) + \frac{\partial}{\partial \tilde{z}}(rW) = 0. \tag{4.4.17}$$

The order of magnitude of v is fixed by the boundary condition (Equation 4.4.11). It is necessary now to consider only the (r, θ) components of Equation (4.4.7). Using the exact expressions (Equations 4.4.12, 4.4.13) and the boundary-layer expansion (Equation 4.4.16), we have

$$2\frac{\alpha}{\delta}\frac{\partial U}{\partial \tilde{z}} + \cdots = \frac{\varepsilon}{\delta^3}\frac{\partial^3 V}{\partial \tilde{z}^3} + \cdots, \tag{4.4.18}$$

$$2\frac{1}{\delta}\frac{\partial V}{\partial \tilde{z}} + \cdots = -\frac{\varepsilon\alpha}{\delta^3}\frac{\partial^3 U}{\partial \tilde{z}^3} + \cdots. \tag{4.4.19}$$

The boundary-layer equations will be ordinary differential equations in agreement with the general ideas for boundary layers that occur on surfaces that are not subcharacteristic. A system of sufficiently high order to account for all the boundary conditions occurs only if all terms shown in Equations (4.4.18) and (4.4.19) are retained. Thus, we have

$$\frac{\alpha}{\delta} = \frac{\varepsilon}{\delta^3}, \qquad \frac{1}{\delta} = \frac{\varepsilon\alpha}{\delta^3}$$

or

$$\delta = \sqrt{\varepsilon}, \qquad \alpha = 1. \tag{4.4.20}$$

The boundary-layer expansion (Equation 4.4.16) is

$$u(r, z; \varepsilon) = U(r, \tilde{z}) + \cdots; \qquad v(r, z; \varepsilon) = V(r, \tilde{z}) + \cdots; \qquad \tilde{z} = \frac{z}{\sqrt{\varepsilon}}; \tag{4.4.21}$$

$$w(r, z; \varepsilon) = \sqrt{\varepsilon}W(r, \tilde{z}) + \cdots.$$

Matching to the outer flow will take place as $\tilde{z} \to \infty$ (r fixed) as a result of the intermediate limit, in the usual way:

$$z_\eta = \frac{z}{\eta}, \qquad \sqrt{\varepsilon} \ll \eta \ll 1; \qquad z = \eta z_\eta \to 0, \qquad \tilde{z} = \frac{\eta}{\sqrt{\varepsilon}} z \to \infty. \tag{4.4.22}$$

Taking account of this, we look for solutions with

$$U(r, \infty) = V(r, \infty) = 0. \tag{4.4.23}$$

Hence the integrated form of Equations (4.4.18) and (4.4.19) can be used:

$$2U = \frac{\partial^2 V}{\partial \tilde{z}^2}, \qquad 2V = -\frac{\partial^2 U}{\partial \tilde{z}^2}. \tag{4.4.24}$$

Elimination produces the boundary-layer equation for the azimuthal component V,

$$\frac{\partial^4 V}{\partial \tilde{z}^4} + 4V = 0. \tag{4.4.25}$$

The boundary conditions for Equation (4.4.25), from Equation (4.4.11), are summarized:

$$\left\{\begin{aligned} & V(r,0) = \kappa r\,; \\ 2U(r,0) = \; & \frac{\partial^2 V}{\partial \tilde{z}^2}(r,0) = 0\,; \\ & V(r,\tilde{z}) \to 0, \qquad \tilde{z} \to \infty. \end{aligned}\right\} \tag{4.4.26}$$

The solution of Equation (4.4.25) can be represented as

$$V(r,\tilde{z}) = \sum_{i=1}^{4} a_i(r)\exp(\lambda_i \tilde{z}), \tag{4.4.27}$$

where the λ_i are the roots of

$$\lambda^4 + 4 = 0. \tag{4.4.28}$$

These are

$$\lambda_{1,2,3,4} = \pm\sqrt{2}\exp\left[\pm i\frac{\pi}{4}\right]. \tag{4.4.29}$$

For decay as $\tilde{z} \to \infty$, only the two roots with negative real parts are relevant:

$$\lambda_{1,2} = -1 \pm i. \tag{4.4.30}$$

The solution (Equation 4.4.27) can thus be written

$$V(r,\tilde{z}) = a_1(r)e^{-\tilde{z}+i\tilde{z}} + b_1(r)e^{-\tilde{z}-i\tilde{z}}$$

or, in real form,

$$V(r,\tilde{z}) = e^{-\tilde{z}}\{A(r)\cos\tilde{z} + B(r)\sin\tilde{z}\}. \tag{4.4.31}$$

The first part of Equation (4.4.26) shows that

$$A(r) = \kappa r \tag{4.4.32}$$

and then

$$\frac{\partial^2 V}{\partial \tilde{z}^2} = e^{-\tilde{z}}\{2\kappa r\sin\tilde{z} - 2B\cos\tilde{z}\}. \tag{4.4.33}$$

Hence, from Equation (4.4.26), we see that $B = 0$. The full boundary-layer solution which matches to unperturbed solid-body rotation is thus given by

$$\begin{gathered} U(r,\tilde{z}) = \kappa r e^{-\tilde{z}}\sin\tilde{z}, \qquad V(r,\tilde{z}) = \kappa r e^{-\tilde{z}}\cos\tilde{z}, \\ W(r,\tilde{z}) = \kappa e^{-\tilde{z}}(\sin\tilde{z} + \cos\tilde{z} - 1). \end{gathered} \tag{4.4.34}$$

The boundary layer of Equation (4.4.34) is an example of a boundary layer which oscillates, but, because of exponential decay, it can be matched to the unperturbed flow. Note, however, from the solution of Equation (4.4.34) or the exact equations, that

$$V + iU = \kappa r e^{-\tilde{z}(1-i)}, \tag{4.4.35}$$

so that

$$\sqrt{V^2 + U^2} = \kappa r e^{-\tilde{z}}, \qquad \tilde{z} = \tan^{-1}\frac{U}{V}. \tag{4.4.36}$$

The projection of the velocity vector on a plane $\tilde{z} = \text{const}$ rotates by $\pi/2$ in passing from $\tilde{z} = 0$ to $\tilde{z} = \infty$, while its magnitude decays exponentially.

The boundary layers which can occur along subcharacteristics ($r = \text{const}$), for example, on the sidewall boundary of a vessel, are more complicated and are described by suitable partial differential equations. Various matchings may have to be used to describe the total flow. Examples of more complicated and even unsteady flows appear in the recent literature, for example in Reference 4.4.1. Boundary layers of the type discussed here, where there is a balance of the stretching and diffusion of vorticity, are called Ekman layers. The same kind of equations occur in meteorology when dealing with the problem of wind near a surface (Reference 4.4.2) and were discussed in regard to the ocean by Ekman (1902).

REFERENCES

4.4.1 H. P. GREENSPAN, and L. N. HOWARD, "On the Time Dependent Motion of a Rotating Fluid," *J. Fluid Mechanics 17* (1963), 385.

4.4.2 B. HAURWITZ, *Dynamic Meteorology*, New York: McGraw-Hill Book Co., 1941.

4.5 Singular boundary-value problems

Just as we found for ordinary differential equations discussed in Section 2.7, there are problems for partial differential equations in which various asymptotic expansions are constructed in various regions, but where the order of the system does not change. The form of the expansions is dominated by boundary conditions. Usually, in one limit or another a region degenerates to a point or line and thus may be singular. Narrow domains, slender bodies, disturbances of a small spatial extent are examples. In these cases, it is often useful, although not always necessary, to construct different expansions in different regions. Expansions valid near the singularity can be matched to expansions valid far away. In this Section, we present several such examples.

4.5.1 *Slender-body theory*

Consider the problem of classical potential theory† which results from the flow of an incompressible inviscid fluid past a slender body-of-revolution. Let lengths be normalized against the length of the body, velocities by U the velocity at infinity along the body axis, and pressure differences by $\rho_\infty U^2$. In view of the irrotationality, a velocity potential exists, and the continuity equation is

$$\frac{\partial^2 \Phi}{\partial x^2} + \frac{\partial^2 \Phi}{\partial r^2} + \frac{1}{r}\frac{\partial \Phi}{\partial r} = 0. \tag{4.5.1}$$

The dimensionless velocity components are

$$u = \frac{\partial \Phi}{\partial x}, \qquad v = \frac{\partial \Phi}{\partial r}, \tag{4.5.2}$$

and the pressure is found from the Bernoulli equation:

$$p = \tfrac{1}{2}(1 - u^2 - v^2). \tag{4.5.3}$$

Let a meridian plane of the body be denoted by

$$r = \delta F(x), \qquad 0 < x < 1, \qquad F(0) = F(1) = 0, \qquad F_{\max} = 1, \tag{4.5.4}$$

so that δ is the small parameter measuring the relative slenderness of a family of bodies whose shape function is $F(x)$ (see Figure 4.22).

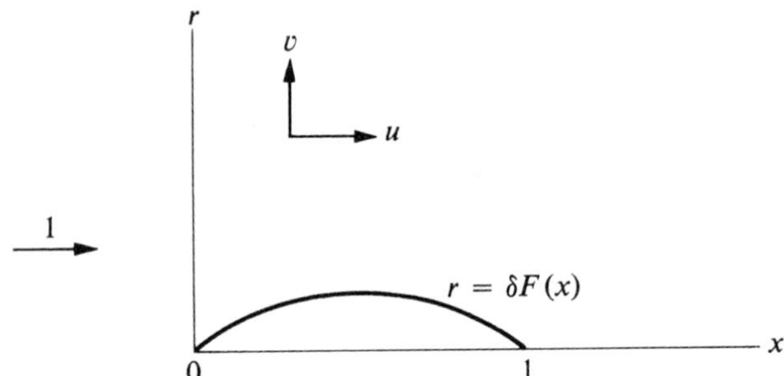

FIGURE 4.22 Flow past a slender body.

The boundary conditions for this potential problem are as follows:

UNIFORM STREAM AT INFINITY

$$\Phi(x, r) \to x, \tag{4.5.5}$$

†There are, of course, analogous problems in classical electric potential theory.

FLOW TANGENT TO BODY SURFACE

$$\frac{v}{u} = \frac{\partial\Phi}{\partial r}(x, \delta F)\bigg/\frac{\partial\Phi}{\partial x}(x, \delta F) = \delta F'(x) \qquad 0 < x < 1. \tag{4.5.6}$$

The exact solution for $\Phi(x, r; \delta)$ of this problem in potential theory depends, in general, on the solution of an integral equation. The flow might be represented as a distribution of singularities either on a line or over the surface; the unknown intensity of the singularities must be found as the solution of the integral equation. The numerical problems are fairly difficult. However, if the body is slender ($\delta \to 0$), the integral equations can be solved approximately. Here we proceed from expansions based on the equations and boundary conditions.

The outer expansion associated with the limit process ($\delta \to 0$, r, x fixed) is based on the idea that the body shrinks to a line on the axis in this limit, and that the uniform stream is undisturbed. The disturbances to the uniform stream are represented by an asymptotic expansion in terms of a sequence that is unknown *a priori* but must be found from the behavior of the flow near the body, that is, from matching. As far as the outer expansion is concerned, the body appears as a line of singularities:

$$\Phi(x, r; \delta) = x + \varepsilon_1(\delta)\phi_1(x, r) + \varepsilon_2(\delta)\phi_2(x, r) + \cdots. \tag{4.5.7}$$

Due to the linearity of the problem, each ϕ_i is an axisymmetric potential satisfying a zero boundary condition at infinity:

$$\frac{\partial^2\phi_i}{\partial x^2} + \frac{\partial^2\phi_i}{\partial r^2} + \frac{1}{r}\frac{\partial\phi_i}{\partial r} = 0, \qquad i = 1, 2, \ldots. \tag{4.5.8}$$

Next, an inner expansion is considered, valid near the boundary, generated by a limit process that preserves the structure of the boundary condition. In this limit, $\delta \to 0$ with (x, r^*) fixed, where

$$r^* = r/\delta \tag{4.5.9}$$

and where $r^* = F(x)$ is the body shape. A uniform stream is again taken as the first term. This is clearly incorrect in the neighborhood of the ends of a body which has a stagnation point, but it is adequate over the major part of the body. Tentatively, let

$$\Phi(x, r; \delta) = x + \mu_1(\delta)\varphi_1(x, r^*) + \mu_2(\delta)\varphi_2(x, r^*) + \cdots, \tag{4.5.10}$$

where now the orders $\mu_i(\delta)$ must be found both from conditions on the surface and conditions of matching. The dominant equation is thus $O(\mu_1/\delta^2)$,

$$\frac{\partial^2\varphi_1}{\partial r^{*2}} + \frac{1}{r^*}\frac{\partial\varphi_1}{\partial r^*} = 0, \tag{4.5.11}$$

and the boundary condition (Equation 4.5.6) becomes

$$\frac{\mu_1(\delta)}{\delta}\frac{\partial\varphi_1}{\partial r^*}(x, F(x)) = (1 + \cdots)\delta F'(x). \tag{4.5.12}$$

Equation (4.5.11) indicates that the first perturbation flow near the body looks like an incompressible flow in a cross-section plane (x = const). The solution is

$$\varphi_1(x, r^*) = A_1(x)\log r^* + B_1(x). \tag{4.5.13}$$

The two unknown functions are found from the boundary condition on the surface and from matching. Thus, we have

$$\frac{\partial\varphi_1}{\partial r^*}(x, r^*) = \frac{A_1(x)}{r^*}. \tag{4.5.14}$$

Thus $A_1(x)$ is proportional to a source strength in the cross-plane problem, and now Equation (4.5.12) reads

$$\frac{\mu_1(\delta)}{\delta}\left\{\frac{A_1(x)}{F(x)}\right\} = \delta F'(x). \tag{4.5.15}$$

Thus, we know that $\mu_1 = \delta^2$ and

$$A_1 = FF' = \frac{1}{2}\frac{d}{dx}F^2. \tag{4.5.16}$$

The source strength A_1 is thus proportional to the rate of change of the cross-sectional area of the body.

Next consider the matching of the two expansions under an intermediate limit $\delta \to 0$ (x, r_η fixed), where

$$r_\eta = \frac{r}{\eta(\delta)} \qquad \text{and} \qquad \eta \to 0, \qquad \frac{\eta}{\delta} \to \infty. \tag{4.5.17}$$

It is not necessary to construct the intermediate expansion. (Its dominant equation is that for φ_1.) Matching to first order occurs if

$$\lim_{\substack{\delta\to 0\\(r_\eta \text{ fixed})}} \{x + \varepsilon_1(\delta)\phi_1(x, r) + \cdots - (x + \mu_1(\delta)\varphi_1(x, r^*) + \cdots)\} = 0.$$

In the intermediate limit, we have $r = \eta r_\eta \to 0$, $r^* = (\eta/\delta)r_\eta \to \infty$ and, thus,

$$\left\{\varepsilon_1(\delta)\phi_1(x, \eta r_\eta) - \delta^2\left(A_1(x)\log\frac{\eta r_\eta}{\delta} + B_1(x)\right) + \cdots\right\} \to 0. \tag{4.5.18}$$

The behavior of $\phi_1(x, r)$ as $r \to 0$ is essential for the matching, and Equation

(4.5.18) indicates that logarithmic behavior of $\phi_1(x, r)$ is essential for matching. Thus, the solution for ϕ_1 can be represented as a line of point sources on the axis $r = 0$, $0 < x < 1$, and this satisfies the boundary condition at infinity:

$$\phi_1(x, r) = \frac{-1}{2\pi^2}\int_0^\infty d\omega \int_{-\infty}^\infty K_0(\omega r)\cos\omega(x - \xi)S_1(\xi)\,d\xi$$

$$= \frac{-1}{4\pi}\int_{-\infty}^\infty \frac{S_1(\xi)}{\sqrt{(x-\xi)^2 + r^2}}\,d\xi. \qquad (4.5.19)$$

The logarithmic behavior near the axis is easily seen from the Fourier integral since

$$K_0(\omega r) = -\log\frac{\omega r \gamma}{2} + O(r^2 \log r), \qquad \gamma = \text{Euler const} = 0.577215. \qquad (4.5.20)$$

It is expected that the source strength distribution S_1 is zero outside the interval (0, 1). Letting $r \to 0$ in Equation (4.5.19), we have that

$$\phi_1(x, r) \to \frac{1}{2\pi^2}\log r \int_{-\infty}^\infty S_1(\xi)\,d\xi \int_0^\infty \cos\omega(x - \xi)\,d\omega + \cdots. \qquad (4.5.21)$$

Interpreting

$$(1/\pi)\int_0^\infty \cos\omega x\,d\omega = \delta(x),$$

we find that

$$\phi_1(x, r) \to (1/2\pi)S_1(x)\log r + \cdots.\dagger \qquad (4.5.22)$$

The matching condition (Equation 4.5.18) is, thus,

$$\left\{\frac{\varepsilon_1(\delta)}{2\pi}S_1(x)\log(\eta r_\eta) + \cdots - \delta^2\left(A_1(x)\log\frac{\eta r_\eta}{\delta} + B_1(x)\right) + \cdots\right\} \to 0. \qquad (4.5.23)$$

It is clear that the term $O(\delta^2 \log \delta)$ cannot be matched in the expansions as they stand, although the term $\log(\eta r_\eta)$ is all right. It is necessary to introduce a larger term in the inner expansion $\mu_0\varphi_0(x, r^*)$ such that

$$\mu_0 = \delta^2 \log \delta \qquad (4.5.24)$$

and $\varphi_0(x, r^*) = A_1(x)$. Thus, the inner expansion is modified to read

$$\Phi(x, r; \delta) = x + \delta^2 \log\delta A_1(x) + \delta^2\{A_1(x)\log r^* + B_1(x)\} + \cdots. \qquad (4.5.25)$$

† Another derivation of this result appears later.

It is easily seen that the equation for φ_1 is not altered by the addition of this term necessary for the matching. It should be remarked that $\log \delta$ is not very much greater than one for practical values of δ ($\delta = .10$, for example), although of larger order in terms of a limit. For practical results, both terms $O(\delta^2 \log \delta)$ and $O(\delta^2)$ are needed. The occurrence of $\log \delta$ is clearly due to the axi-symmetric nature of the problem. The matching condition (Equation 4.5.23) is now modified to

$$\left\{\frac{\varepsilon_1(\delta)}{2\pi} S_1(x) \log (\eta r_\eta) + \cdots \varepsilon_2(\delta)\phi_2(x, \eta r_\eta) + \cdots - (\delta^2 \log \delta A_1(x) \right.$$
$$\left. + \delta^2 A_1(x) \log \frac{\eta r_\eta}{\delta} + \delta^2 B_1(x) + \cdots)\right\} \to 0, \quad (4.5.26)$$

Thus, for matching, we have

$$\varepsilon_1(\delta) = \delta^2, \qquad \frac{1}{2\pi} S_1(x) = A_1(x) = \frac{1}{2}\frac{d}{dx} F^2(x), \qquad 0 < x < 1. \quad (4.5.27)$$

The complete outer potential $\phi_1(x, r)$ is now determined, since the source strength $S_1(x)$ in Equation (4.5.19) is now known. The determination of $B_1(x)$ and various other higher terms depends on further terms in the series (Equation 4.5.22) for $\phi_1(x, r)$ as $r \to 0$. The form of the expansion follows directly from the equation

$$\frac{\partial}{\partial r}\left(r \frac{\partial \phi_1}{\partial r}\right) = -r \frac{\partial^2 \phi_1}{\partial x^2} \quad (4.5.28)$$

by substitution of an expansion in r into both sides of the equation

$$\frac{\partial}{\partial r}\left(r \frac{\partial \phi_1}{\partial r}\right) = -\frac{r}{2\pi} \log r S_1''(x) + \cdots. \quad (4.5.29)$$

Integration of Equation (4.5.29) shows that

$$\phi_1(x, r) = \frac{1}{2\pi} S_1(x) \log r + T_1(x) - \frac{S_1''(x)}{2\pi}\left(\frac{r^2}{4} \log r - \frac{r^2}{4}\right)$$
$$+ \frac{r^2}{2} T_1''(x) + O(r^4 \log r). \quad (4.5.30)$$

The occurrence of derivatives of S_1 (and T_1) in this expansion show that smoothness requirements must be imposed on the body shape if this type of expansion is to be valid. Discontinuities in slope, curvature, etc., produce local regions where this discussion is not valid; suitable local expansions must be used. The important function $T_1(x)$, which is actually essential for finding the pressure distribution, cannot be found by the process leading to Equation (4.5.30). Instead, a more detailed analysis must be applied to the integral (Equation 4.5.19). To carry this out, write Equation (4.5.19) as

$$-4\pi\phi_1(x, r) = \int_0^{x-\alpha(r)} + \int_{x-\alpha(r)}^{x+\alpha(r)} + \int_{x+\alpha(r)}^{1} \tag{4.5.31}$$

since the difficulty appears at $\xi = x, r \to 0, 0 < x < 1$. Here $\alpha(r)$ is a function to be determined ($\alpha \to 0, r \to 0$), which measures in a certain way the effective range of the singularity. Let

$$I_1(x, r) = \int_{x-\alpha(r)}^{x+\alpha(r)} \frac{S_1(\xi)\, d\xi}{\sqrt{(x-\xi)^2 + r^2}} = \int_{-sh^{-1}(\alpha/r)}^{sh^{-1}(\alpha/r)} S_1(x + rsh\theta)\, d\theta. \tag{4.5.32}$$

To obtain an expansion of I_1, first expand the integral, assuming the necessary smoothness of $S_1(\xi)$,

$$I_1 = \int_{-sh^{-1}(\alpha/r)}^{sh^{-1}(\alpha/r)} \left\{ S_1(x) + \frac{r^2}{2} sh^2\theta S_1''(x) + \cdots \right\} d\theta$$

since the term $O(r)$ is identically zero. Integration yields

$$I_1 = 2S_1(x) sh^{-1}\left(\frac{\alpha}{r}\right) + \frac{r^2}{4} S_1''(x) \left\{ \frac{\alpha}{r} \sqrt{1 + \frac{\alpha^2}{r^2}} - sh^{-1}\left(\frac{\alpha}{r}\right) \right\} + \cdots. \tag{4.5.33}$$

Assuming now that $r/\alpha \to 0$, we can use the expansion of sh^{-1},

$$sh^{-1}\left(\frac{\alpha}{r}\right) = \log\left(\frac{\alpha}{r} + \sqrt{\frac{\alpha^2}{r^2} + 1}\right) = \log\frac{2\alpha}{r} + \frac{1}{4}\frac{r^2}{\alpha^2} + O\left(\frac{r^4}{\alpha^4}\right). \tag{4.5.34}$$

Thus, the expansion for $I_1(x, r)$ is

$$I_1(x, r) = 2S_1(x)\left\{ \log\frac{2\alpha}{r} + \frac{1}{4}\frac{r^2}{\alpha^2} + \cdots \right\} + \frac{1}{2} S_1''(x) \left\{ \alpha^2\left(1 + \frac{1}{2}\frac{r^2}{\alpha^2} + \cdots\right) \right.$$
$$\left. - r^2\left(\log\frac{2\alpha}{r} + \frac{1}{4}\frac{r^2}{\alpha^2} + \cdots\right)\right\}. \tag{4.5.35}$$

The expansion of the outer integrals I_2, I_3, as $r \to 0$ must be such that $\alpha(r)$ disappears from the result. For these integrals, the expansion $r \to 0$ can be carried out directly since there is no singularity in the range,

$$I_2 = \int_0^{x-\alpha(r)} \frac{S_1(\xi)}{\sqrt{(x-\xi)^2 + r^2}}\, d\xi = \int_0^{x-\alpha(r)} \frac{S_1(\xi)}{x-\xi} \left\{ 1 - \frac{1}{2}\frac{r^2}{(x-\xi)^2} + \cdots \right\} d\xi, \tag{4.5.36}$$

and, similarly for I_3,

$$I_3 = \int_{x+\alpha(r)}^{1} \frac{S_1(\xi)\, d\xi}{\sqrt{(x-\xi)^2 + r^2}}. \tag{4.5.37}$$

Integration by parts yields

$$I_2 = -(\log \alpha)S_1(x-\alpha) + (\log x)S_1(0) + \int_0^{x-\alpha(r)} S_1'(\xi) \log (x-\xi)\, d\xi + O\left(\frac{r^2}{\alpha^2}\right).$$

Assuming now that the body is sufficiently pointed at nose and tail† so that $\lim_{x\to 0} (\log x)S_1(x) \to 0$ and $\lim_{x\to 1} [\log (1-x)]S_1(x) \to 0$, I_2 and I_3 combine to yield

$$I_2 + I_3 = -2(\log \alpha)S_1(x) + \int_0^1 S_1'(\xi) \operatorname{sgn}(x-\xi) \log |x-\xi|\, d\xi + O(r^2/\alpha^2). \tag{4.5.38}$$

Combining Equations (4.5.35) and (4.5.38), we find the first two terms in $\phi_1(x, r)$, and the remainder follows from Equation (4.5.30):

$$-4\pi\phi_1(x, r) = -2S_1(x) \log r + 2S_1(x) \log 2 + \int_0^1 S_1'(\xi) \log (x-\xi)\, d\xi + \cdots$$

or

$$T_1(x) = -\frac{1}{2\pi} S_1(x) \log 2 + \frac{1}{4\pi} \int_0^1 S_1'(\xi) \operatorname{sgn}(x-\xi) \log |x-\xi|\, d\xi. \tag{4.5.39}$$

Now the matching (Equation 4.5.26) can be completed to determine the unknown function $B_1(x)$ and to indicate the general form of the expansion. We use the fact that $\phi_2(x, r)$ is an axisymmetric potential with an expansion, as $r \to 0$, of the same form as $\phi_1(x, r)$:

$$\begin{aligned}
\Bigg[\delta^2 &\left(\frac{1}{2\pi} S_1(x) \log \eta r_\eta + T_1(x) - \frac{S_1''}{2\pi} \frac{\eta^2 r_\eta^2}{4} \log \eta r_\eta + O(\eta^2 r_\eta^2) \right) \\
&+ \varepsilon_2(\delta) \left(\frac{1}{2\pi} S_2(x) \log \eta r_\eta + T_2(x) + \cdots \right) - \delta^2 \log \delta A_1(x) \\
&- \delta^2 \left\{ A_1(x) \log \frac{\eta r_\eta}{\delta} + B_1(x) \right\} - \mu_2(\delta)\varphi_2\left(x, \frac{\eta}{\delta} r_\eta\right) \\
&\qquad - \mu_3(\delta)\varphi_3\left(x, \frac{\eta}{\delta} r_\eta\right) - \mu_4(\delta)\varphi_4\left(x, \frac{\eta}{\delta} r_\eta\right) \Bigg] \to 0.
\end{aligned} \tag{4.5.40}$$

---

†Near the nose, $F(x) \sim x^n$, $n > \frac{1}{2}$, is permissible (zero radius of curvature). The problem of a blunter nose also requires special treatment—an example is given later. Here $n > \frac{1}{2}$ corresponds to an integrable pressure singularity in our approximation.

For matching, we see that

$$B_1(x) = T_1(x). \tag{4.5.41}$$

The contributions $\mu_2\varphi_2$, $\mu_3\varphi_3$, and $\mu_4\varphi_4$ in the inner expansion form a set analogous to μ_0 and μ_1, so that matching can be carried out and the boundary conditions of tangent flow are accounted for. It can be verified that the expansions are matched if

$$\mu_2 = \delta^4 \log^2 \delta, \qquad \mu_3 = \delta^4 \log \delta, \qquad \mu_4 = \delta^4, \qquad \varepsilon_2 = \delta^4 \log \delta,$$

and φ_4 is found from

$$\frac{\partial^2 \varphi_4}{\partial r^{*2}} + \frac{1}{r^*}\frac{\partial \varphi_4}{\partial r^*} = -\frac{\partial^2 \varphi_1}{\partial x^{*2}} = -A_1''(x)\log r^* - B_1''(x), \tag{4.5.42}$$

so that

$$\varphi_2 = A_4(x),$$

$$\varphi_3 = A_4(x)\log r^* + B_3(x),$$

$$\varphi_4 = A_4(x)\log r^* + B_4(x) - \frac{A_1''}{4}(r^{*2}\log r^* - r^{*2}) + \frac{r^{*2}}{4}B_1''.$$

The corresponding source strengths are found from the boundary conditions and matching, and the procedure can be continued, although it is doubtful whether it is of practical value to obtain many terms.

As far as the dominant behavior is concerned, the inner expansion is summarized as follows:

$$\begin{aligned}
\Phi(x, r; \delta) &= x + (\delta^2 \log \delta)A_1(x) + \delta^2\{A_1(x)\log r^* + B_1(x)\} + O(\delta^4 \log^2 \delta),\\
u = \Phi_x(x, r; \delta) &= 1 + (\delta^2 \log \delta)A_1'(x)\\
&\quad + \delta^2\{A_1'(x)\log r^* + B_1'(x)\} + O(\delta^4 \log^2 \delta),
\end{aligned} \tag{4.5.43}$$

$$v = \Phi_r(x, r; \delta) = \delta\frac{A_1(x)}{r^*} + O(\delta^3),$$

where

$$A_1(x) = S_1(x) = \frac{1}{2}\frac{d}{dx}F^2(x) = FF',$$

$$B_1(x) = T_1(x) = -\frac{1}{2\pi}S_1(x)\log 2 + \frac{1}{4\pi}\int_0^1 S_1'(\xi)\,\mathrm{sgn}\,(x - \xi)\log|x - \xi|\,d\xi.$$

Note that the net source strength is zero for a closed body:

$$\int_0^1 S_1(x)\,dx = \frac{F^2(1)}{2} - \frac{F^2(0)}{2} = 0$$

in the perturbation term of dominant order, as of course is true for the exact theory for any δ.

The pressure distribution on the surface $p_b(x)$ also has an expansion in terms of δ and is easily calculated from the inner expansion (Equation 4.5.43) as

$$p_b(x) = p(x, \delta F(x)) = -2\delta^2\left\{S_1' \log(\delta F) + B_1' + \frac{F'^2}{2}\right\} + O(\delta^4 \log^2 \delta). \tag{4.5.44}$$

It can also be verified that the drag coefficient C_{D} given by

$$C_{\mathrm{D}} = \frac{4}{\delta^2}\int_0^1 p_b(x)F(x)F'(x)\,dx \tag{4.5.45}$$

is zero for the terms $O(\delta^2 \log \delta, \delta^2)$ in agreement with the general result (D'Alembert paradox) for incompressible flow.

In this example, the use of an inner expansion is not strictly necessary in the sense that the inner expansion is really completely contained in the outer expansion. However, it is useful in making explicit the behavior near the boundary and in emphasizing the different natures of the expansion as $\delta \to 0$ for a point fixed on the boundary and a point fixed in space. In this way, the different expansions are associated with limit processes. For more complicated differential equations, the idea of local behavior near a singular line or point can be essential.

BLUNT NOSE. LOCAL EXPANSION The local nonuniformity of the slender-body expansion near a blunt nose is now investigated, and a method, based on a local solution, of eliminating the difficulty is now sketched. As mentioned in the footnote on p. 188, some difficulty occurs for a nose which is so blunt that $F(x) \sim \sqrt{x}$, but if $F(x) \sim x^n$, $n < \frac{1}{2}$, the pressure force, at least in the first approximation, is integrable. Thus, we consider here a slender body whose shape function $F(x)$ has the following expansion near the nose:

$$F(x) = \sqrt{2ax}\{1 + bx + \cdots\}, \qquad F'(x) = \frac{1}{2}\sqrt{\frac{2a}{x}} + O(x^{1/2}),$$
$$F''(x) = -\frac{1}{4}\frac{\sqrt{2a}}{x^{3/2}} + O(x^{-1/2}). \tag{4.5.46}$$

The radius of curvature R_c at the nose is

$$R_c \to \frac{\delta^3(F'^3)}{\delta F''} \to \delta^2 a \qquad \text{as} \quad x \to 0. \tag{4.5.47}$$

The slender-body inner expansion of the potential is Equation (4.5.43), but near the nose we find that the source strength is

$$A_1(x) = FF'(x) = a + O(x). \tag{4.5.48}$$

Furthermore, for the function $B_1(x)$ we have to return to the integration following Equation (4.5.36) and retain the boundary term at the nose which was dropped out for sufficiently pointed bodies with $A_1(0) \to 0$. Thus, we have

$$B_1(x) = -A_1(x)\log 2 - A_1(0)\log x + \cdots + \int_0^1 A_1'(\xi)\,\mathrm{sgn}\,(x - \xi)\log|x - \xi|\,d\xi \tag{4.5.49}$$

or, as $x \to 0$,

$$B_1(x) \to -a\log 2 - (a/2)\log x + \cdots. \tag{4.5.50}$$

Thus, for the potential, we obtain

$$\Phi = x + a\delta^2 \log \delta + \delta^2\{a \log r^* - a\log 2 - (a/2)\log x + \cdots\} \quad \text{as} \quad x \to 0. \tag{4.5.51}$$

On the body surface, $r^* = \sqrt{2ax}$, Φ is finite. However, the velocity perturbation is

$$u = \Phi_x = 1 - \frac{a\delta^2}{2x} + \cdots, \qquad v = a\frac{\delta}{r^*}, \tag{4.5.52}$$

so that the local surface pressure, p_b, from the Bernoulli equation (4.5.3), is

$$2p_b = 1 - \left(1 - \frac{a\delta^2}{x} + \cdots\right)^2 - \left(\frac{a\delta}{\sqrt{2ax}} + \cdots\right)^2 = \delta^2\frac{a}{2x} + O(\delta^4). \tag{4.5.53}$$

The term of $O(\delta^2)$ shows an unphysically large compression and, in fact, the total force on the nose which is proportional to $\int p_b FF'\,dx$ is infinite. In order to give a better representation of the flow near the nose, we can try to find a local expansion based on a limit process which preserves the structure of the flow near the nose. Since we are interested in the neighborhood of a point, both $x, r \to 0$ in the limit, and it is clear that all terms in the basic equations (Equation 4.5.1) should be retained. Thus, the general form has

$$\tilde{x} = \frac{x}{\alpha(\delta)}, \qquad \tilde{r} = \frac{r}{\alpha(\delta)} \quad \text{fixed}$$

in the limit. But now considering that $r_b \sim \delta\sqrt{x}$ as $x \to 0$, we see that $\alpha(\delta) = \delta^2$ in order to keep the typical body structure near the nose. Thus, let

$$\tilde{x} = \frac{x}{\delta^2}, \qquad \tilde{r} = \frac{r}{\delta^2}. \tag{4.5.54}$$

The asymptotic expansion near the nose is

$$\Phi = x + \varepsilon_1(\delta)\tilde{\phi}_1(\tilde{x}, \tilde{r}) + \cdots, \tag{4.5.55}$$

where $\tilde{\phi}_1$ is a potential:

$$\frac{\partial^2 \tilde{\phi}_1}{\partial \tilde{x}^2} + \frac{\partial^2 \tilde{\phi}_1}{\partial \tilde{r}^2} + \frac{1}{\tilde{r}}\frac{\partial \tilde{\phi}_1}{\partial \tilde{r}} = 0. \tag{4.5.56}$$

As far as the first approximation goes, the body is represented by

$$\tilde{r}_b = \sqrt{2a\tilde{x}}. \tag{4.5.57}$$

Then the problem is one of flow past a paraboloid. The surface-boundary condition (Equation 4.5.6) becomes

$$\frac{[\varepsilon_1(\delta)/\delta^2](\partial\tilde{\phi}_1/\partial\tilde{r})(\tilde{x}, \sqrt{2a\tilde{x}}) + \cdots}{1 + [\varepsilon_1(\delta)/\delta^2](\partial\tilde{\phi}_1/\partial\tilde{x})(\tilde{x}, \sqrt{2a\tilde{x}}) + \cdots} = \frac{1}{2}\sqrt{\frac{2a}{\tilde{x}}}, \tag{4.5.58}$$

from which we see that the proper choice is

$$\varepsilon_1(\delta) = \delta^2. \tag{4.5.59}$$

Note that the free-stream term in Equation (4.5.55) is just the same order ($x = \delta^2\tilde{x}$) as the term $\varepsilon_1(\delta)\tilde{\phi}_1$. The potential of the paraboloid with the boundary condition (Equation 4.5.58) can be written

$$\phi_1 = \frac{1}{2}a\log\left\{\sqrt{\left(\tilde{x} - \frac{a}{2}\right)^2 + \tilde{r}^2} - \left(\tilde{x} - \frac{a}{2}\right)\right\}. \tag{4.5.60}$$

There is no arbitrary constant here, due to the form of Equation (4.5.58). The x-term is already matched (Equation 4.5.55). This solution can be matched to the previous inner expansion to remove the singularity at the nose and enable a uniformly valid approximation to be constructed. For the matching, an intermediate limit can be used with r^* fixed and x_η fixed, where

$$x_\eta = \frac{x}{\eta}, \qquad \delta^2 \ll \eta \ll \delta. \tag{4.5.61}$$

Under this limit, we have

$$\tilde{x} = \frac{\eta}{\delta^2} x_\eta \to \infty, \qquad x = \eta x_\eta \to 0, \qquad \tilde{r} = \frac{r^*}{\delta} \to \infty. \tag{4.5.62}$$

Thus, we obtain

$$\sqrt{\left(\tilde{x} - \frac{a}{2}\right)^2 + r^2} = \sqrt{\left(\frac{\eta}{\delta^2} x_\eta - \frac{a}{2}\right)^2 + \frac{r^{*2}}{\delta^2}}$$

$$\to \frac{\eta}{\delta^2} x_\eta \left\{1 + \frac{1}{2} \frac{\delta^2}{\eta^2} \frac{r^{*2}}{x_\eta^2} + \cdots\right\} \qquad \text{if } \frac{\delta}{\eta} \to 0$$

and

$$\sqrt{\left(\tilde{x} - \frac{a}{2}\right)^2 + r^2} - \left(\tilde{x} - \frac{a}{2}\right) \to \frac{r^{*2}}{2\eta x_\eta} + \cdots. \tag{4.5.63}$$

By adding suitable constants which do not affect the velocity, it is seen that the potential of Equation (4.5.60) matches to the $\log r^*$, $\log x$ terms in Equation (4.5.51). Thus, near the nose the pressure should be computed from the velocity components as found from Equation (4.5.60),

$$\frac{\partial \Phi}{\partial r} = \frac{a}{2} \frac{1}{\sqrt{(\tilde{x} - a/2)^2 + \tilde{r}^2} - (x^2 - a/2)} \frac{\tilde{r}}{\sqrt{(\tilde{x} - a/2)^2 + \tilde{r}^2}} \to \frac{1}{2} \frac{\sqrt{2a\tilde{x}}}{\tilde{x} + a/2}$$

$$\text{on the surface,} \tag{4.5.64}$$

$$\frac{\partial \Phi}{\partial x} = 1 + \frac{a}{2} \frac{1}{\sqrt{(\tilde{x} - a/2)^2 + \tilde{r}^2} - (\tilde{x} - a/2)} \left\{\frac{\tilde{x} - a/2}{\sqrt{(\tilde{x}^2 - a/2)^2 + \tilde{r}^2}} - 1\right\}$$

$$\to \frac{\tilde{x}}{\tilde{x} + a/2} \qquad \text{on the surface.} \tag{4.5.65}$$

This is a typical example of how a local solution, in this case flow past a paraboloid, can be used to improve the behavior near a singularity. A composite expansion can be written by adding the local and outer expansions and subtracting the common part.

4.5.2 Low Reynolds-number viscous flow past a circular cylinder

For this problem, the Navier–Stokes equations (Equation 4.2.3) are again considered to describe the flow. There is uniform flow at infinity, and the body is at the origin. Since the size of the body was used as the

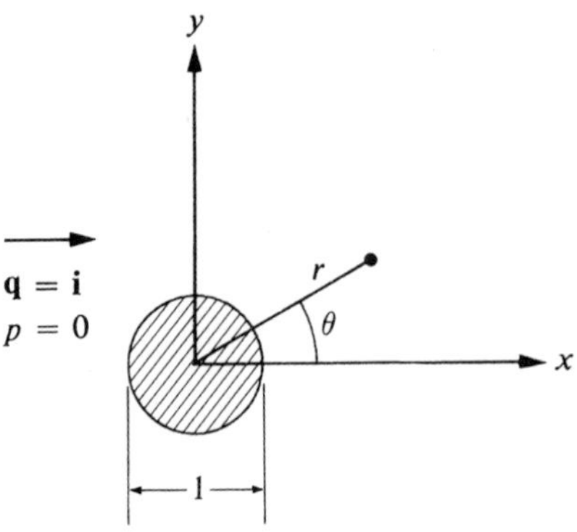

FIGURE 4.23 Problem in inner variables.

characteristic length in writing the system (Equation 4.2.3), the body diameter is one (see Figure 4.23). The boundary condition of no-slip,

$$\mathbf{q} = 0 \qquad \text{on} \quad r = \sqrt{x^2 + y^2} = \tfrac{1}{2}, \tag{4.5.2.1}$$

and conditions at infinity serve to define the problem. We are interested in a low Reynolds number, so that in Equation (4.2.3) we have

$$\varepsilon = \frac{1}{\text{Re}} = \frac{\nu}{UL} \to \infty. \tag{4.5.2.2}$$

The variables based on L are inner variables (Stokes variables in the notation of References 4.5.2.1, 4.5.2.2, 4.5.2.3), since the boundary remains fixed in the limit. As it turns out, the inner problem which is Stokes flow cannot satisfy the complete boundary condition at infinity, so that some suitable outer expansion, valid near infinity, must also be constructed. Both inner and outer expansions, which can be identified with the usual Stokes and Oseen flow approximations, respectively, are described here, and the matching is carried out. The model example corresponding to the kind of singular boundary-value problem that occurs here has already been discussed in Section 2.7.2.

The inner expansion is based on Re $\to 0$, $\varepsilon \to \infty$ in Equation (4.2.3), but if pressure is measured in units of ρU^2, both inertia and pressure terms drop out of the limiting momentum equations. There are not enough variables if continuity is to be considered, so that the physical pressure (difference from infinity) should be measured in terms of $U\mu/L$. Or let

$$p^*(x, y) = \frac{1}{\varepsilon} p(x, y) = (\text{Re})\, p(x, y). \tag{4.5.2.3}$$

This is in accord with Stokes' idea of a balance between viscous stresses and pressure forces, at least near the body, for slow flow. Thus, in inner variables, the Navier–Stokes system can be written

$$\operatorname{div} \mathbf{q} = 0, \tag{4.5.2.4a}$$

$$\operatorname{Re}(\mathbf{q} \cdot \nabla \mathbf{q}) = -\operatorname{grad} p^* - \operatorname{curl} \boldsymbol{\omega}, \qquad \boldsymbol{\omega} = \operatorname{curl} \mathbf{q}. \tag{4.5.2.4b}$$

The inner expansion, associated with the limit process (Re → 0, x, y fixed) has the form

$$\mathbf{q}(x, y; \operatorname{Re}) = \alpha_0(\operatorname{Re})\mathbf{q}_0(x, y) + \alpha_1(\operatorname{Re})\mathbf{q}_1(x, y) + \cdots, \tag{4.5.2.5a}$$

$$p^*(x, y; \operatorname{Re}) = \alpha_0(\operatorname{Re})p_0^*(x, y) + \alpha_1(\operatorname{Re})p_1^*(x, y) + \cdots. \tag{4.5.2.5b}$$

Taking the limit of the Navier–Stokes equations (Equation 4.5.2.4) shows that the first term of the inner expansion satisfies the usual Stokes equations:

$$\operatorname{div} \mathbf{q}_0 = 0, \tag{4.5.2.6a}$$

$$0 = \operatorname{grad} p_0^* - \operatorname{curl} \boldsymbol{\omega}_0, \qquad \boldsymbol{\omega}_0 = \operatorname{curl} \mathbf{q}_0. \tag{4.5.2.6b}$$

A fairly general discussion of the solutions to Equation (4.5.2.6) can be given while taking account of the boundary conditions on the surface, so that the behavior at infinity can be ascertained. It is convenient to introduce the stream function $\psi(x, y)$ satisfying continuity identically by

$$\mathbf{q} = \operatorname{curl} \boldsymbol{\psi}, \qquad \boldsymbol{\psi} = \psi(x, y)\mathbf{k}, \qquad q_x = \frac{\partial \psi}{\partial y}, \qquad q_y = -\frac{\partial \psi}{\partial x}. \tag{4.5.2.7}$$

The equation for the vorticity $\boldsymbol{\omega}_0 = \omega_0(x, y)\mathbf{k}$ is

$$\omega_0(x, y) = -\nabla^2 \psi_0(x, y). \tag{4.5.2.8}$$

Further, taking the curl of the momentum equation (Equation 4.5.2.6b) shows that

$$\operatorname{curl}\operatorname{curl} \boldsymbol{\omega}_0 = 0 \qquad \text{or} \qquad \nabla^2 \omega_0 = 0. \tag{4.5.2.9}$$

Thus, the vorticity field is a harmonic function and can be represented, in general, outside the circular cylinder $r = \frac{1}{2}$ by a series with unknown coefficients. The velocity field must be symmetric with respect to the x-axis, and the vorticity field antisymmetric. Thus, the general form is the familiar solution of Laplace's equation in cylindrical coordinates,

$$\omega_0(r, \theta) = \sum_{n=0}^{\infty} (a_n r^n + b_n r^{-n}) \sin n\theta. \tag{4.5.2.10}$$

The general solution for $\psi_0(r, \theta)$ satisfying Equation (4.5.2.8) is

$$\frac{\partial^2\psi_0}{\partial r^2} + \frac{1}{r}\frac{\partial\psi_0}{\partial r} + \frac{1}{r^2}\frac{\partial^2\psi_0}{\partial\theta^2} = -\sum_{n=0}^{\infty}(a_n r^n + b_n r^{-n})\sin n\theta, \quad (4.5.2.11)$$

and the boundary condition of no-slip

$$\psi_0\left(\frac{1}{2}, \theta\right) = \frac{\partial\psi_0}{\partial r}\left(\frac{1}{2}, \theta\right) = 0, \quad (4.5.2.12)$$

can now be found. Thus, let

$$\psi_0(r, \theta) = \sum_{n=1}^{\infty}\Psi^{(n)}(r)\sin n\theta, \quad (4.5.2.13)$$

so that we have

$$L^{(n)}\Psi^{(n)} \equiv \frac{d^2\Psi^{(n)}}{dr^2} + \frac{1}{r}\frac{d\Psi^{(n)}}{dr} - \frac{n^2}{r^2}\Psi^{(n)} = -a_n r^n - b_n r^{-n}. \quad (4.5.2.14)$$

It can be verified that

$$L^{(n)}r^m = (m^2 - n^2)r^{m-2}, \quad (4.5.2.15)$$

so that by choosing $m = n + 2$, we have

$$L^{(n)}r^{n+2} = (4n + 4)r^n, \quad (4.5.2.16)$$

which is good for all $n \neq -1$. Further, for $n = -1$, we obtain

$$L^{(n)}r\log r = 2/r. \quad (4.5.2.17)$$

Thus, introducing new constants, the general solution (Equation 4.5.2.14) is

$$\Psi^{(1)} = A_1 r^3 + B_1 r\log r + C_1 r + \frac{D_1}{r}, \quad (4.5.2.18a)$$

$$\Psi^{(n)} = A_n r^{2+n} + B_n r^{2-n} + C_n r^n + \frac{D_n}{r^n}, \qquad n = 2, 3, \ldots \quad (4.5.2.18b)$$

and

$$\frac{d\Psi^{(1)}}{dr} = 3A_1 r^2 + B_1(\log r + 1) + C_1 - \frac{D_1}{r^2}, \quad (4.5.2.19a)$$

$$\frac{d\Psi^{(n)}}{dr} = (2 + n)A_n r^{1+n} + (2 - n)B_n r^{1-n} + nC_n r^{n-1} - n\frac{D_n}{r^{n+1}}, \quad n = 2, 3, \ldots. \quad (4.5.2.19b)$$

By applying the boundary condition at the body surface $r = \frac{1}{2}$ (Equation

4.5.2.12), we obtained two relations between the four constants A_n, B_n, C_n, D_n. Further determination of the solution must come from the boundary conditions at infinity, which would read

$$q_x = \sin\theta \frac{\partial \psi}{\partial r}(r, \theta) + \frac{\cos\theta}{r}\frac{\partial \psi}{\partial \theta}(r, \theta) = 1 \qquad \text{as} \quad r \to \infty, \quad (4.5.2.20)$$

$$q_y = -\cos\theta \frac{\partial \psi}{\partial r}(r, \theta) + \frac{\sin\theta}{r}\frac{\partial \psi}{\partial \theta}(r, \theta) = 0, \qquad r \to \infty \quad (4.5.2.21)$$

or

$$\frac{\partial \psi}{\partial r}(r, \theta) \to \sin\theta, \qquad r \to \infty, \qquad \frac{1}{r}\frac{\partial \psi}{\partial \theta}(r, \theta) \to \cos\theta, \qquad r \to \infty. \quad (4.5.2.22)$$

If the condition of Equation (4.5.2.22) is imposed to fix $C_1 = 1, A_1 = B_1 = A_n = C_n = 0$, then the two boundary conditions at the wall can not be satisfied. Thus, the condition has to be given up and replaced by a condition of matching at infinity. The inner expansion is not uniform at infinity. The situation is possibly a little clearer for the corresponding problem for a sphere, where, although the first term of the inner expansion can satisfy the conditions at infinity, the second can not and becomes larger than the first at some distance from the origin. In general, only one more constant B_1 is needed, so that we can choose

$$B_1 \neq 0, \qquad A_1 = 0, \qquad A_n = 0, \qquad C_n = 0, \qquad n = 2, 3, \ldots, \quad (4.5.2.23)$$

and obtain the weakest possible divergence of the solution at infinity. This has to be verified by matching. Thus, from the boundary condition at the surface (Equation 4.5.2.12) applied to Equations (4.5.2.18) and (4.5.2.19) we obtain

$$\begin{aligned}
\Psi^{(1)}\left(\frac{1}{2}\right) &= 0 = \frac{B_1}{2}\log\frac{1}{2} + \frac{C_1}{2} + 2D_1, \\
\Psi^{(n)}\left(\frac{1}{2}\right) &= 0 = B_n 2^{n-2} + 2^n D_n, \qquad n = 2, 3, \ldots; \\
\frac{d\Psi^{(1)}}{dr}\left(\frac{1}{2}\right) &= 0 = B_1\left(\log\frac{1}{2} + 1\right) + C_1 - 4D_1, \\
\frac{d\Psi^{(n)}}{dr}\left(\frac{1}{2}\right) &= 0 = (2 - n)\beta_n 2^{n-1} - nD_n 2^{n+1}, \qquad n = 2, 3, \ldots.
\end{aligned} \quad (4.5.2.24)$$

Thus, from the conditions at the surface of the circular cylinder, we have

$$B_n = D_n = 0, \qquad n = 2, 3, \ldots, \quad (4.5.2.25)$$

and we are left with two relations between the three constants B_1, C_1, and D_1:

$$(\tfrac{1}{2}\log\tfrac{1}{2})B_1 + \tfrac{1}{2}C_1 + 2D_1 = 0, \qquad (\log\tfrac{1}{2} + 1)B_1 + C_1 - 4D_1 = 0. \tag{4.5.2.26}$$

Thus, the first term of the inner expansion becomes

$$\psi_0(x, r) = [B_1 r \log r + C_1 r + (D_1/r)] \sin\theta, \tag{4.5.2.27}$$

and

$$q_x = \alpha_0(\mathrm{Re})\{B_1 \log r + C_1 + B_1 \sin^2\theta + (D_1/r^2)\cos 2\theta\} + \alpha_1(\mathrm{Re})q_x + \cdots. \tag{4.5.2.28}$$

Now, in order to construct the outer expansions, a suitable outer variable has to be chosen. It was a basic idea of S. Kaplun to use the characteristic length ν/U for defining the expansion in the far field. Thus, in these units the body radius is very small and approaches zero in the limit. It can then be anticipated that the first term of the outer expansion is the undisturbed stream, since the body of infinitesimal size has no arresting power. Compare this procedure with that in the model example in Section 2.7.2. The formalities involve a limit procedure with $\tilde{x}$, $\tilde{y}$ fixed, $\mathrm{Re} \to 0$, where

$$\tilde{x} = (\mathrm{Re})x, \qquad \tilde{y} = (\mathrm{Re})y \tag{4.5.2.29}$$

since x, y are based on the diameter. In these units, the body surface itself is

$$\tilde{r} = \sqrt{\tilde{x}^2 + \tilde{y}^2} = \tfrac{1}{2}, \qquad \mathrm{Re} \to 0. \tag{4.5.2.30}$$

If the Navier–Stokes equations (Equation 4.5.2.4) are written in these units, the parameter Re disappears. The pressure is again based on ρU^2:

$$\widetilde{\operatorname{div}}\, \mathbf{q} = 0, \tag{4.5.2.31a}$$

$$\mathbf{q}\cdot\tilde{\nabla}\mathbf{q} + \tilde{\nabla}p = -\widetilde{\operatorname{curl}}\,\boldsymbol{\omega}, \qquad \boldsymbol{\omega} = \widetilde{\operatorname{curl}}\,\mathbf{q}, \tag{4.5.2.31b}$$

where $(\tilde{\ })$ means space derivatives with respect to $(\tilde{x}, \tilde{y})$. The form of the outer expansion is thus assumed to be a perturbation about the uniform free stream. Thus, we have

$$q_x(x, y; \mathrm{Re}) = 1 + \beta(\mathrm{Re})u(\tilde{x}, \tilde{y}) + \beta_1(\mathrm{Re})u_1(\tilde{x}, \tilde{y}) + \cdots, \tag{4.5.2.32a}$$

$$q_y(x, y; \mathrm{Re}) = \beta(\mathrm{Re})v(\tilde{x}, \tilde{y}) + \cdots, \tag{4.5.2.32b}$$

$$p(x, y; \mathrm{Re}) = \beta(\mathrm{Re})\tilde{p}(\tilde{x}, \tilde{y}) + \cdots. \tag{4.5.2.32c}$$

From this expansion, it is clear that the first approximation equation is linearized about the free stream. The transport operator is

$$\mathbf{q} \cdot \tilde{\nabla} = \frac{\partial}{\partial \tilde{x}} + \beta(\text{Re})\left(u\frac{\partial}{\partial \tilde{x}} + v\frac{\partial}{\partial \tilde{y}}\right) + \cdots. \tag{4.5.2.33}$$

Thus, we have

$$\frac{\partial u}{\partial \tilde{x}} + \frac{\partial v}{\partial \tilde{y}} = 0, \tag{4.5.2.34a}$$

$$\frac{\partial u}{\partial \tilde{x}} + \frac{\partial \tilde{p}}{\partial \tilde{x}} = \frac{\partial^2 u}{\partial \tilde{x}^2} + \frac{\partial^2 u}{\partial \tilde{y}^2}, \tag{4.5.2.34b}$$

$$\frac{\partial v}{\partial \tilde{x}} + \frac{\partial \tilde{p}}{\partial \tilde{y}} = \frac{\partial^2 v}{\partial \tilde{x}^2} + \frac{\partial^2 v}{\partial \tilde{y}^2}. \tag{4.5.2.34c}$$

These are the equations proposed by Oseen as a model for high Reynolds-number flow, but they appear here as part of an actual approximation scheme for low Re. The idea of the matching of the two expansions can now be discussed. If the methods used previously are followed, a class of intermediate limits is considered in which x_η, y_η are held fixed and in which

$$x_\eta = \eta(\text{Re})x, \qquad y_\eta = \eta(\text{Re})y, \qquad \eta \to 0 \tag{4.5.2.35}$$

and

$$\text{Re} \ll \eta(\text{Re}) \ll 1.$$

Therefore, in this limit, we know that

$$r = \frac{r_\eta}{\eta} \to \infty, \qquad \tilde{r} = \frac{\text{Re}}{\eta}, r_\eta \to 0. \tag{4.5.2.36}$$

Assuming that the two expansions are valid in an overlap domain, we can compare the intermediate forms of inner and outer expansions (Equations 4.5.2.28, 4.5.2.32a) for q_x:

$$\lim_{\substack{\varepsilon \to 0, \\ r_\eta \text{ fixed}}} \left\{ \alpha_0(\text{Re})\left[B_1 \log \frac{r_\eta}{\eta(\varepsilon)} + C_1 + B_1 \sin^2\theta + D_1 \frac{\eta^2(\varepsilon)}{r_\eta^2}\cos 2\theta\right] + \alpha_1(\text{Re})q_1 \right.$$
$$\left. + \cdots - 1 - \beta(\text{Re})u\left(\frac{\text{Re}}{\eta}x_\eta, \frac{\text{Re}}{\eta}y_\eta\right) - \cdots \right\} = 0. \tag{4.5.2.37}$$

It is clear from Equation (4.5.2.37) that a solution of the Oseen equation

(Equation 4.5.2.34) must be found, in which

$$u(\tilde{x}, \tilde{y}) \to a \log \tilde{r} + \cdots \qquad \text{as} \quad \tilde{r} \to 0;$$

$$u(\tilde{x}, \tilde{y}) \to a \log \frac{\text{Re}\, r_\eta}{\eta} + \cdots \qquad \text{under the intermediate limit} \tag{4.5.2.38}$$

if the expansions are to be matched and the dominant remaining terms are

$$-\alpha_0(\text{Re})B_1 \log \eta(\varepsilon) + \cdots - 1 + \beta(\text{Re})a \log \eta(\varepsilon) + \beta(\text{Re})a \log \left(\frac{1}{\text{Re}}\right) + \cdots.$$

Matching is accomplished if

$$\alpha_0(\text{Re}) = \beta(\text{Re}), \qquad B_1 = a, \tag{4.5.2.39}$$

and

$$\beta(\text{Re}) = \frac{1}{\log(1/\text{Re})}, \qquad a = 1. \tag{4.5.2.40}$$

Thus, Equation (4.5.2.38) provides the necessary boundary condition for the solution of the first outer approximation. The stream function, pressure, and other velocity component can also be considered and matched. In this way, the complete first approximation to the flow near the body is found (cf. Equation 4.5.2.26):

$$B_1 = 1, \qquad C_1 = -\tfrac{1}{2} \log \tfrac{1}{2} - \tfrac{1}{2}, \qquad D_1 = \tfrac{1}{8}. \tag{4.5.2.41}$$

The continuation of this procedure enables the various higher approximations to be carried out.

Note that the nonlinear terms of the Navier–Stokes equations, when expressed in inner variables (Equation 4.5.2.4b), are $O(\text{Re})$, and hence transcendentally small compared to $\beta(\text{Re}) = 1/[\log(1/\text{Re})]$ as $\text{Re} \to 0$. In particular, when successive terms of the inner expansions are constructed, each satisfies the same Stokes equations (Equation 4.5.2.6). The nonlinear effects appear only explicitly in the outer equation and outer expansion. Thus, the nonlinearity indicates the existence of terms,

$$\beta_1(\text{Re}) = \beta^2(\text{Re}) = \log^2 \left(\frac{1}{\text{Re}}\right), \tag{4.5.2.42}$$

so that $(u_1, v_1, \tilde{p}_1)$ satisfy nonhomogeneous Oseen equations. Of course, terms of intermediate order satisfying the homogeneous Oseen equations may appear between (u, u_1) to complete the matching. For the incompressible case, it turns out that the outer expansion includes the inner expansion, and that a uniformly valid solution is found from the outer expansion with a boundary condition satisfied on $\tilde{r} = \mathrm{Re}/2$. Such a result can not be expected in the more general compressible case.

A much more sophisticated version of this problem and the general problem of low Re flow appears in References 4.5.2.1, 4.5.2.2, and 4.5.2.3. The ideas are now sketched. The treatment of matching these is based on the observation that Stokes equations are obtained as the limiting form of Navier–Stokes under the whole class of limits of the intermediate form

$$x_\xi = \frac{\tilde{x}}{\xi}, \qquad y_\xi = \frac{\tilde{y}}{\xi}. \tag{4.5.2.43}$$

Thus an intermediate expansion of a more general type is considered, and each term consists of a Stokes solution with constants depending on Re, for example,

$$q_x = \sum_{n=0} \varepsilon^{*n} U_n(x, y; \mathrm{Re}) + \cdots, \qquad q_y\dagger = \cdots. \tag{4.5.2.44}$$

In these papers, we have

$$\varepsilon^* = 1 \bigg/ \left(\log \frac{8}{\mathrm{Re}} + \frac{1}{2} - \gamma \right), \qquad \gamma = \text{Euler's constant} = 0.577. \tag{4.5.2.45}$$

This parameter is equivalent to β of Equation (4.5.2.40) for the first term but simplifies the calculation of further terms.

The nth partial sum of Equation (4.5.2.44) is uniformly valid to order ε^n in the (convex) set

$$\operatorname{ord} \mathrm{Re} \leq \operatorname{ord} \xi < \varepsilon^{*n}. \tag{4.5.2.46}$$

Note then, when $\xi = \mathrm{Re}$, then $x_\xi = \tilde{x}/\mathrm{Re} = x$, the inner variable. The outer or Oseen expansion has the same form as before,

$$q_x = 1 + \sum_{n=1} \varepsilon^{*n} q_n(\tilde{x}, \tilde{y}), \tag{4.5.2.47}$$

and the nth partial sum of Equation (4.5.2.47) is valid for

$$\operatorname{ord} \varepsilon^{*n} \leq \operatorname{ord} \xi \leq \operatorname{ord} 1. \tag{4.5.2.48}$$

The Oseen limit is nonuniform near the body, and hence both expansions are matched to the intermediate expansion as follows. Try to find $U_0(x, y; \mathrm{Re})$ uniformly valid to order one in the intermediate domain

$$q_x - U_0 \to 0 \qquad \text{uniformly in} \qquad \tfrac{1}{2}\mathrm{Re} \leq \tilde{r} < \xi(\mathrm{Re}) \quad \text{for any} \quad \xi \to 0. \tag{4.5.2.49}$$

†In what follows, we write only q_x as a symbol for the whole flow.

But the Oseen approximation is valid in the following sense (r fixed in limit):

$$(q_x - 1) \to 0 \qquad \text{uniformly in} \quad A \le \tilde{r}, \qquad A = \text{any const} > 0. \tag{4.5.2.50}$$

By applying the extension theorem (cf. Section 2.9 and Reference 4.2.3.2), the domain of validity of 1, the first Oseen term, can be extended so that it overlaps the domain of validity of U_0. Hence, the matching condition is

$$\lim_{\substack{\varepsilon \to 0, \\ x_\xi y_\xi \text{ fixed}}} (1 - U_0) = 0 \qquad \text{for} \quad \text{ord}\, \xi_0(\varepsilon^*) < \text{ord}\, \xi < 1. \tag{4.5.2.51}$$

Since under the class of limits (Equation 4.5.2.49) the Navier–Stokes equations yield to Stokes equation, it is suggested that $U_0(x, y; \text{Re})$ be a Stokes solution in (x_ξ, y_ξ) satisfying the no-slip condition on the surface $r_\xi = (1/2)(\text{Re}/\xi)$. Only those Stokes solutions which grow as slowly as possible toward infinity need be considered. Thus, comparing Equation (4.5.2.28) and noting that $U_0 = 0$ on the surface, we have

$$U_0 = \varepsilon^*(\text{Re}) \log \left(\frac{r_\xi}{\frac{1}{2}(\text{Re}/\xi)} \right) + \cdots. \tag{4.5.2.52}$$

The matching condition (Equation 4.5.2.51) thus gives

$$\varepsilon^* \log \frac{1}{\text{Re}} = 1 + b_1 \varepsilon + b_2 \varepsilon^2 + \cdots, \tag{4.5.2.53}$$

where the b_i can be chosen for convenience. The procedure is carried further, and physical interpretations are given for the various terms, for example the first Oseen correction appears as the flow due to a singular force at the origin whose strength is the Stokes drag. The formula for the drag force per unit span,

$$\frac{D}{4\pi\mu U} = \varepsilon^*[1 - 0.87\varepsilon^* + O(\varepsilon^{*2})], \tag{4.5.2.54}$$

is given. Further discussion is devoted to the case of the sphere, where the nonuniformity appears at a later stage and to the case of cylinders of arbitrary cross section, for which Equation (4.5.2.54) holds when L is suitably defined. Similar results appear also in Reference 4.5.2.4.

REFERENCES

4.5.2.1 S. Kaplun, "Low Reynolds Number Flow past a Circular Cylinder," *Journal of Math. and Mech.* 6, 5 (1957), 595–603.

4.5.2.2 S. KAPLUN, and P. A. LAGERSTROM, "Asymptotic Expansions of Navier–Stokes Solutions for Small Reynolds Numbers," *Journal of Math. and Mech.*, 6, *5* (1957), 515–593.

4.5.2.3 P. A. LAGERSTROM, Note on the Preceding Two Papers. *Journal of Math. and Mech.*, 6, *5* (1957), 605–606.

4.5.2.4 I. PROUDMAN, and J. R. A. PEARSON, "Expansions at Small Reynolds Number for the flow past a Sphere and a Circular Cylinder," *Journal of Fluid Mechanics*, 2, Part 3 (1957).

4.5.3 One-dimensional heat conduction

In many examples, the geometrical shape of the domain of the problem introduces a small parameter. For such thin domains, it is often possible to introduce various asymptotic expansions based on the limit $\varepsilon \to 0$. The terms in these asymptotic expansions can correspond to simplified models for the physical process. In this Section, one-dimensional heat conduction is derived from a three-dimensional equation. In Section 4.5.4, elastic shell theory is derived from the three-dimensional linear elasticity equations, and there are many other examples. In general, the boundary conditions for the simplified equations have to be derived from matching with a more complicated boundary layer involving more independent variables.

Consider steady heat-conduction in a long rod of circular cross section whose shape is given by

$$S(X, R) = 0 = R - bF(X/L), \qquad 0 \le X \le L \tag{4.5.3.1}$$

(see Figure 4.24). Assume that the side of the rod is insulated, so that $\partial T/\partial n = 0$, and assume that the temperature $T(X, R)$ is prescribed on the

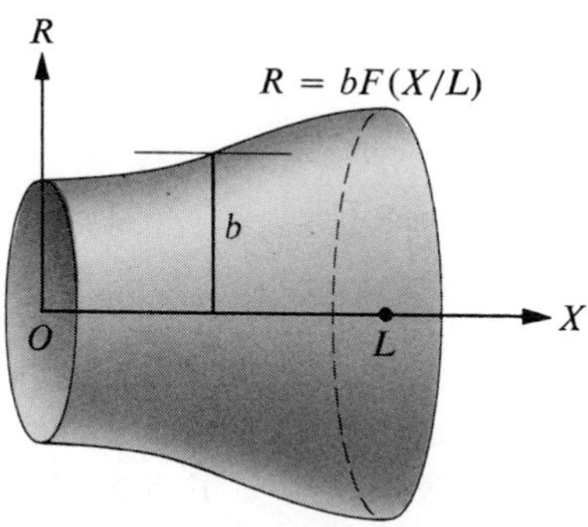

FIGURE 4.24 Quasi-one-dimensional heat conduction.

ends and is written in the form

$$T(0, R) = T^*\phi\left(\frac{R}{b}\right), \qquad T(L, R) = T^*\psi\left(\frac{R}{b}\right), \tag{4.5.3.2}$$

so that heat flows down the rod. We are interested in the case where $b/L \ll 1$. Here T^* is a characteristic temperature, and the equation for steady heat flow with constant thermal properties is Laplace's equation with axial symmetry,

$$\frac{\partial^2 T}{\partial R^2} + \frac{1}{R}\frac{\partial T}{\partial R} + \frac{\partial^2 T}{\partial X^2} = 0. \tag{4.5.3.3}$$

The boundary condition on the insulated surface $S = 0$ can be expressed as

$$\nabla T \cdot \nabla S = 0 \qquad \text{on} \quad S = 0$$

or

$$\frac{\partial T}{\partial R} = \frac{b}{L}F'\left(\frac{X}{L}\right)\frac{\partial T}{\partial X} \qquad \text{on} \quad R = bF\left(\frac{X}{L}\right). \tag{4.5.3.4}$$

The entire problem can be expressed in the following suitable dimensionless coordinates:

$$r = \frac{R}{b}, \qquad x = \frac{X}{L}, \qquad \theta(x, r; \varepsilon) = \frac{T(x, R)}{T^*},$$

where $\varepsilon = b/L$. In terms of these variables, Equation (4.5.3.3) becomes

$$\frac{\partial^2 \theta}{\partial r^2} + \frac{1}{r}\frac{\partial \theta}{\partial r} + \varepsilon^2\frac{\partial^2 \theta}{\partial x^2} = 0, \tag{4.5.3.5}$$

and the problem is specified by the following boundary conditions:

ends $$\theta(0, r) = \phi(r), \qquad \theta(1, r) = \psi(r), \tag{4.5.3.6}$$

side $$\frac{\partial \theta}{\partial r}(x, F(x)) = \varepsilon^2 F'(x)\frac{\partial \theta}{\partial x}(x, F(x)). \tag{4.5.3.7}$$

We now assume that a limiting solution, independent of ε, appears as $\varepsilon \to 0$ and represents θ by the following asymptotic expansion, which we expect to be valid away from the ends of the rod:

$$\theta(x, r; \varepsilon) = \theta_0(x, r) + \varepsilon^2\theta(x, r) + \cdots. \tag{4.5.3.8}$$

The corresponding limit process has $\varepsilon \to 0$, (x, r) fixed.

In general, an arbitrary order could be chosen for the θ_0 term, but matching would show it to be of $O(1)$. The second term is of order ε^2, so that a nonhomogeneous equation for θ_1 results. Terms of intermediate order could be inserted if needed. The sequence of equations approximating Equation (4.5.3.5) is

$$\frac{\partial^2\theta_0}{\partial r^2} + \frac{1}{r}\frac{\partial\theta_0}{\partial r} = 0, \tag{4.5.3.9}$$

$$\frac{\partial^2\theta_1}{\partial r^2} + \frac{1}{r}\frac{\partial\theta_1}{\partial r} = -\frac{\partial^2\theta_0}{\partial x^2}, \tag{4.5.3.10}$$

$$\vdots$$

All subsequent equations are of the form of Equation (4.5.3.10). The boundary condition (Equation 4.5.3.7) has the expansion

$$\frac{\partial\theta_0}{\partial r}(x, F(x)) + \varepsilon^2\frac{\partial\theta_1}{\partial r}(x, F(x)) + \cdots = \varepsilon^2 F'(x)\left\{\frac{\partial\theta_0}{\partial x}(x, F(x)) + \cdots\right\},$$

so that, on the insulated boundary, we have

$$\frac{\partial\theta_0}{\partial r}(x, F(x)) = 0, \tag{4.5.3.11}$$

$$\frac{\partial\theta_1}{\partial r}(x, F(x)) = F'(x)\frac{\partial\theta_0}{\partial x}(x, F(x)). \tag{4.5.3.12}$$

Next the solution must be investigated. We have

$$\theta_0(x, r) = A_0(x) + B_0(x)\log r. \tag{4.5.3.13}$$

If we require finite temperature at the axis, then $B_0 = 0$, and the basic approximation is a one-dimensional temperature distribution:

$$\theta_0(x, r) = A_0(x). \tag{4.5.3.14}$$

This distribution automatically satisfies the boundary condition (Equation 4.5.3.11). In this case, further information about $A_0(x)$ cannot be found without considering the equation for θ_1 and its boundary condition. Equation (4.5.3.10) is now

$$\frac{\partial^2\theta_1}{\partial r^2} + \frac{1}{r}\frac{\partial\theta_1}{\partial r} = -\frac{d^2A_0}{dx^2}, \tag{4.5.3.15}$$

which, if we disregard the log r term, has the solution

$$\theta_1(x, r) = A_1(x) - \frac{r^2}{4}\frac{d^2 A_0}{dx^2}. \tag{4.5.3.16}$$

Information about A_1 is found from the equation for θ_2, etc. Now the boundary condition on the insulated surface (Equation 4.5.3.12) becomes

$$-\frac{F(x)}{2}\frac{d^2 A_0}{dx^2} = F'(x)\frac{dA_0}{dx} \tag{4.5.3.17}$$

or

$$\frac{d}{dx}\left(F^2(x)\frac{dA_0}{dx}\right) = 0. \tag{4.5.3.18}$$

Remembering that $F(x)$ is proportional to the radius of a cross section, we see that Equation (4.5.3.18) is the equation for one-dimensional heat conduction. It arises here as a formal consequence of the insulation boundary condition. For the uniform accuracy of this approximation over the center section of the rod, $F(x)$ has to be sufficiently smooth.

Now, boundary conditions for Equation (4.5.3.5) as $x \to 0, 1$ have to be found by studying the solution in the neighborhood of the ends. Near $x = 0$, the only distinguished limit which preserves enough structure in (4.5.3.5) to allow for boundary conditions and matching is one in which $\tilde{x} = x/\varepsilon$ is fixed. Thus, consider the asymptotic expansion valid near $x = 0$,

$$\theta(x, r; \varepsilon) = \vartheta(\tilde{x}, r) + \cdots, \qquad \tilde{x} = x/\varepsilon. \tag{4.5.3.19}$$

Then the full equation results for ϑ:

$$\frac{\partial^2 \vartheta}{\partial r^2} + \frac{1}{r}\frac{\partial \vartheta}{\partial r} + \frac{\partial^2 \vartheta}{\partial \tilde{x}^2} = 0, \tag{4.5.3.20}$$

but the boundary condition on the insulated surface is somewhat simplified. Equation (4.5.3.7) becomes

$$\frac{\partial \vartheta}{\partial r}(\tilde{x}, F(\varepsilon\tilde{x})) + \cdots = \varepsilon^2 F'(\varepsilon\tilde{x})\frac{1}{\varepsilon}\frac{\partial \vartheta}{\partial \tilde{x}}(\tilde{x}, F(\varepsilon\tilde{x})) + \cdots. \tag{4.5.3.21}$$

Thus, as $\varepsilon \to 0$, we have

$$\frac{\partial \vartheta}{\partial r}(\tilde{x}, r_0) = 0, \tag{4.5.3.22}$$

where $r_0 = F(0)$. Again the assumption that F is smooth has been used. It can be seen from Equation (4.5.3.21) that the next term in the boundary-layer expansion (Equation 4.5.3.19) is $O(\varepsilon)$, but this is not considered here. At the end $x = 0$, we have

$$\vartheta(0, r) = \phi(r), \qquad 0 \le r \le r_0. \tag{4.5.3.23}$$

Thus, the problem to be solved is that of heat flow in an insulated cylinder. The extent in the $\tilde{x}$ direction is infinite, since matching according to any intermediate limit makes $(\tilde{x} \to \infty,\ x \to 0)$. The matching condition here takes the simple form

$$\vartheta(\infty, r) = A_0(0). \tag{4.5.3.24}$$

It remains to be shown that $\vartheta(\tilde{x}, r) \to \text{const.}$ as $\tilde{x} \to \infty$ and to evaluate the constant. The solution to the problem for ϑ can be expressed, by separation of variables in terms of functions like

$$e^{-\lambda\tilde{x}} J_0(\lambda r), \qquad \lambda \ge 0,$$

and the transcendental equation for the eigenvalues λ_n follows from Equation (4.5.3.22):

$$\lambda_n J_0'(\lambda_n r) = 0. \tag{4.5.3.25}$$

There are an infinite set of roots starting with $\lambda_0 = 0, \lambda_1, \lambda_2, \lambda_3, \ldots,$ and an infinite complete set of eigenfunctions. Thus, we have

$$\vartheta(x, r) = a_0 + \sum_{n=1}^{\infty} a_n e^{-\lambda_n \tilde{x}} J_0(\lambda_n r). \tag{4.5.3.26}$$

From the equation for $J_0(\lambda r)$,

$$\frac{d}{dr}\left\{r \frac{dJ_0}{dr}\right\} + \lambda^2 J_0(\lambda r) = 0, \tag{4.5.3.27}$$

it follows by integration from 0 to r_0 that

$$\int_0^{r_0} J_0(\lambda_n r) r\, dr = 0. \tag{4.5.3.28}$$

Thus, the constant a_0 is determined from

$$\int_0^{r_0} \vartheta(x, r) r\, dr = \frac{r_0^2}{2} a_0 = \int_0^{r_0} \vartheta(0, r) r\, dr$$

or

$$a_0 = \frac{2}{r_0^2} \int_0^{r_0} \phi(r) r\, dr. \tag{4.5.3.29}$$

Thus, the matching condition (Equation 4.5.3.24) states that the (weighted) average temperature at the end should be used as the boundary condition for the one-dimensional heat flow:

$$A(0) = (2/r_0^2)\int_0^{r_0} \phi(r)r\,dr, \qquad r_0 = F(0). \tag{4.5.3.30}$$

Similar considerations apply near $X = 1$, so that we have

$$A(1) = (2/r_1^2)\int_0^{r_1} \psi(r)r\,dr, \qquad r_1 = F(1), \tag{4.5.3.31}$$

and the net heat flow can then be calculated to $O(\varepsilon)$.

The other coefficients in the expansion (Equation 4.5.3.26) can be calculated from the usual orthogonality properties of the eigenfunctions:

$$\int_0^{r_0} J_0(\lambda_n r)J_0(\lambda_m r)r\,dr = \begin{cases} 0, & n \neq m, \\ \gamma_m^2, & n = m. \end{cases} \tag{4.5.3.32}$$

The correctness of the one-dimensional approximation depended to a large extent on the type of boundary conditions. The problems below illustrate this point.

Problems

4.5.1 Consider steady heat conduction in a cylindrical rod, $0 \le X \le L$, $0 \le R \le a$, with the following boundary conditions of temperature prescribed on all surfaces.

at $X = 0$: $T(0, R) = T^*F(R/a)$,
at $X = L$: $T(L, R) = T^*G(R/a)$,
at $R = a$: $T(X, a) = T^*H(X)$.

Construct asymptotic expansions of the solution for $T/T^* = \theta(x, r; \varepsilon)$, when $x = X/L$, $r = R/a$, and $\varepsilon = a/L \to 0$.

Construct suitable boundary-layer solutions for the ends, and show how they match to the expansion valid away from the ends.

Does the solution constructed here represent one-dimensional heat conduction?

4.5.2 Consider a plane sound wave of frequency ω, wavelength λ incident on a sphere of radius a. Construct matched inner and outer expansions for the case $a/\lambda \ll L$. Complete the first two terms in the inner expansion.

The acoustic velocity potential satisfies the wave equation

$$\frac{\partial^2\phi}{\partial x^2} + \frac{\partial^2\phi}{\partial y^2} + \frac{\partial^2\phi}{\partial z^2} - \frac{1}{c^2}\frac{\partial^2\phi}{\partial t^2} = 0, \qquad c = \text{sound speed}.$$

The incoming plane wave is represented by (in complex notation)

$$\phi = A \exp\left[i\omega\left(t - \frac{x}{c}\right)\right].$$

The boundary condition at the surface of a rigid sphere is $\partial\phi/\partial r = 0$.

4.5.4 Elastic-shell theory. Spherical shell

By an elastic shell, we mean a thin region of elastic material which responds to a load in a special way due to its geometrical properties. The theory of elastic shells can be derived in a systematic way, by the use of perturbation expansions, from the three-dimensional equations of elasticity. This is not the method usually followed in various books. Rather, shell equations are derived from overall assumptions about the total forces and moments acting on an infinitesimal element. These forces and moments are often thought of as average across the cross section of a shell or else corresponding strain-energy methods are used. (See References 4.5.4.1, 4.5.4.2, and 4.5.4.3.)

Perturbation theory corroborates the approximate equations in certain cases and further provides a method for incorporating the boundary layers which inevitably arise. If some stage of the approximation corresponds to simplified shell theory, one can not expect to satisfy full-elasticity boundary conditions.

The basic small parameter ε of shell theory is the thickness over a characteristic length, say the sphere radius. The calculations here are based wholly on linear elasticity theory, that is, on small strains. Thus, the loads that are applied must be thought of as being sufficiently small so that the structure remains in the linear elastic range. Since the loads then occur linearly in the problem, they need not be considered in the perturbation scheme; all results are proportional to the loads. However, if large deformations or nonlinearities are to be considered, then the mutual dependence of load (made dimensionless with an elastic modulus) and ε is of vital importance.

In this Section we consider a simple special example of shell theory; namely, a segment of a spherical shell fastened rigidly around the edges and loaded by axi-symmetric pressure forces on the inner surface. (See Figure 4.25.) The problem is sufficiently general to illustrate all the essential features of shell theory. First, the outer expansion valid away from the boundary is constructed and is shown to contain the membrane theory of thin shells. Then, the various boundary layers which must be added are discussed briefly.

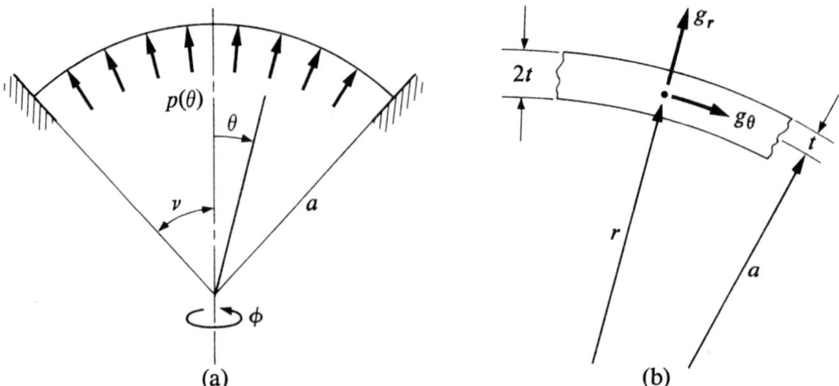

FIGURE 4.25 (a) Spherical segment, (b) detail of thickness.

The exact boundary-value problem demands a solution of the full equations for elasticity (written, for example, in terms of the displacements $(q_r, q_\theta, q_\phi \equiv 0)$) in polar coordinates (r, θ, ϕ) subject to the boundary conditions of prescribed stresses on the free surfaces and zero displacements on the fixed edges:

$$T_{rr}(a + t, \theta) = T_{r\theta}(a + t, \theta) = 0, \qquad 0 \leq \theta \leq \nu;$$
$$T_{rr}(a - t, \theta) = -p(\theta), \qquad T_{r\theta}(a - t, \theta) = 0, \qquad 0 \leq \theta \leq \nu; \tag{4.5.4.1}$$
$$q_r(r, \nu) = q_\theta(r, \nu) = 0, \qquad a - t \leq r \leq a + t.$$

Away from the edge $(\theta = \nu)$, it can be expected that the solution to this problem should behave something like that of the full sphere under pressure. An exact solution of the latter problem (Reference 4.5.4.1, p. 142) is available for uniform pressure. A study of this exact solution shows that the deflections have an expansion starting with terms $O(1/\varepsilon)$, and that the hoop stresses $T_{\theta\theta}$, $T_{\phi\phi}$ are also $O(1/\varepsilon)$, as would be expected from an overall force balance. These facts can be used to start the expansion of our problem corresponding to membrane theory which is valid away from the edge $\theta = \nu$.

Our procedure is first to construct the membrane-theory expansion assumed valid away from the boundary, and then to construct the necessary boundary layer. A convenient starting point is the stress-equilibrium equations (Reference 4.5.4.1, p. 91) (div $T = 0$);

$$\frac{\partial T_{rr}}{\partial r} + \frac{1}{r}\frac{\partial T_{r\theta}}{\partial \theta} + \frac{1}{r}(2T_{rr} - T_{\theta\theta} - T_{\phi\phi} + T_{r\theta}\cot\theta) = 0, \tag{4.5.4.2}$$

$$\frac{\partial T_{r\theta}}{\partial r} + \frac{1}{r}\frac{\partial T_{\theta\theta}}{\partial \theta} + \frac{1}{r}[(T_{\theta\theta} - T_{\phi\phi})\cot\theta + 3T_{r\theta}] = 0. \tag{4.5.4.3}$$

The stress components are related to the strain components with the help of the elastic constants (λ, μ):

$$T_{rr} = \lambda\Delta + 2\mu\frac{\partial q_r}{\partial r}, \qquad T_{\theta\theta} = \lambda\Delta + 2\mu\left(\frac{1}{r}\frac{\partial q_\theta}{\partial \theta} + \frac{q_r}{r}\right),$$

$$T_{\phi\phi} = \lambda\Delta + 2\mu\left(\frac{\cot\theta}{r}q_\theta + \frac{q_r}{r}\right), \qquad \frac{1}{\mu}T_{r\theta} = \frac{\partial q_\theta}{\partial r} - \frac{q_\theta}{r} + \frac{1}{r}\frac{\partial q_r}{\partial \theta}, \tag{4.5.4.4}$$

$$T_{r\phi} = T_{\theta\phi} \equiv 0,$$

where dilatation is

$$\Delta = \operatorname{div}\mathbf{q} = \frac{\partial q_r}{\partial r} + \frac{2}{r}q_r + \frac{1}{r}\frac{\partial q_\theta}{\partial \theta} + \frac{\cot\theta}{r}q_\theta. \tag{4.5.4.5}$$

Note also that

$$E = \text{modulus of elasticity} = \frac{\mu(3\lambda + 2\mu)}{\lambda + \mu},$$

$$\sigma = \text{Poisson ratio} = \frac{\lambda}{2(\lambda + \mu)}.$$

Now consider a limit process $\varepsilon \to 0$ and coordinates fixed inside the shell $(\tilde{r}, \theta)$, where

$$\tilde{r} = \frac{r - a}{t} = \frac{r/a - 1}{\varepsilon}, \qquad -1 \le \tilde{r} \le 1, \qquad \frac{\partial}{\partial r} = \frac{1}{\varepsilon}\frac{\partial}{\partial \tilde{r}}. \tag{4.5.4.6}$$

The stresses in a thin shell thus have an asymptotic expansion of the form

$$T_{rr}(r, \theta; \varepsilon) = T(\tilde{r}, \theta) + \cdots, \qquad T_{r\theta}(r, \theta; \varepsilon) = S(\tilde{r}, \theta) + \cdots,$$

$$T_{\theta\theta}(r, \theta; \varepsilon) = \frac{H(\theta)}{\varepsilon} + \cdots, \qquad T_{\phi\phi}(r, \theta; \varepsilon) = \frac{J(\theta)}{\varepsilon} + \cdots. \tag{4.5.4.7}$$

If, in fact, stress $O(1/\varepsilon)$ were allowed in T_{rr}, $T_{r\theta}$, the equilibrium equations would immediately show that these stresses are functions of θ only, and the boundary conditions would show that these terms are zero.

The hoop stress terms $O(1/\varepsilon)$ here are assumed to depend only on θ; this mirrors their behavior for the full sphere where they are constant across the thickness. This can also be proved by a detailed consideration of the displacement equations and expansions. It is sufficient here to show consistency with the equations and boundary conditions. The equilibrium equations

(Equations 4.5.4.2 and 4.5.4.3) have terms $O(1/\varepsilon)$, which are

$$\frac{\partial T}{\partial \tilde{r}} - (H + J) = 0, \tag{4.5.4.8}$$

$$\frac{\partial S}{\partial \tilde{r}} + \frac{dH}{d\theta} + (H - J)\cot\theta = 0. \tag{4.5.4.9}$$

Here we have used $r/a = 1 + \varepsilon\tilde{r}$, $a/r = 1 - \varepsilon\tilde{r} + \cdots$. These approximate stress-balance equations can be integrated at once to yield

$$T(\tilde{r}, \theta) = \tau(\theta) + \{H(\theta) + J(\theta)\}\tilde{r}, \tag{4.5.4.10}$$

$$S(\tilde{r}, \theta) = \sigma(\theta) - \tilde{r}(dH/d\theta) - \tilde{r}(H - J)\cot\theta, \tag{4.5.4.11}$$

where $\tau(\theta)$, $\sigma(\theta)$ are functions of integration. Now, applying the boundary conditions (Equations 4.5.4.1), we have four relations:

$$0 = T(1, \theta) = \tau(\theta) + H(\theta) + J(\theta),$$

$$-p(\theta) = T(-1, \theta) = \tau - (H + J),$$

$$0 = S(1, \theta) = \sigma - \frac{dH}{d\theta} - (H - J)\cot\theta,$$

$$0 = S(-1, \theta) = \sigma + \frac{dH}{d\theta} + (H - J)\cot\theta.$$

Elimination from this system provides the basic equations for H, J:

$$H + J = \frac{p}{2} = -\tau, \tag{4.5.4.12}$$

$$\frac{dH}{d\theta} + (H - J)\cot\theta = 0 = \sigma \tag{4.5.4.13}$$

or, in terms of H itself,

$$\frac{d}{d\theta}(H\sin^2\theta) = \frac{p}{2}\sin\theta\cos\theta. \tag{4.5.4.14}$$

The integral of (Equation 4.5.4.14), which has H bounded as $\theta \to 0$, is

$$H(\theta) = \frac{1}{\sin^2\theta}\int_0^\theta \frac{p(\alpha)}{2}\sin\alpha\cos\alpha\, d\alpha. \tag{4.5.4.15}$$

Here J follows from Equation (4.5.4.12):

$$J(\theta) = \frac{p(\theta)}{2} - \frac{1}{\sin^2\theta}\int_0^\theta \frac{p(\alpha)}{2}\sin\alpha\cos\alpha\, d\alpha. \tag{4.5.4.16}$$

For the special case where p = const, the classical result is obtained:

$$H = J = p/4 = \text{const.} \tag{4.5.4.17}$$

Since τ, σ are given by Equations (4.5.4.12) and (4.5.4.13), we now have the $O(1)$ distribution of shear and normal stress across the section:

$$T(\tilde{r}, \theta) = -\frac{p(\theta)}{2}(1 - \tilde{r}), \tag{4.5.4.18}$$

$$S(\tilde{r}, \theta) = 0. \tag{4.5.4.19}$$

It is of interest now, and essential for matching later, to obtain the form of the deflection which corresponds to this distribution of stresses. As for the full sphere, the dominant terms of the deflection are $O(1/\varepsilon)$ and are functions of θ alone. The justification is similar to that given before. Thus, tentatively assume that

$$\frac{q_r}{a} = \frac{u(\theta)}{\varepsilon} + u_1(\tilde{r}, \theta) + \cdots, \tag{4.5.4.20}$$

$$\frac{q_\theta}{a} = \frac{v(\theta)}{\varepsilon} + v_1(\tilde{r}, \theta) + \cdots. \tag{4.5.4.21}$$

The stresses produced by this set of displacements are now studied. From Equation (4.5.4.5), we have

$$\Delta = \frac{1}{\varepsilon}\left\{\frac{\partial u_1}{\partial \tilde{r}} + 2u + \frac{dv}{d\theta} + v \cot\theta\right\} + \cdots, \tag{4.5.4.22}$$

so that the expansion for T_{rr} starts out as

$$T_{rr} = \frac{1}{\varepsilon}\left\{\lambda\left(2u + \frac{dv}{d\theta} + v\cot\theta\right) + (\lambda + 2\mu)\frac{\partial u_1}{\partial \tilde{r}}\right\} + \cdots. \tag{4.5.4.23}$$

However, this term must be identically zero, since no T_{rr} of $O(1/\varepsilon)$ occurs in the problem. Thus, we have

$$\frac{\partial u_1}{\partial \tilde{r}} = -\frac{\lambda}{\lambda + 2\mu}\left(2u + \frac{dv}{d\theta} + v\cot\theta\right). \tag{4.5.4.24}$$

There is, in consequence, a dilatation of $O(1/\varepsilon)$ corresponding to the general stretching of the shell:

$$\Delta = \frac{1}{\varepsilon}\frac{2\mu}{\lambda + 2\mu}\left\{2u + \frac{dv}{d\theta} + v\cot\theta\right\} + \cdots. \tag{4.5.4.25}$$

Equations (4.5.4.12) and (4.5.4.13) can now be expressed as equations for the displacement of the shell:

$$T_{\theta\theta} + T_{\phi\phi} = 2(\lambda + \mu)\Delta - 2\mu\left(\frac{\partial q_r}{\partial r} + \frac{q_r}{r}\right)$$

$$= 2(\lambda + \mu)\frac{1}{\varepsilon}\left\{\frac{2\mu}{\lambda + 2\mu}\right\}\left\{2u + \frac{dv}{d\theta} + v\cot\theta\right\} - \frac{2\mu}{\varepsilon}\left(\frac{\partial u_1}{\partial \tilde{r}}\right)$$

or

$$H + J = \frac{2\mu(3\lambda + 2\mu)}{\lambda + 2\mu}\left\{2u + \frac{dv}{d\theta} + v\cot\theta\right\} + \cdots. \qquad (4.5.4.26)$$

Similarly, we obtain

$$T_{\phi\phi} - T_{\theta\theta} = \frac{2\mu}{\varepsilon}\left(v\cot\theta - \frac{dv}{d\theta}\right) + \cdots$$

or

$$J - H = 2\mu\left(v\cot\theta - \frac{dv}{d\theta}\right) + \cdots. \qquad (4.5.4.27)$$

Thus, Equation (4.5.4.12) directly becomes

$$\frac{dv}{d\theta} + v\cot\theta + 2u = \frac{p(\theta)}{4\mu}\frac{\lambda + 2\mu}{3\lambda + 2\mu} \qquad (4.5.4.28)$$

and, after a little elimination, Equation (4.5.4.13) becomes

$$\frac{du}{d\theta} - v = \frac{1}{2\mu}\frac{\lambda + \mu}{3\lambda + 2\mu}\frac{dp(\theta)}{d\theta}. \qquad (4.5.4.29)$$

Equations (4.5.4.28) and (4.5.4.29) form the basic system of equations for the shape of the shell and are identical with the membrane equations mentioned in Reference 4.5.4.1, p. 584.

The equation for the tangential displacement alone, from Equations (4.5.4.28) and (4.5.4.29), is

$$\frac{d^2v}{d\theta^2} + \cot\theta\frac{dv}{d\theta} + (2 - \csc^2\theta)v = -\frac{1}{4\mu}\frac{dp}{d\theta}. \qquad (4.5.4.30)$$

A particular solution corresponding to a rigid displacement is a solution of the homogeneous equations

$$v_p = A\sin\theta, \qquad u_p = -A\cos\theta. \qquad (4.5.4.31)$$

The complete solution for the case $p = \text{const}$ is, thus,

$$u = u_\infty - A\cos\theta, \qquad v = A\sin\theta, \qquad (4.5.4.32)$$

where the constant u_∞ is the radial displacement of the full sphere under uniform pressure:

$$u_\infty = \frac{1}{8\mu}\frac{\lambda + 2\mu}{3\lambda + 2\mu}p. \tag{4.5.4.33}$$

It is clear that the solution represented by Equation (4.5.4.32) can not satisfy the boundary condition of no displacement at $\theta = v$, even with a particular choice of the rigid displacement A. In fact, no such rigid displacement of $O(1/\varepsilon)$ is to be expected in this problem. Some kind of a boundary layer is needed near $\theta = v$.

If displacements q_r, q_θ of the same order occur in a thin layer near $O(\varepsilon)$ in thickness near $\theta = v$, plane-strain elasticity equations result. These are expressed in $(\theta^* = [\theta - v]/\varepsilon, \bar{r})$. However, it is easy to show that no solution of these plane-strain equations in the "elasticity" boundary layer exists which matches to the membrane expansion. For matching, we would need

$$\frac{q_r}{a} = \frac{u^*(\tilde{r}, \theta^*)}{\varepsilon} + \cdots, \qquad \frac{q_\theta}{a} = \frac{v^*(\tilde{r}, \theta^*)}{\varepsilon} + \cdots, \tag{4.5.4.34}$$

and $u^* \to u_\infty$, $v^* \to 0$, $\theta^* \to -\infty$ $(A = 0)$.

Thus, some intermediate boundary layer must be constructed, and its width must be greater than that of the elasticity layer. That is, a boundary-layer expansion is sought, in which

$$\tilde{\theta} = \frac{\theta - v}{\delta(\varepsilon)}, \qquad \tilde{r} = \frac{(r/a) - 1}{\varepsilon}, \qquad (\delta(\varepsilon) \gg \varepsilon) \tag{4.5.4.35}$$

are fixed. Note that

$$\cot\theta = \cot v - \delta(1 + \cot^2 v)\tilde{\theta}. \tag{4.5.4.36}$$

Returning to the stress equations, we assume an asymptotic expansion of the form

$$T_{rr}(r, \theta; \varepsilon) = \tau(\tilde{r}, \tilde{\theta}) + \cdots, \tag{4.5.4.37}$$

$$T_{\theta\theta}(r, \theta; \varepsilon) = (1/\varepsilon)h(\tilde{r}, \tilde{\theta}) + \cdots, \tag{4.5.4.38}$$

$$T_{\phi\phi}(r, \theta; \varepsilon) = (1/\varepsilon)g(\tilde{r}, \tilde{\theta}) + \cdots, \tag{4.5.4.39}$$

$$T_{r\theta}(r, \theta; \varepsilon) = \beta(\varepsilon)\sigma(\tilde{r}, \tilde{\theta}) + \cdots. \tag{4.5.4.40}$$

The orders of the hoop stresses are in accord with overall equilibrium ideas, the order of the normal stress with the boundary conditions, and the order of the shear is here undetermined. A large shear can be expected to be produced if substantial bending takes place near the boundary. Other possibilities should be investigated and ruled out. This assumption leads to an expansion capable of being matched. The dominant equations of stress equilibrium are, thus,

$$\frac{1}{\varepsilon}\frac{\partial \tau}{\partial \tilde{r}} + \frac{\beta(\varepsilon)}{\delta(\varepsilon)}\frac{\partial \sigma}{\partial \tilde{\theta}} - \frac{1}{\varepsilon}(h + g) = 0, \tag{4.5.4.41}$$

$$\frac{\beta}{\varepsilon}\frac{\partial \sigma}{\partial \tilde{r}} + \frac{1}{\varepsilon\delta}\frac{\partial h}{\partial \tilde{\theta}} = 0. \tag{4.5.4.42}$$

In order for Equation (4.5.4.42) to yield a nontrivial equation, we need

$$\beta(\varepsilon) = \frac{1}{\delta(\varepsilon)}. \tag{4.5.4.43}$$

Then, the distinguished limit of Equation (4.5.4.41) occurs for $1/\varepsilon = \beta/\delta$ or

$$\delta = \sqrt{\varepsilon}, \qquad \beta(\varepsilon) = 1/\sqrt{\varepsilon}, \tag{4.5.4.44}$$

fixing the order of the boundary-layer thickness and shear stress. The resulting equations include all the terms of the "elasticity" boundary layer, and thus have at least the possibility of matching to an elasticity boundary layer.

Rewriting the basic equations (Equations 4.5.4.41, 4.5.4.42), we have

$$\frac{\partial \tau}{\partial \tilde{r}} + \frac{\partial \sigma}{\partial \tilde{\theta}} - (h + g) = 0,$$

$$\frac{\partial \sigma}{\partial \tilde{r}} + \frac{\partial h}{\partial \tilde{\theta}} = 0.$$

Next, consider the displacement field corresponding to the assumed orders of stress in Equations (4.5.4.38) through (4.5.4.40):

$$\frac{q_r}{a} = \frac{U(\tilde{\theta})}{\varepsilon} + U_1(\tilde{r}, \tilde{\theta}) + \cdots, \tag{4.5.4.45}$$

$$\frac{q_\theta}{a} = \frac{V(\tilde{\theta}, \tilde{r})}{\sqrt{\varepsilon}} + \sqrt{\varepsilon}V_1(\tilde{r}, \tilde{\theta}) + \cdots. \tag{4.5.4.46}$$

It is necessary that $U = U(\tilde{\theta})$ only, so that dilatation of $O(1/\varepsilon^2)$ does not occur. Then, for the dilatation Δ, we have

$$\Delta = \frac{1}{\varepsilon}\left\{\frac{\partial U_1}{\partial \tilde{r}} + 2U + \frac{\partial V}{\partial \tilde{\theta}}\right\} + \cdots, \tag{4.5.4.47}$$

and the expressions for the $O(1/\varepsilon)$ components of hoop stress are

$$h = \lambda\frac{\partial U_1}{\partial \tilde{r}} + (\lambda + 2\mu)\frac{\partial V}{\partial \tilde{\theta}} + 2(\lambda + \mu)U, \tag{4.5.4.48}$$

$$g = \lambda\frac{\partial U_1}{\partial \tilde{r}} + \lambda\frac{\partial V}{\partial \tilde{\theta}} + 2(\lambda + \mu)U, \tag{4.5.4.49}$$

$$h + g = 2\lambda\frac{\partial U_1}{\partial \tilde{r}} + 2(\lambda + \mu)\left\{\frac{\partial V}{\partial \theta} + 2U\right\}. \tag{4.5.4.50}$$

Considering next the normal stress T_{rr}, we have

$$T_{rr} = \frac{1}{\varepsilon}\left\{\lambda\left(\frac{\partial U_1}{\partial \tilde{r}} + 2U + \frac{\partial V}{\partial \tilde{\theta}}\right) + 2\mu\frac{\partial U_1}{\partial \tilde{r}}\right\} + \tau(\tilde{r}, \tilde{\theta}) + \cdots. \tag{4.5.4.51}$$

Again, the term $O(1/\varepsilon)$ in T_{rr} must vanish. This provides an expression for $\partial U_1/\partial \tilde{r}$ in terms of U, V and allows h, g to be expressed completely in terms of these quantities:

$$\frac{\partial U_1}{\partial \tilde{r}} = -\frac{\lambda}{\lambda + 2\mu}\left(\frac{\partial V}{\partial \theta} + 2U\right). \tag{4.5.4.52}$$

We have, thus,

$$h = 4\mu\frac{\lambda + \mu}{\lambda + 2\mu}\frac{\partial V}{\partial \tilde{\theta}} + 2\mu\frac{3\lambda + 2\mu}{\lambda + 2\mu}U, \tag{4.5.4.53}$$

$$h + g = 2\mu\frac{3\lambda + 2\mu}{\lambda + 2\mu}\left(\frac{\partial V}{\partial \tilde{\theta}} + U\right). \tag{4.5.4.54}$$

A similar argument can be applied to the shear stress:

$$\frac{1}{\mu}T_{r\theta} = \frac{1}{\varepsilon^{3/2}}\frac{\partial V}{\partial \tilde{r}} + \frac{1}{\sqrt{\varepsilon}}\frac{\partial V_1}{\partial \tilde{r}} - \frac{V}{\sqrt{\varepsilon}} + (1 - \varepsilon\tilde{r} + \cdots)\left\{\frac{1}{\varepsilon^{3/2}}\frac{dU}{d\tilde{\theta}} + \frac{1}{\sqrt{\varepsilon}}\frac{\partial U_1}{\partial \tilde{\theta}}\right\} + \cdots.$$

The term $O(1/\varepsilon^{3/2})$ must vanish:

$$\frac{\partial V}{\partial \tilde{r}} + \frac{dU}{d\tilde{\theta}} = 0, \tag{4.5.4.55}$$

which is one of the basic differential equations for the shell deflection. Also, the term $O(1/\sqrt{\varepsilon})$ is

$$\frac{\sigma(\tilde{r}, \tilde{\theta})}{\mu} = \frac{\partial V_1}{\partial \tilde{r}} - V + \frac{\partial U_1}{\partial \tilde{\theta}} - \tilde{r}\frac{dU}{d\tilde{\theta}}. \tag{4.5.4.56}$$

The consequence of Equation (4.5.4.55) is a linear variation of tangential displacement across the cross section

$$V(\tilde{r}, \tilde{\theta}) = A(\tilde{\theta}) - \tilde{r}\frac{dU}{d\tilde{\theta}}, \tag{4.5.4.57}$$

and a corresponding linear variation of the hoop stresses from Equations (4.5.4.53) and (4.5.4.54). Introducing some special notation, we have

$$h = h^{(0)}(\tilde{\theta}) + \tilde{r}h^{(1)}(\tilde{\theta}), \tag{4.5.4.58}$$

$$g = g^{(0)}(\tilde{\theta}) + \tilde{r}g^{(1)}(\tilde{\theta}), \tag{4.5.4.59}$$

where

$$h^{(0)} = 4\mu\frac{\lambda + \mu}{\lambda + 2\mu}\frac{dA}{d\tilde{\theta}} + 2\mu\frac{3\lambda + 2\mu}{\lambda + 2\mu}U,$$

$$h^{(1)} = -4\mu\frac{\lambda + \mu}{\lambda + 2\mu}\frac{d^2U}{d\tilde{\theta}^2},$$

$$h^{(0)} + g^{(0)} = 2\mu\frac{3\lambda + 2\mu}{\lambda + 2\mu}\left(\frac{dA}{d\tilde{\theta}} + 2U\right),$$

$$h^{(1)} + g^{(1)} = -2\mu\frac{3\lambda + 2\mu}{\lambda + 2\mu}\frac{d^2U}{d\tilde{\theta}^2}.$$

The tangential equilibrium equation (Equation 4.5.4.42) can now be integrated in the form

$$\sigma(\tilde{r}, \tilde{\theta}) = \sigma^{(0)}(\tilde{\theta}) - \tilde{r}\frac{dh^{(0)}}{d\tilde{\theta}} - \frac{\tilde{r}^2}{2}\frac{dh^{(1)}}{d\tilde{\theta}}. \tag{4.5.4.60}$$

The boundary condition states that $\sigma(\pm 1, \tilde{\theta}) = 0$, so that we have

$$\frac{dh^{(0)}}{d\tilde{\theta}} = 0 \tag{4.5.4.61}$$

and

$$\sigma^{(0)} = \frac{1}{2}\frac{dh^{(1)}}{d\tilde{\theta}}. \tag{4.5.4.62}$$

The shear stress has a parabolic distribution across the thickness

$$\sigma(\tilde{r}, \tilde{\theta}) = (1 - \tilde{r}^2)\tfrac{1}{2}(dh^{(1)}/d\tilde{\theta}). \tag{4.5.4.63}$$

A similar study of the radial equilibrium equation (Equation 4.5.4.41), using Equations (4.5.4.62), (4.5.4.58), and (4.5.4.59), allows the basic differential equation for the shell deflection to be found, and from its solution all the stresses can also be found. Integration of Equation (4.5.4.41) shows that

$$\tau(\tilde{r}, \tilde{\theta}) = \tau^{(0)}(\tilde{\theta}) + \tilde{r}\tau^{(1)}(\tilde{\theta}) + \tilde{r}^2\tau^{(2)}(\tilde{\theta}) + \tilde{r}^3\tau^{(3)}(\tilde{\theta}), \qquad (4.5.4.64)$$

where

$$\tau^{(1)} = -\tfrac{1}{2}(d^2h^{(1)}/d\tilde{\theta}^2) + h^{(0)} + g^{(0)},$$
$$\tau^{(2)} = \tfrac{1}{2}\{h^{(1)} + g^{(1)}\},$$
$$\tau^{(3)} = \tfrac{1}{6}(d^2h^{(1)}/d\tilde{\theta}^2).$$

The boundary conditions at $\tilde{r} = \pm 1$ are

$$\tilde{r} = +1, \qquad 0 = \tau^{(0)} + \tau^{(1)} + \tau^{(2)} + \tau^{(3)}, \qquad (4.5.4.65)$$

$$\tilde{r} = -1, \qquad -p(v) = \tau^{(0)} - \tau^{(1)} + \tau^{(2)} - \tau^{(3)} \qquad (4.5.4.66)$$

or

$$\tau^{(1)} + \tau^{(3)} = \frac{p(v)}{2} = -\frac{1}{3}\frac{d^2h^{(1)}}{d\tilde{\theta}^2} + h^{(0)} + g^{(0)}. \qquad (4.5.4.67)$$

Equations (4.5.4.61) and (4.5.4.67) provide the basic systems of equations. Equation (4.5.4.61) states that $h^{(0)} = \text{const}$ or

$$2(\lambda + \mu)(dA/d\tilde{\theta}) + (3\lambda + 2\mu)U = (3\lambda + 2\mu)U_\infty, \qquad (4.5.4.68)$$

where $U \to U_\infty$ as $\tilde{\theta} \to -\infty$, for matching the constant u of the membrane solution as $\theta \to v$; $dA/d\tilde{\theta} \to 0$, $\tilde{\theta} \to -\infty$. Equation (4.5.4.67) is, from the definitions of $h^{(0)}$, $h^{(1)}$, $q^{(0)}$,

$$\frac{4}{3}\mu\frac{\lambda + \mu}{\lambda + 2\mu}\frac{d^4U}{d\tilde{\theta}^4} + 2\mu\frac{3\lambda + 2\mu}{\lambda + 2\mu}\left(\frac{dA}{d\tilde{\theta}} + 2U\right) = \frac{p(v)}{2} \qquad (4.5.4.69)$$

For the special case of $p(\theta) = \text{const} = p$, which is all that will be considered further, the elimination of $dA/d\tilde{\theta}$ from Equations (4.5.4.68) and (4.5.4.69) results in

$$\frac{d^4U}{d\tilde{\theta}^4} + 4\kappa^4U = \text{const} = 4\kappa^4U_\infty, \qquad (4.5.4.70)$$

where

$$4\kappa^4 = \frac{3}{4}\frac{(3\lambda + 2\mu)(\lambda + 2\mu)}{(\lambda + \mu)^2}, \qquad U_\infty = \frac{1}{8\mu}\frac{\lambda + 2\mu}{3\lambda + 2\mu}p.$$

Equation (4.5.4.70) looks exactly like the equation of beam on an elastic foundation and has oscillatory decaying solutions as $\tilde{\theta} \to -\infty$. Discarding the solutions which grow as $\tilde{\theta} \to -\infty$ and making $U(\tilde{\theta}) = 0$ as $\tilde{\theta} = 0$ to approach the fixed boundary condition at $\theta = \nu$, we have

$$U(\tilde{\theta}) = U_\infty\{1 - e^{\kappa\tilde{\theta}} \cos \kappa\tilde{\theta}\} + b\, e^{\kappa\tilde{\theta}} \sin \kappa\tilde{\theta}, \tag{4.5.4.71}$$

where the constant b is arbitrary. Next, from Equation (4.5.4.68), we calculate $A(\tilde{\theta})$:

$$A(\tilde{\theta}) = A_\infty + \frac{3\lambda + 2\mu}{4(\lambda + \mu)\kappa}\{(U_\infty + b)\cos \kappa\tilde{\theta} + (U_\infty - b)\sin \kappa\tilde{\theta}\}\, e^{\kappa\tilde{\theta}} \tag{4.5.4.72}$$

and

$$\frac{dU}{d\tilde{\theta}} = \kappa\{(U_\infty + b)\sin \kappa\tilde{\theta} - (U_\infty - b)\cos \kappa\tilde{\theta}\}\, e^{\kappa\tilde{\theta}}. \tag{4.5.4.73}$$

This solution should match to the elasticity boundary layer as $\tilde{\theta} \to 0$, $\tilde{\theta}^* \to -\infty$. The entire matching process can be expressed in terms of a suitable intermediate limit as usual, but here the details are omitted. The behavior of the "bending-layer" solution as $\tilde{\theta} \to 0$ is

$$U(\tilde{\theta}) \to (b - U_\infty)\kappa\tilde{\theta} + b\kappa^2\tilde{\theta}^2 + (U_\infty + b)\frac{\kappa^3\tilde{\theta}^3}{3} + \cdots,$$

$$\frac{dU}{d\tilde{\theta}} \to \kappa(b - U_\infty) + 2b\kappa^2\tilde{\theta} + (U_\infty + b)\kappa^3\tilde{\theta}^2 + \cdots,$$

$$A \to A_\infty + \frac{3\lambda + 2\mu}{4\kappa(\lambda + \mu)}\{U_\infty + b\} + 2U_\infty\kappa\tilde{\theta} + \cdots, \tag{4.5.4.74}$$

and, from Equation (4.5.4.57),

$$V \to A_\infty + \frac{3\lambda + 2\mu}{4\kappa(\lambda + \mu)}\{V_\infty + b\} - \tilde{r}\kappa(b - U_\infty) + 0(\tilde{\theta}).$$

All attempts at matching this behavior to that of an "elasticity" boundary layer as $\theta^* \to -\infty$ fail, except if Equation (4.5.4.74) is made to satisfy the boundary condition at $\tilde{\theta} = 0$ exactly; that is, the elasticity boundary layer is included in Equation (4.5.4.74). Thus, the arbitrary constants (A_∞, b) must be chosen so that $V = 0$ at $\tilde{\theta} = 0$:

$$b - U_\infty = 0, \qquad A_\infty + \frac{3\lambda + 2\mu}{4\kappa(\lambda + \mu)}(U_\infty + b) = 0. \tag{4.5.4.75}$$

Thus, the bending boundary layer satisfies the fixed-edge boundary condition exactly. As far as Equation (4.5.4.70) is concerned, this means that a fixed edge forces the boundary conditions. Thus, we have

$$U(\tilde{\theta}) = \frac{dU}{d\tilde{\theta}} = 0 \quad \text{at} \quad \tilde{\theta} = 0. \tag{4.5.4.76}$$

A consequence of this solution is that

$$V(\tilde{r}, \tilde{\theta}) \to A_\infty = -\frac{3\lambda + 2\mu}{2(\lambda + \mu)\kappa} U_\infty \tag{4.5.4.77}$$

as $\tilde{\theta} \to -\infty$. A term must be added to the membrane solution to match this deflection. This term can be a rigid displacement of $O(1/\sqrt{\varepsilon})$. In particular, we could have

$$\begin{aligned} \frac{q_r}{a} &= \frac{u(\theta)}{\varepsilon} - \frac{A_\infty \cos\theta}{\sqrt{\varepsilon}} + \cdots, \\ \frac{q_\theta}{a} &= \frac{v(\theta)}{\varepsilon} + \frac{A_\infty \sin\theta}{\sqrt{\varepsilon}} + \cdots, \end{aligned} \tag{4.5.4.78}$$

and this is the ultimate effect of the rigid boundary on the main part of the shell. The presence of an $O(1/\sqrt{\varepsilon})$ term in q_r implies a higher-order bending layer, etc.

It should be noted in conclusion that the considerations above are not valid for a shallow shell where ν is small. To study a shallow shell, $\nu(\varepsilon)$ must be assigned an order by studying the various limits.

REFERENCES

4.5.4.1 A. E. H. Love, *A Treatise on the Mathematical Theory of Elasticity*, 4th ed., England: Cambridge University Press, 1927.

4.5.4.2 V. Z. Vlasov, *Allgemeine Schalentheorie und ihre Anwendung in der Technik* (translated from Russian), Berlin: Akademie Verlag, 1958.

4.5.4.3 S. Timoshenko and S. Woinowsky-Krieger, *Theory of Plates and Shells*, 2nd ed., New York: McGraw-Hill Book Co., 1959.

CHAPTER 5

Derivation of Approximate Equations. Several Parameters. Similarity Laws

In this Chapter, several examples are presented in which the main aim is the systematic derivation of approximate equations. This procedure is connected with perturbation theory. Strictly speaking, there is no difference with that which has been presented already. However, when the first-approximation equation of a certain expansion procedure covers a sufficiently broad class of problems, it is often referred to as an approximate equation, such as the transonic equation, or a nonlinear water-wave equation. Typical to one class of these problems is the occurrence of several parameters and the specification of a relation between them which is necessary for a distinguished limit. The parameter that is held fixed in the limit is often called a similarity parameter, and certain global results which depend on this similarity parameter are called "laws of similitude." From the point of view of perturbation theory, these laws are valid to a certain order. For another class of problems, it is the far field which provides the distinguished limit.

5.1 Expansion procedures of thin airfoil theory at various Mach numbers

We consider now a simplified version of some of the expansion procedures used in airfoil theory. The usual assumption of the steady flow of a perfect, inviscid gas is made. The main question is the simplification of the rather complicated equations of motion when the perturbations are small (slender airfoils) and the free-stream Mach number can range from zero to infinity. The dependence on the two parameters, thickness ratio δ and Mach number at infinity M_∞, is an essential part of the considerations.

For simplicity, only families of shapes at zero angle of attack are considered. The airfoils are symmetric about the x-axis (Figure 5.1), and the flow at upstream infinity is uniform with magnitude U. The unit of length is the airfoil chord.

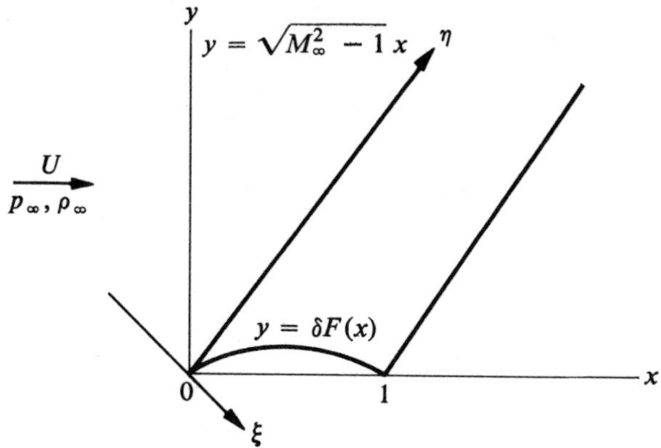

FIGURE 5.1 Thin airfoil: linearized supersonic flow field.

If $\mathbf{q} = (q_x, q_y)$ is the velocity, the boundary conditions are

$$\mathbf{q} = U\mathbf{i} \qquad \text{at upstream infinity,} \tag{5.1.1}$$

$$\frac{q_y(x, \delta F(x))}{q_x(x, \delta F(x))} = \delta F'(x) \qquad \text{tangent flow at body surface.} \tag{5.1.2}$$

By symmetry, it is sufficient to consider that $y \geq 0$.

The equations to be solved come from conservation of mass, momentum, and energy, plus an equation of state. We must add shock-jump conditions to these equations, since there is a possibility for shock waves to occur whenever the flow is locally supersonic ($M > 1$). The shock-jump conditions are integral forms of the conservation laws mentioned above. A principal difficulty, associated with the intrinsic nonlinearity of the problem, is that the location of the shock waves is unknown in advance and must be found as part of the problem. Some of these difficulties are overcome when the shock waves are sufficiently weak, in which case jump conditions appear naturally in the solutions.

In all cases, for a perfect gas we can use the invariant corresponding to constant total enthalpy,

$$\frac{q^2}{2} + \frac{a^2}{\gamma - 1} = \frac{U^2}{2} + \frac{a_\infty^2}{\gamma - 1}, \tag{5.1.3}$$

where a = local speed of sound $= \sqrt{\partial p/\partial \rho} = \sqrt{\gamma RT}, \gamma = c_p/c_v$ = const. The only mechanism for entropy production and for the introduction of rotation into this model flow is a shock wave. The entropy is, thus, constant along a streamline but can jump across a shock wave. Isentropic flow, however, implies irrotational flow. As long as the Mach number is not too large, the flow can be assumed isentropic and irrotational. This assumption is not necessary but can be proved. Omission of the details will allow us to obtain the final result quickly. For details see (Reference 5.1.1). Thus, the momentum equation can be written

$$(\mathbf{q} \cdot \nabla)\mathbf{q} = \nabla\left(\frac{q^2}{2}\right) = -\frac{1}{\rho}\nabla p = -\left(\frac{dp}{d\rho}\right)\frac{\nabla\rho}{\rho} = -a^2\frac{\nabla\rho}{\rho}. \tag{5.1.4}$$

The remaining information is contained in the continuity equation:

$$\operatorname{div}(\rho\mathbf{q}) = \mathbf{q} \cdot \nabla\rho + \rho\nabla \cdot \mathbf{q} = 0. \tag{5.1.5}$$

Now, from Equation (5.1.4), we have

$$\mathbf{q} \cdot \nabla\left(\frac{q^2}{2}\right) = -a^2\frac{\mathbf{q} \cdot \nabla\rho}{\rho}, \tag{5.1.6}$$

and the use of the continuity equation enables ρ to be eliminated,

$$\mathbf{q} \cdot \nabla\frac{q^2}{2} = a^2\nabla \cdot \mathbf{q}. \tag{5.1.7}$$

Note that, as $a \to \infty$, the usual equation of incompressible flow results.

Introducing now the potential $\Phi(x, y; M_\infty, \delta)$ of the irrotational flow, we have

$$q_x = \frac{\partial\Phi}{\partial x}, \qquad q_y = \frac{\partial\Phi}{\partial y}. \tag{5.1.8}$$

Equations (5.1.7) and (5.1.3) form the basic system of equations, and Equations (5.1.1) and (5.1.2) the boundary conditions:

$$(a^2 - \Phi_x^2)\Phi_{xx} - 2\Phi_x\Phi_y\Phi_{xy} + (a^2 - \Phi_y^2)\Phi_{yy} = 0, \tag{5.1.9}$$

$$\frac{a^2}{\gamma - 1} + \frac{\Phi_x^2 + \Phi_y^2}{2} = \frac{a_\infty^2}{\gamma - 1} + \frac{U^2}{2}, \tag{5.1.10}$$

$$\Phi_y(x, \delta F(x)) = \delta F'(x)\Phi_x(x, \delta F(x)), \tag{5.1.11}$$

$$\Phi \to Ux \qquad \text{at upstream infinity.} \tag{5.1.12}$$

Corresponding equations hold in (x, y, z). Equation (5.1.9) is quasi-linear; it is of elliptic type when the flow is locally subsonic, $\Phi_x^2 + \Phi_y^2 < a^2$, and hyperbolic when the flow is locally supersonic, $\Phi_x^2 + \Phi_y^2 > a^2$.

The problem is often simplified by various small disturbance approximations corresponding to thin airfoils. We will now discuss these expansions and the limit processes associated with them.

5.1.1 *Linearized theory*

The content of this theory is equivalent to acoustics. The limit process considered is

$$\delta \to 0 \qquad (x, y; M_\infty \text{ fixed}). \tag{5.1.13}$$

The first term of the expansion represents a uniform free stream. Let

$$\Phi(x, y; M_\infty, \delta) = U\{x + \varepsilon_1(\delta)\phi_1(x, y; M_\infty) + \varepsilon_2(\delta)\phi_2(x, y; M_\infty) + \cdots\}. \tag{5.1.14}$$

The order of $\varepsilon_1(\delta)$ is fixed from the boundary condition (Equation 5.1.11), since we have

$$\Phi_y(x, y; M_\infty, \delta) = U\{\varepsilon_1(\delta)\phi_{1_y}(x, y; M_\infty) + \varepsilon_2(\delta)\phi_{2_y}(x, y; M_\infty) + \cdots\}, \tag{5.1.15}$$

$$\Phi_x(x, y; M_\infty; \delta) = U\{1 + \varepsilon_1\phi_{1_x} + \varepsilon_2\phi_{2_x} + \cdots\}. \tag{5.1.16}$$

Thus, the boundary condition (Equation 5.1.11) has the expansion

$$\begin{aligned} \varepsilon_1\phi_{1_y}(x, 0) + \varepsilon_1\delta F(x)\phi_{1_{yy}}(x, 0) + \cdots + \varepsilon_2\phi_{2_y}(x, 0) + \cdots \\ = \delta F'(x)\{1 + \varepsilon_1\phi_{1_x}(x, 0) + \cdots\}, \qquad 0 < x < 1. \end{aligned} \tag{5.1.17}$$

It follows that $\varepsilon_1 = \delta$, and that reasonable boundary conditions for ϕ_2 appear if $\varepsilon_2 = \varepsilon_1\delta = \delta^2$. Here a power-series expansion of the solution near $y = 0$ has been assumed. In the plane-flow case, this turns out to be all right—an inner expansion in the manner of Section 4.5.1 would give this result trivially. For axial symmetry, of course, the situation is different, and a treatment along the lines of Section 4.5.1 is needed. Thus, Equation (5.1.14) is

$$\Phi = U\{x + \delta\phi_1 + \delta^2\phi_2 + \cdots\}. \tag{5.1.18}$$

Now, Equation (5.1.10) has the expansion

$$a^2 = a_\infty^2 - (\gamma - 1)U^2\delta\phi_{1_x} + O(\delta^2), \tag{5.1.19}$$

and the basic equation (Equation 5.1.9) is

$$\begin{aligned} &(a_\infty^2 - (\gamma - 1)U^2\delta\phi_{1_x} - U^2 - 2U^2\delta\phi_{1_x} + \cdots)(\delta\phi_{1_{xx}} + \delta^2\phi_{2_{xx}} + \cdots) \\ &-2U^2\delta^2\phi_{1_y}\phi_{1_{xy}} + \cdots + (a_\infty^2 - (\gamma - 1)U^2\delta\phi_{1_x} + \cdots) \\ &\qquad \times (\delta\phi_{1_{yy}} + \delta^2\phi_{2_{yy}} + \cdots) = 0. \end{aligned} \tag{5.1.20}$$

First- and second-order approximate equations result:

$$O(\delta):\ (M_\infty^2 - 1)\phi_{1_{xx}} = \phi_{1_{yy}} = 0, \tag{5.1.21}$$

$$O(\delta^2):\ (M_\infty^2 - 1)\phi_{2_{xx}} - \phi_{2_{yy}} = M_\infty^2[(\gamma - 1)M_\infty^2 - 2]\phi_{1_x}\phi_{1_{xx}} - 2M_\infty^2\phi_{1_y}\phi_{1_{xy}}. \tag{5.1.22}$$

Equation (5.1.21) has been used to simplify the right-hand side of Equation (5.1.22). Equation (5.1.21) is the steady version of the acoustic equation which results from a Galilean transformation with speed U. Equation (5.1.22) corresponds to a second-order version of acoustics. Equation (5.1.21) is of elliptic type for subsonic flight ($M_\infty < 1$), and of hyperbolic type for ($M_\infty > 1$), which in itself indicates that the expansion cannot be valid when M_∞ is close to unity. While it is true that the expansion becomes valid if δ is sufficiently small, the dependence on the parameter M_∞ may make the expansion not very useful. Some study of the properties of the solutions ϕ_1, ϕ_2 enables us to mark out the range of validity of the expansions with respect to both parameters (δ, M_∞).

The boundary conditions on the body surface which apply to Equations (5.1.21) and (5.1.22) are

$$\phi_{1_y}(x, 0) = F'(x), \tag{5.1.23}$$

$$\phi_{2_y}(x, 0) = \phi_{1_x}(x, 0)F'(x) - F(x)\phi_{1_{yy}}(x, 0) = \phi_{1_x}(x, 0)F'(x) - (M_\infty^2 - 1)\phi_{1_{xx}}(x, 0)F(x). \tag{5.1.24}$$

Consider now the supersonic case $M_\infty > 1$ which is the simpler to analyze. The solution of Equation (5.1.21), with the boundary conditions of tangent flow (Equation 5.1.23) and the further restrictions that only downstream running waves come from the body (due to the boundary conditions at upstream infinity), is

$$\phi_1(x, y) = -\frac{1}{\sqrt{M_\infty^2 - 1}}F(x - \sqrt{M_\infty^2 - 1}\,y), \qquad 0 < x - \sqrt{M_\infty^2 - 1}\,y < 1. \tag{5.1.25}$$

Note that

$$\phi_{1_y}(x, y) = F'(x - \sqrt{M_\infty^2 - 1}\,y)$$

so that Equation (5.1.23) is satisfied. From this potential, the first-order flow field and pressure can be found. For example, we have

$$\frac{p - p_\infty}{\rho_\infty U^2} = -\delta\phi_{1_x} = \frac{\delta}{\sqrt{M_\infty^2 - 1}}F'(x - \sqrt{M_\infty^2 - 1}\,y). \tag{5.1.26}$$

The potential is constant outside the wave zone $0 < x - \sqrt{M_\infty^2 - 1}\, y < 1$, and there is a jump of pressure, for example, across $x = \sqrt{M_\infty^2 - 1}\, y$ if $F'(0) \neq 0$. This jump is a linearized version of a shock wave. It is clear already that the expansion is not a good approximation unless

$$\delta/\sqrt{M_\infty^2 - 1} \ll 1,$$

but more precise information is obtained from the second approximation.

Introduce the characteristic coordinates of the first approximation,

$$\xi = x - \sqrt{M_\infty^2 - 1}\, y, \qquad \eta = x + \sqrt{M_\infty^2 - 1}\, y, \tag{5.1.27}$$

and note that the right-hand side of Equation (5.1.22) is

$$[(\gamma - 1)M_\infty^2 - 2]\frac{M_\infty^2}{M_\infty^2 - 1}F'(\xi)F''(\xi) - 2M_\infty^2 F'(\xi)F''(\xi)$$
$$= \frac{(\gamma + 1)M_\infty^4}{M_\infty^2 - 1}F'(\xi)F''(\xi),$$

so that Equation (5.1.22) becomes

$$\phi_{2_{\xi\eta}} = \frac{\gamma + 1}{4}\frac{M_\infty^4}{(M_\infty^2 - 1)^2}F'(\xi)F''(\xi). \tag{5.1.28}$$

Thus, the general solution for ϕ_2 can be written in $0 < \xi < 1$ as

$$\phi_2(\xi, \eta) = \frac{\gamma + 1}{8}\frac{M_\infty^4}{(M_\infty^2 - 1)^2}\eta F'^2(\xi) + G(\xi). \tag{5.1.29}$$

The arbitrary function $G(\xi)$ can be found from the boundary condition of Equation (5.1.24). Without working out the details, we see that the order of magnitude of the second term is now clear, so that the original expansion (Equation 5.1.14) now becomes

$$\phi(x, y; M_\infty, \delta) = U\left\{x - \frac{\delta}{\sqrt{M_\infty^2 - 1}}F(x - \sqrt{M_\infty^2 - 1}\, y)\right.$$
$$\left. + O\left(\frac{\delta^2(\gamma + 1)M_\infty^4}{(M_\infty^2 - 1)^2}(x + \sqrt{M_\infty^2 - 1}\, y)\right)\right\}. \tag{5.1.30}$$

We can say that the first two terms provide a valid approximation if $\delta\phi_2 \ll \phi_1$ or if

$$\frac{(\gamma + 1)\delta M_\infty^4}{(M_\infty^2 - 1)^{3/2}}(x + \sqrt{M_\infty^2 - 1}\, y) \ll 1. \tag{5.1.31}$$

The occurrence of nonuniformity with respect to the parameter M_∞ and the coordinates is a typical feature of expansion procedures with more than one parameter. Each nonuniformity indicated by Equation (5.1.31) corresponds to a different physical phenomenon. The type of nonuniformity and the conditions necessary for the linearized expansion to be a good approximation are indicated below, by eliminating unessential factors from Equation (5.1.31):

TRANSONIC REGIME

$$M_\infty \approx 1 \qquad (\eta \text{ fixed}), \qquad \frac{\delta}{(M_\infty^2 - 1)^{3/2}} \ll 1,$$

FAR FIELD

$$(x + \sqrt{M_\infty^2 - 1}\, y) \approx \infty \qquad (M_\infty \text{ fixed}), \qquad \delta(x + \sqrt{M_\infty^2 - 1}\, y) \ll 1,$$

HYPERSONIC REGIME

$$M_\infty \approx \infty \qquad (\eta \text{ fixed}), \qquad \delta M_\infty \ll 1.$$

The first two nonuniformities, transonic and far field, represent cumulative effects. For a body flying close to the speed of sound, small waves accumulate at the body and their nonlinear interaction eventually becomes important. The fact that the angle of a small wave is given incorrectly leads to a cumulative effect which means that even the location of the wave zone is given incorrectly in the far field. Lastly, the hypersonic difficulty is caused by an underestimation of the effects of the nonlinearity in producing pressure changes. In fact, the physical basis of linearized theory is invalid when $\delta M_\infty \sim O(1)$, since then the shock waves are strong, entropy effects must be included, and the basic equations must be reexamined.

Each of the regimes indicated above can be treated by introducing a suitable modified expansion procedure. The outline of the procedure for the transonic and hypersonic regimes is sketched in the following Sections.

5.1.2 *Transonic theory*

Linearized theory predicts catastrophic failure at $M_\infty = 1$ (cf. Equation 5.1.26), but the trouble is mathematical and not physical; the orders of magnitude of certain terms have been estimated incorrectly.

In order to arrive at the correct limit process and expansion, go to the heart of the matter and set $M_\infty = 1$. If a suitable expansion can be found for $M_\infty = 1$, then it can certainly be extended to some neighborhood of $M_\infty = 1$ by considering that $M_\infty \to 1$ at a certain rate as $\delta \to 0$. It is clear, however, that the limit process $\delta \to 0$ with $M_\infty = 1$ cannot be carried out in the original system of coordinates, since this will merely produce the same result as in linearized theory. Instead, a coordinate $\tilde{y}$,

$$\tilde{y} = \beta(\delta)y, \tag{5.1.32}$$

must be kept fixed. Actually, we expect $\beta(\delta) \to 0$, since linearized theory indicates a larger extent of the perturbation field in the y-direction as $M_\infty \to 1$. We are striving for an expansion which has a possibility of satisfying the boundary conditions on the body† and, if possible, at infinity, so that the x-coordinate is fixed. Then $\beta(\delta)$ is to be found from these considerations, so that a distinguished limit process exists.

EXPANSION PROCESS FOR $M_\infty = 1$

Instead of Equation (5.1.14), consider

$$\Phi(x, y; \delta) = U\{x + \varepsilon(\delta)\varphi(x, \tilde{y}) + \cdots\}. \tag{5.1.33}$$

The dominant terms which now appear correspond to those in the first and second approximations (Equations 5.1.21, 5.1.22) with the orders adjusted appropriately $(\partial/\partial y \to \beta(\partial/\partial\tilde{y}))$.‡ Thus, from Equation (5.1.9), we find that

$$\varepsilon\beta^2\varphi_{\tilde{y}\tilde{y}} + \cdots = (\gamma + 1)\varepsilon^2\varphi_x\varphi_{xx} - 2\beta^2\varepsilon^2\varphi_{\tilde{y}}\varphi_{x\tilde{y}} + \cdots. \tag{5.1.34}$$

The distinguished limit occurs if $\beta \to 0$ as $\varepsilon \to 0$, in such a way that

$$\varepsilon\beta^2 = \varepsilon^2 \qquad \text{or} \qquad \beta = \sqrt{\varepsilon}. \tag{5.1.35}$$

All terms except the first two in Equation (5.1.34) are negligible, so that we obtain the transonic equation for $M_\infty = 1$:

$$\varphi_{\tilde{y}\tilde{y}} = (\gamma + 1)\varphi_x\varphi_{xx} \qquad (M_\infty = 1). \tag{5.1.36}$$

This quasi-linear equation is of changing type:

$\varphi_x < 0$, locally subsonic, elliptic type;

$\varphi_x > 0$, locally supersonic, hyperbolic type.

The attempt to construct solutions to this equation leads to interesting and difficult problems (cf. Reference 5.1.2), but it is clear that this equation has the possibility of describing the physical phenomena correctly and, in fact, various experimental results indicate that it is very good for airfoils and nozzles of a practical shape. The problem is not complete until we discuss

---

†In the case of axial symmetry, a suitable inner expansion can be used.

‡We can show that third- and higher-order-type terms cannot contribute to the dominant transonic approximations.

the boundary conditions which serve to fix the orders of magnitude.† On the body, Equation (5.1.11) now becomes

$$\varepsilon\beta\varphi_{\tilde{y}}(x, 0) + \cdots = \delta F'(x), \tag{5.1.37}$$

so that

$$\varepsilon\beta = \delta. \tag{5.1.38}$$

A comparison of Equations (5.1.38), and (5.1.35) shows us that

$$\varepsilon = \delta^{3/2}, \qquad \beta = \delta^{1/3} \tag{5.1.39}$$

for the distinguished limit. The boundary condition at upstream infinity is

$$\varphi \to 0, \qquad x \to -\infty. \tag{5.1.40}$$

This expansion procedure can also be carried to higher orders. The successive equations φ_2, φ_3 are *linear* but have variable coefficients depending on the lower approximations. This is typical for expansions where the first term satisfies a nonlinear equation (cf. van der Pol Oscillator, Section 2.6).

EXTENSION TO MACH NUMBERS M_∞ CLOSE TO ONE

The concept of the limit process leading to the expansion must now be widened to consider $M_\infty \to 1$ as $\delta \to 0$, this can be expressed as

$$M_\infty^2 = 1 + K\nu(\delta), \qquad \nu(\delta) \to 0. \tag{5.1.41}$$

The quantity K is held fixed in the limit and may be $O(1)$. Here $K \equiv 0$ corresponds to $M_\infty = 1$. A significant order is to be found for $\nu(\delta)$. The expansion has the form

$$\Phi(x, y; M_\infty, \delta) = U\{x + \delta^{2/3}\varphi(x, \tilde{y}; K) + \cdots\}, \qquad \tilde{y} = \delta^{1/3}y, \tag{5.1.42}$$

and again the dominant terms come from the first and second approximations (Equations 5.1.21, 5.1.22). Thus, we have

$$-\nu(\delta)\delta^{2/3}K\varphi_{xx} + \cdots + \delta^{4/3}\varphi_{\tilde{y}\tilde{y}} = \delta^{4/3}(\gamma + 1)\varphi_x\varphi_{xx} + \cdots. \tag{5.1.43}$$

The distinguished case is evidently $\nu(\delta) = \delta^{2/3}$; if $\nu(\delta) \gg \delta^{2/3}$, then a meaningless equation results, and if $\nu(\delta) \ll \delta^{2/3}$, the flow is that of $M_\infty = 1$, and the approximation is less general. The resulting transonic equation is

$$[K + (\gamma + 1)\varphi_x]\varphi_{xx} - \varphi_{\tilde{y}\tilde{y}} = 0, \tag{5.1.44}$$

with boundary conditions as before. The parameter K, which appears in

† The orders are different for axial symmetry: $\varphi_{rr} + (1/\tilde{r})\varphi_r = (\gamma + 1)\varphi_x\varphi_{xx}$, $\varepsilon = \delta^2$, $\beta = \delta$ (cf. Reference 5.1.1).

the expansion, is often called a similarity parameter:

$$K = \frac{M_\infty^2 - 1}{\delta^{2/3}} \qquad \text{(transonic similarity parameter)}, \tag{5.1.45}$$

and similarity rules or laws of similitude are expressed in terms of K. For example, the pressure at a given abscissa on a thin airfoil is expressed as

$$\frac{p - p_\infty}{\rho_\infty U^2 \delta^{2/3}} = -\varphi_x(x, 0; K) = fn(K). \tag{5.1.46}$$

This sort of rule can be tested by experiments on a family of affine shapes varying (δ, M_∞) so that K is fixed. Note that the existence of the parameter K was implied in the discussion of the validity of linearized theory, when it was seen that linearized theory was valid for $K \gg 1$. The uniformity of the expansion (Equation 5.1.42) both with respect to the parameter K and the coordinates $(x, \tilde{y})$ can be studied as before.

The shock relations that go with Equation (5.1.44) can be derived from the integral form of Equation (5.1.44) applied across the discontinuity surface plus the requirement that the resultant jump in velocity is normal to the shock surface. Equation (5.1.44) is a divergence expression, so that integration across the shock yields

$$\left\{K[\varphi_x] + \frac{\gamma + 1}{2}[\varphi_x^2]\right\}n_1 \cdot = [\varphi_{\tilde{y}}]n_2, \qquad [\;] = \text{jump}, \tag{5.1.47}$$

where (n_1, n_2) are the components of the normal $\mathbf{n}$ to the shock surface in $(x, \tilde{y})$. Our second requirement is

$$[\varphi_x]n_2 = [\varphi_{\tilde{y}}]n_1. \tag{5.1.48}$$

The combination of Equations (5.1.48) and (5.1.47) expresses the jump conditions, giving the transonic form of a shock polar curve:

$$K[\varphi_x]^2 + \frac{\gamma + 1}{2}[\varphi_x^2][\varphi_x] = [\varphi_{\tilde{y}}]^2. \tag{5.1.49}$$

Finally, it is clear that there is some sort of matching between the transonic expansion and the linearized expansion. Near infinity where $\varphi_x \to 0$, the transonic equation (Equation 5.1.44) approaches the linear equation (Equation 5.1.21) in form. The regions near infinity come closer to the airfoil for larger K. Hence, in some sense the linearized supersonic results should be obtained from transonic solutions as K gets large. Details of this matching have not been worked out. However, in general the distinguished limit contains more information.

5.1.3 *Hypersonic theory*

The discussion at the end of Section 5.1.1 shows that the linearized approximation is not valid when M_∞ is so large that $M_\infty\delta \sim O(1)$. In these circumstances, the Mach wave $x = \sqrt{M_\infty^2 - 1}\, y \doteq M_\infty y$ is of the same order from the body as the body thickness δ; the body is in this sense no longer thin, and the shock waves are strong. However, small disturbances to the free stream are still produced, and an expansion procedure can be constructed. It is reasonable that a coordinate $\tilde{y} \sim M_\infty y$ be held fixed, so that details of the wave structure are preserved. The expansion procedure must now be applied to the exact equations of motion, since a potential does not exist if any shock waves appear. Some aspects of the procedure are sketched below. For the equations of motion in (q_x, q_y, p, ρ), we have the following.

$$\begin{aligned}
&\text{(a)} \quad \text{continuity:} && \frac{\partial(\rho q_x)}{\partial x} + \frac{\partial(\rho q_y)}{\partial y} = 0;\\
&\text{(b)} \quad x\text{-momentum:} && q_x\frac{\partial q_x}{\partial x} + q_y\frac{\partial q_x}{\partial y} = -\frac{1}{\rho}\frac{\partial p}{\partial x};\\
&\text{(c)} \quad y\text{-momentum:} && q_x\frac{\partial q_y}{\partial x} + q_y\frac{\partial q_y}{\partial y} = -\frac{1}{\rho}\frac{\partial p}{\partial y};\\
&\text{(d)} \quad \text{energy } \rho\text{:} && \left(q_x\frac{\partial}{\partial x} + q_y\frac{\partial}{\partial y}\right)\left\{\frac{1}{\gamma - 1}\frac{p}{\rho} + \frac{q_x^2 + q_y^2}{2}\right\}\\
& && \qquad = -p\left\{\frac{\partial q_x}{\partial x} + \frac{\partial q_y}{\partial y}\right\}.
\end{aligned} \tag{5.1.50}$$

The perfect-gas expression for internal energy per mass $(1/(\gamma - 1))(p/\rho)$ has been used in the energy equations. The energy equation can be replaced by the condition that the entropy is constant along a streamline (but not across shock waves). Thus, we have

$$\left(q_x\frac{\partial}{\partial x} + q_y\frac{\partial}{\partial y}\right)\left(\frac{p}{\rho^\gamma}\right) = 0.$$

A study of the shock relations show that corresponding to a $q_y \sim O(\delta)$, we have perturbations in $p \sim O(\delta^2)$, in $\rho \sim O(1)$, and in $q_x \sim O(\delta^2)$. The basic idea used is that the nose shock angle to the free stream is of order δ. The perturbation is normal to the shock, so that the true velocity perturbations have different orders (cf. transonic case). For further details, consult

Reference 5.1.3. Thus, with the limit process

$$\delta \to 0 \qquad (x, \tilde{y}; H \text{ fixed}); \qquad \tilde{y} = \frac{y}{\delta}, \qquad H = \frac{1}{M_\infty^2 \delta^2},$$

we associate the following expansion:

$$\begin{aligned}
&\text{(a)} \quad \frac{q_x(x, y; M_\infty, \delta)}{U} = 1 + \delta^2 u(x, \tilde{y}; H) + \cdots, \\
&\text{(b)} \quad \frac{q_y(x, y; M_\infty, \delta)}{U} = \delta v(x, \tilde{y}; H) + \cdots, \\
&\text{(c)} \quad \frac{p(x, y; M_\infty, \delta)}{\rho_\infty U^2} = \delta^2 P(x, \tilde{y}; H) + \cdots, \\
&\text{(d)} \quad \frac{\rho(x, y; M_\infty; \delta)}{\rho_\infty} = \sigma(x, \tilde{y}; H) + \cdots.
\end{aligned} \tag{5.1.51}$$

The derivative along a streamline becomes

$$\frac{1}{U}\left\{q_x \frac{\partial}{\partial x} + q_y \frac{\partial}{\partial y}\right\} \to \frac{\partial}{\partial x} + v\frac{\partial}{\partial \tilde{y}} + O(\delta^2). \tag{5.1.52}$$

The dominant terms of Equation (5.1.50) are as follows.

$$\begin{aligned}
&\text{(a)} \quad \text{continuity:} \quad \frac{\partial \sigma}{\partial x} + \frac{\partial(\sigma v)}{\partial \tilde{y}} = 0; \\
&\text{(b)} \quad x\text{-momentum:} \quad \frac{\partial u}{\partial x} + v\frac{\partial u}{\partial \tilde{y}} = -\frac{1}{\sigma}\frac{\partial P}{\partial x}; \\
&\text{(c)} \quad y\text{-momentum:} \quad \frac{\partial v}{\partial x} + v\frac{\partial v}{\partial \tilde{y}} = -\frac{1}{\sigma}\frac{\partial P}{\partial \tilde{y}}; \\
&\text{(d)} \quad \text{energy:} \quad \sigma\left(\frac{\partial}{\partial x} + v\frac{\partial}{\partial \tilde{y}}\right)\left(\frac{1}{\gamma - 1}\frac{P}{\sigma} + u + \frac{v^2}{2}\right) = -P\frac{\partial v}{\partial \tilde{y}}; \\
&\text{(e)} \quad \text{entropy:} \quad \left(\frac{\partial}{\partial x} + v\frac{\partial}{\partial \tilde{y}}\right)\left(\frac{P}{\sigma^\gamma}\right) = 0.
\end{aligned} \tag{5.1.53}$$

In the free stream we have

$$P = \frac{p_\infty}{\rho_\infty v^2 \delta^2} = \frac{1}{\gamma M_\infty^2 \delta^2} = \frac{H}{\gamma}.$$

The simplification achieved in this expansion process is the uncoupling of the u-momentum equation so that, for example, the system (a), (c), and (e) of

Equation (5.1.53) forms a complete system for (P, σ, v). The same remark applies to the shockwave relations that are not written out here and to the boundary condition of tangent flow on the airfoil surface (not applied at $y = 0$, now):

$$v(x, F(x)) = F'(x). \tag{5.1.54}$$

The equations (a), (c), and (e), shock relations, and boundary conditions are exactly analogous to those for unsteady one-dimensional motion $(t \leftrightarrow x)$ for the shock wave and flow produced by a piston moving with velocity v.

The similarity of hypersonic flows is thus expressed by the hypersonic similarity parameter $H = 1/M_\infty^2\delta^2$. The expansion is uniformly valid as $H \to 0$, corresponding to $M_\infty \to \infty$. For small H, the hypersonic solution joins on to linearized theory for $M_\infty \gg 1$, again in a sense which has not been made precise.

The nonlinear equations which appear for hypersonic theory are still difficult to solve, but some simplification and similarity has been discovered.

In all these expansions—linearized, transonic, hypersonic—various other local nonuniformities may appear due to a local violation of assumed order of magnitude. The blunt nose region of a slender body in hypersonic flow is an example. Near the nose, a different expansion must be used to describe the flow, and the effect spreads downstream along streamlines forming a layer (entropy layer) near the body surface where some variables are estimated incorrectly. In constructing the local expansions and solutions in these regions and layers, the ideas of matching have once more to be used (cf. Reference 5.1.3). The stagnation point of a body in transonic or linearized subsonic flow would demand a similar treatment if flow details were wanted. Very often, however, such details are unnecessary for overall results.

REFERENCES

5.1.1 J. D. Cole, and A. F. Messiter, "Expansion Procedures and Similarity Laws for Transonic Flow," *Zeitschrift für angewandte Mathematik und Physik*, VIII, *1* (1957), 1–25.

5.1.2 K. G. Guderley, *Theorie schallnaher Strömungen*, Springer-Verlag, 1957.

5.1.3 W. D. Hayes, and R. F. Probstein, *Hypersonic Flow Theory*, 2nd ed., Vol. I, New York: Academic Press, 1966.

5.2 Near-field and far-field equations

Some examples of near-field and far-field equations relating to wave propagation are discussed in this Section. In the first example, sound waves are produced by a piston and propagate to a large distance. The ordinary acoustic theory which keeps the sound speed constant is valid near the piston, but the cumulative effects of variation in the sound speed produce errors in the far field. This shows up at first as a nonuniformity of the acoustic perturbation procedure. Thus, it is necessary to use a different limit process and expansion procedure to construct suitable approximate equations for the far fields. These turn out to be nonlinear and to demand shock waves. These approximate equations must be such that their solutions can match to the near-field equations. The second example concerns the propagation of long waves on shallow water. For small amplitude, the near field is again given by the usual shallow-water linear wave equations, but because of cumulative nonlinear effects, the far field demands a different description. This second example also contains some features of the singular boundary-value problems of Section 4.5, since shallow water is a thin domain.

An essentially different method has been used to study this type of problem. In one formulation, the characteristic parameters (α, β) are held fixed, and limit-process expansions are carried out for both the original dependent $(u, v, p, \ldots,)$ and independent variables $(x, t, \ldots,)$. In this way an attempt is made to account for the variation in sound speed by allowing the characteristics to bend. In terms of perturbation theory, the expansion of u expressed in (x, t) is not of limit-process type but rather of the more general type (cf. Equation 1.2.5) which was used extensively in Section 3. As a result, special rules are sometimes introduced, such as the statement that the second approximation shall not have a stronger singularity than the first, in order to guarantee the asymptotic character of the expansions. However, these methods, either in characteristic parameters or by some other expansion of both dependent and independent variables, do not seem to be able to give a uniformly valid solution for near and far fields in a variety of cases, and hence are not discussed here.

Some detailed discussion of both methods as well as the application to other physically interesting examples including viscous effects, chemical reactions, and radiation, is presented by W. Lick in Reference 5.2.1.

5.2.1 Piston problem of acoustics

Consider the classical problem of the one-dimensional propagation of waves in a tube produced by piston motion at the end. The waves are described within the framework of an ideal (inviscid, non heat-conducting, etc.) gas. Various shock waves and regions of nonuniform flow are produced which propagate down the tube. The shock waves are treated as discontinuities. In actual practice, their structure and thickness depends on viscous and similar effects, but this thickness is supposed to be very small compared to the dimensions of interest. It is interesting to note, however, that a procedure similar to the one used here can also be used in the viscous case. When the piston motion is weak, that is, when velocities are produced which are small compared to the sound speed determined by the ambient state, then acoustics gives the usual first approximation. In acoustics, the special treatment of shock jumps can be forgotten, and they appear naturally in the linearized solution. The first step in our analysis of the problem is to work out first- and second-order acoustics. It is sufficient to consider isentropic flow, since only weak shock waves are to be produced, and the entropy changes are actually third-order in the shock jumps. This enables us to start the discussion with the following simple versions of the continuity and momentum equations:†

$$\frac{\partial c}{\partial \bar{t}} + q\frac{\partial c}{\partial \bar{x}} + \frac{\gamma - 1}{2}c\frac{\partial q}{\partial \bar{x}} = 0, \qquad \text{continuity}; \tag{5.2.1}$$

$$\frac{\partial q}{\partial \bar{t}} + q\frac{\partial q}{\partial \bar{x}} + \frac{2}{\gamma - 1}c\frac{\partial c}{\partial \bar{x}} = 0, \qquad \text{momentum}. \tag{5.2.2}$$

Here q and c are the flow velocity and local speed of sound, respectively, $\bar{x}$ is the distance, and $\bar{t}$ the time. In deriving these equations, the isentropic law for a perfect gas,

$$p/\rho^{\gamma} = \text{const}, \tag{5.2.3}$$

is assumed to apply throughout, where p = pressure, ρ = density, γ = ratio of specific heats and, by definition,

$$\begin{aligned} c^2 &= \frac{\partial p}{\partial \rho} = \frac{\gamma p}{\rho} = (\text{const})\gamma\rho^{\gamma-1}, \\ 2\frac{dc}{c} &= (\gamma - 1)\frac{d\rho}{\rho}. \end{aligned} \tag{5.2.4}$$

An alternate form of Equation (5.2.1) and (5.2.2) expressing the rates of changes of the Riemann invariants is derived by addition and subtraction of these equations:

$$\left\{\frac{\partial}{\partial \bar{t}} + (q - c)\frac{\partial}{\partial \bar{x}}\right\}\left\{\frac{c}{\gamma - 1} - \frac{q}{2}\right\} = 0, \tag{5.2.5}$$

$$\left\{\frac{\partial}{\partial \bar{t}} + (q + c)\frac{\partial}{\partial \bar{x}}\right\}\left\{\frac{c}{\gamma - 1} + \frac{q}{2}\right\} = 0. \tag{5.2.6}$$

†This of course is not necessary; continuity, momentum, and energy plus shock jumps could be used, but this method is simpler.

The first of these equations states that the Riemann invariant $c/(\gamma - 1) - (q/2)$ does not change along the path of a left running sound wave propagating at the speed c relative to the fluid; the second corresponds to right running waves $(+\bar{x})$.

Consider now the gas initially at rest (state p_0, ρ_0). The problem is specified by the motion of a piston with a characteristic time T, such that the distance traveled is small compared to $c_0 T$; c_0 = ambient speed of sound $= (\gamma p_0/\rho_0)^{1/2}$ (see Figure 5.2). This defines the small parameter of

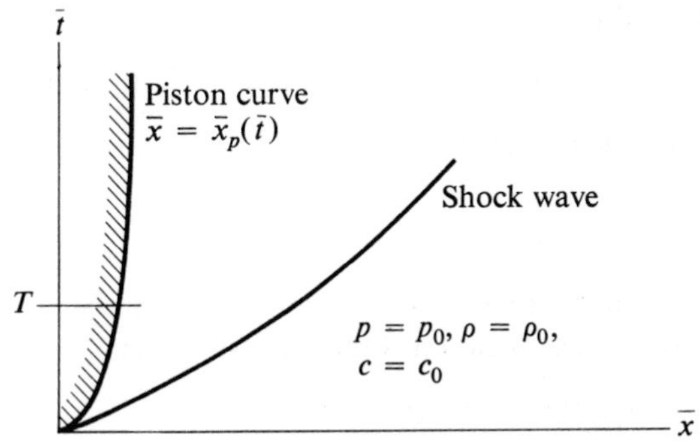

FIGURE 5.2 Piston problem.

the problems ε, and the piston curve $\bar{x}_p(\bar{t})$ can be represented in terms of the dimensionless function f by

$$\bar{x}_p(\bar{t}) = \varepsilon c_0 T f\left(\frac{\bar{t}}{T}\right). \tag{5.2.7}$$

The corresponding piston speed q_p is

$$q_p = \frac{d\bar{x}_p}{d\bar{t}} = \varepsilon c_0 f'\left(\frac{\bar{t}}{T}\right) \tag{5.2.8}$$

and is thus much less than c_0. Thus, the following dimensionless variables can be introduced:

$$u(x, t) = \frac{q(\bar{x}, \bar{t})}{c_0}, \qquad a(x, t) = \frac{c(\bar{x}, \bar{t})}{c_0}, \qquad x = \frac{\bar{x}}{c_0 T}, \qquad t = \frac{\bar{t}}{T}. \tag{5.2.9}$$

Equations (5.2.1) and (5.2.2) and (5.2.5) and (5.2.6) are unchanged in form:

$$\frac{\partial a}{\partial t} + u\frac{\partial a}{\partial x} + \frac{\gamma - 1}{2} a \frac{\partial u}{\partial x} = 0, \tag{5.2.10}$$

$$\frac{\partial u}{\partial t} + u\frac{\partial u}{\partial x} + \frac{2}{\gamma - 1}a\frac{\partial a}{\partial x} = 0 \tag{5.2.11}$$

or

$$\left(\frac{\partial}{\partial t} + (u - a)\frac{\partial}{\partial x}\right)\left(\frac{a}{\gamma - 1} - \frac{u}{2}\right) = 0, \tag{5.2.12}$$

$$\left(\frac{\partial}{\partial t} + (u + a)\frac{\partial}{\partial x}\right)\left(\frac{a}{\gamma - 1} + \frac{u}{2}\right) = 0. \tag{5.2.13}$$

The boundary conditions are that

$$t = 0, \qquad x > 0, \qquad u = 0, \qquad a = 1 \qquad \text{(initial state)}, \tag{5.2.14}$$

and on the piston surface ($x = \varepsilon f(t)$) the velocity of the gas is equal to the piston speed:

$$u(\varepsilon f(t), t) = \varepsilon f'(t), \qquad t > 0. \tag{5.2.15}$$

The expansion procedure of acoustics has the limit process ($\varepsilon \to 0, x, t$ fixed), and thus the acoustic expansion has the following form:

$$u(x, t) = \varepsilon u_1(x, t) + \varepsilon^2 u_2(x, t) + \cdots, \tag{5.2.16}$$

$$a(x, t) = 1 + \varepsilon a_1(x, t) + \varepsilon^2 a_2(x, t) + \cdots. \tag{5.2.17}$$

In the first few terms, only powers of ε appear, due to the simple occurrence of quadratic terms in the equations. From Equations (5.2.10) and (5.2.11), the first- and second-approximation equations are

$$\frac{\partial a_1}{\partial t} + \frac{\gamma - 1}{2}\frac{\partial u_1}{\partial x} = 0, \tag{5.2.18}$$

$$\frac{\partial u_1}{\partial t} + \frac{2}{\gamma - 1}\frac{\partial a_1}{\partial x} = 0, \tag{5.2.19}$$

$$\frac{\partial a_2}{\partial t} + \frac{\gamma - 1}{2}\frac{\partial u_2}{\partial x} = -u_1\frac{\partial a_1}{\partial x} - \frac{\gamma - 1}{2}a_1\frac{\partial u_1}{\partial x}, \tag{5.2.20}$$

$$\frac{\partial u_2}{\partial t} + \frac{2}{\gamma - 1}\frac{\partial a_2}{\partial x} = -u_1\frac{\partial u_1}{\partial x} - \frac{2}{\gamma - 1}a_1\frac{\partial a_1}{\partial x}. \tag{5.2.21}$$

For fixed t, the limit process $\varepsilon \to 0$ can be applied to the boundary condition (Equation 5.2.15) to produce

$$u(0, t) + \varepsilon f(t)u_x(0, t) + O(\varepsilon^2) = \varepsilon f'(t). \tag{5.2.22}$$

The assumption that the expansion (Equation 5.2.16) is valid in $x \geq 0$

enables the terms in (Equation 5.2.22) to be calculated:

$$\varepsilon u_1(0, t) + \varepsilon^2 u_2(0, t) + \varepsilon^2 f(t) u_{1_x}(0, t) + O(\varepsilon^3) = \varepsilon f'(t). \qquad (5.2.23)$$

The first- and second-order boundary conditions† for Equations (5.2.18), (5.2.19), (5.2.20) and (5.2.21) are, thus,

$$u_1(0, t) = f'(t), \qquad t \geq 0; \qquad (5.2.24)$$

$$u_2(0, t) = -u_{1_x}(0, t) f(t), \qquad t \geq 0. \qquad (5.2.25)$$

The first system is evidently equivalent to the simple wave equation with sound speed equal to unity in the units chosen:

$$\frac{\partial^2 u_1}{\partial t^2} - \frac{\partial^2 u_1}{\partial x^2} = 0. \qquad (5.2.26)$$

The general solution contains both outgoing $F(t - x)$ and incoming $G(t + x)$ waves, but it is clear from the physical problem that to the dominant order only outgoing waves should appear in the solution. This checks with the number of boundary conditions and enables a unique solution to be found. Thus, let

$$u_1(x, t) = F(t - x). \qquad (5.2.27)$$

It follows from the boundary condition (Equation 5.2.24) that u_1 is expressed in terms of the given piston speed by

$$u_1(x, t) = \begin{cases} f'(t - x), & t > x; \\ 0, & t < x; \end{cases} \qquad (5.2.28)$$

and Equation (5.2.18) or (5.2.19) gives

$$a_1(x, t) = \begin{cases} \dfrac{\gamma - 1}{2} f'(t - x), & t > x, \\ 0, & t < x. \end{cases} \qquad (5.2.29)$$

Note that the Riemann invariant $a_1/(\gamma - 1) - u_1/2$ for incoming waves is const $= 0$ in this flow. The flow is that of a simple wave of compression or expansion, the velocity and state being constant along one family ($t - x =$ const) of characteristics of the ambient state (see Figure 5.3). If the velocity (and correspondingly the pressure) undergoes a positive jump at

$$t = 0, \qquad f'(0+) > 0,$$

†Strictly speaking, an inner expansion in coordinates ($\tilde{x} = x/\varepsilon, t$) should be constructed to account for the boundary condition which is not applied at x fixed. However, the device in Equation (5.2.23) which transfers the boundary condition to the axis is equivalent to matching.

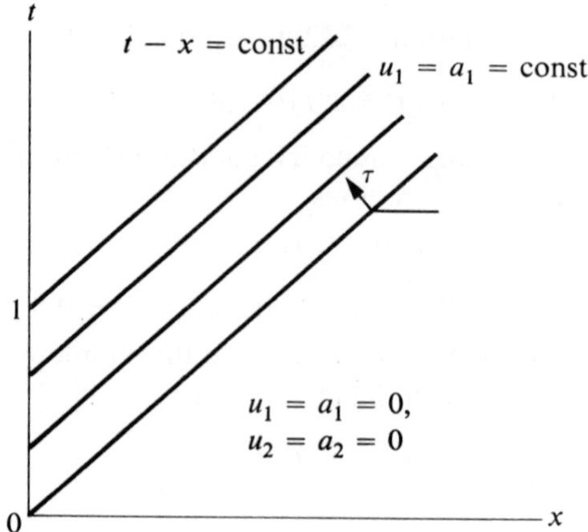

FIGURE 5.3 Wave patterns.

then this jump propagates with unit speed and is the acoustic approximation to the shock wave actually produced. Now, the second-order approximation can be considered by using Equations (5.2.28) and (5.2.29) in the right-hand sides of Equations (5.2.20) and (5.2.21) and by using the second-order boundary condition Equation (5.2.25). The equations to be solved are

$$\frac{\partial a_2}{\partial t} + \frac{\gamma - 1}{2}\frac{\partial u_2}{\partial x} = \frac{\gamma^2 - 1}{4} f'(\tau) f''(\tau), \qquad \tau = t - x > 0, \quad (5.2.30)$$

$$\frac{\partial u_2}{\partial t} + \frac{2}{\gamma - 1}\frac{\partial a_2}{\partial x} = \frac{\gamma + 1}{2} f'(\tau) f''(\tau), \qquad \tau = t - x > 0, \quad (5.2.31)$$

and the boundary condition is

$$u_2(0, t) = f(t) f''(t), \qquad t > 0. \quad (5.2.32)$$

The solution can be split into a particular solution satisfying Equations (5.2.30) and (5.2.31) with the right-hand sides plus a solution of the homogeneous equations expressed as arbitrary functions of $(t + x, t - x)$. Just as before, the solution of the homogeneous system representing incoming waves is put equal to zero, and then the boundary condition (Equation 5.2.33) serves to determine the solution uniquely. Note that even including the right-hand sides of Equations (5.2.30) and (5.2.31), the Riemann invariant for the incoming wave family is still equal to zero; that is,

$$a_2(x, t) = \frac{\gamma - 1}{2} u_2(x, t). \quad (5.2.33)$$

Thus, it is easy to verify that the solution of Equations (5.2.30) and (5.2.31) under the boundary condition (Equation 5.2.32) is

$$u_2(x, t) = \frac{\gamma + 1}{2} x f'(\tau) f''(\tau) + f(\tau) f''(\tau), \qquad \tau = t - x > 0, \tag{5.2.34}$$

$$a_2(x, t) = \frac{\gamma^2 - 1}{4} x f'(\tau) f''(\tau) + \frac{\gamma - 1}{2} f(\tau) f''(\tau), \qquad \tau = t - x > 0. \tag{5.2.35}$$

Here the first term is the particular solution, and in this term the coefficient x can be interpreted as a reflected-wave contribution [that is, $x \equiv \frac{1}{2}(t + x) - \frac{1}{2}(t - x)$]. In this representation, the sound waves of the second approximation are generated by an apparent distribution of sources and forces.

Thus, the final result of first- and second-order acoustics can be written

$$u(x, t; \varepsilon) = \varepsilon f'(\tau) + \varepsilon^2 \left\{ f(\tau) f''(\tau) + \frac{\gamma + 1}{2} x f'(\tau) f''(\tau) \right\} + O(\varepsilon^2), \tag{5.2.36}$$

$$a(x, t; \varepsilon) = 1 + \frac{\gamma - 1}{2} \varepsilon f'(\tau) + \frac{\gamma - 1}{2} \varepsilon^2 \left\{ f(\tau) f''(\tau) + \frac{\gamma - 1}{2} x f'(\tau) f''(\tau) \right\} + O(\varepsilon^2). \tag{5.2.37}$$

Various reasons for nonuniformity of the expansion are evident when the second term is compared to the first. The particular nonuniformity of interest to this Section is that of the far field. The second term of the expansion is comparable with the first when we have

$$\varepsilon x \sim O(1). \tag{5.2.38}$$

Near the wave front, this is equivalent to $\varepsilon t \sim O(1)$. In physical units, the distance away from the piston at which the acoustic formula becomes invalid is, thus, roughly

$$O\left(\frac{\bar{x}}{\bar{x}_p}\right) \sim \left(\frac{c_0}{q_p}\right)^2. \tag{5.2.39}$$

If the piston speed is only $\frac{1}{10}$ of the sound speed, nonlinear effects begin to be important at a distance of the order of 100 times the piston displacement. Other nonuniformities appear, for example, when f'' is very large, but these are not discussed here. We only note here the second-order acoustic formula for the pressure on the piston. This follows from the fact that the Riemann invariant $[a/(\gamma - 1)] - (u/2) = 0$ to second-order, so that, in terms of the pressure on the piston, we have

$$\frac{p}{p_0} = \left(\frac{c}{c_0}\right)^{2\gamma/(\gamma-1)} = \left(1 + \frac{\gamma - 1}{2}\frac{q_p}{c_0}\right)^{2\gamma/(\gamma-1)} = 1 + \gamma\frac{q_p}{c_0} + \frac{\gamma(\gamma + 1)}{4}\left(\frac{q_p}{c_0}\right)^2 + \cdots. \tag{5.2.40}$$

Now the far field (cf. Equation 5.2.38) can be studied by constructing another asymptotic expansion associated with a different limit process. Not surprisingly, coordinates should be chosen which are more or less fixed in the outgoing waves as $\varepsilon \to 0$. We start out fairly generally by considering limits ($\varepsilon \to 0$, τ^*, x^* fixed) where

$$\tau^* = \delta(\varepsilon)\tau = \delta(\varepsilon)(t - x), \tag{5.2.41}$$

$$x^* = \nu(\varepsilon)x. \tag{5.2.42}$$

Here δ, ν are to be found from the requirement that nontrivial equations result whose solutions can be matched to the expansion Equations (5.2.36) and (5.2.37). Now it turns out that there is no singular behavior of u, a in the equations of the outer expansion, so that for matching, the orders of the perturbations to the ambient state are the same in the far field as in the near field. Thus we can assume an asymptotic expansion of the form

$$u(x, t; \varepsilon) = \varepsilon u^*(x^*, \tau^*) + \cdots, \tag{5.2.43}$$

$$a(x, t; \varepsilon) = 1 + \varepsilon a^*(x^*, \tau^*) + \cdots. \tag{5.2.44}$$

Because of the evident importance of the Riemann invariants in this whole problem, it is convenient to carry out the far-field expansion on the equations in the form of Equations (5.2.12) and (5.2.13). Thus, note that

$$\frac{\partial}{\partial t} \to \delta(\varepsilon)\frac{\partial}{\partial \tau^*}, \qquad \frac{\partial}{\partial x} \to \nu(\varepsilon)\frac{\partial}{\partial x^*} - \delta\frac{\partial}{\partial \tau^*}, \qquad u - a = -1 + \varepsilon(u^* - a^*),$$

$$u + a = 1 + \varepsilon(u^* + a^*),$$

and the derivatives following the local sound waves become

$$\frac{\partial}{\partial t} + (u - a)\frac{\partial}{\partial x} \to 2\delta\frac{\partial}{\partial \tau^*} - \nu\frac{\partial}{\partial x^*} + O(\varepsilon\nu, \varepsilon\delta), \qquad \text{incoming}, \tag{5.2.45}$$

$$\frac{\partial}{\partial t} + (u + a)\frac{\partial}{\partial x} \to \nu\frac{\partial}{\partial x^*} - \delta\varepsilon(u^* + a^*)\frac{\partial}{\partial \tau^*} + O(\varepsilon\nu), \qquad \text{outgoing}. \tag{5.2.46}$$

In order to have an expansion in which the local sound speed of the outgoing waves depends on the state, the nonlinear terms in Equation (5.2.46) must be retained; that is, we must choose

$$\nu(\varepsilon) = \delta(\varepsilon)\varepsilon. \tag{5.2.47}$$

With this choice, Equations (5.2.12) and (5.2.13) become, respectively,

$$\frac{\partial}{\partial \tau^*}\left(\frac{a^*}{\gamma - 1} - \frac{u^*}{2}\right) = 0, \tag{5.2.48}$$

$$\left(\frac{\partial}{\partial x^*} - (u^* + a^*)\frac{\partial}{\partial \tau^*}\right)\left(\frac{a^*}{\gamma - 1} + \frac{u^*}{2}\right) = 0. \tag{5.2.49}$$

The integral of Equation (5.2.48) is

$$\frac{a^*}{\gamma - 1} - \frac{u^*}{2} = R(x^*). \tag{5.2.50}$$

The system (Equations 5.2.49, 5.2.50) is thus reducible to a first-order non-linear equation. Conditions in the nature of initial conditions are provided in the matching with the inner expansion and, as a consequence, the solutions for (u^*, a^*) can be joined to the initial ambient state only by a jump, the shock wave. In this case, it is necessary to work out the appropriate approximate shock-jump conditions, starting from the exact shock relations. If C is the shock speed, the shock-relations can be written

$$p_s - p_0 = \rho_0 C q_s, \qquad \text{momentum}; \tag{5.2.51}$$

$$\frac{\rho_0}{\rho_s} = 1 - \frac{q_s}{C}, \qquad \text{continuity}; \tag{5.2.52}$$

$$C^2 - \frac{\gamma + 1}{2} C q_s - c_0^2 = 0, \qquad \text{wave speed}. \tag{5.2.53}$$

Here $(\ )_s$ denotes conditions immediately behind the shock wave propagating into a uniform region of rest with the state $(\ )_0$. The wave-speed formula can be derived from an energy equation with the use of continuity and momentum.

The shock speed C is also close to the acoustic speed c_0, since the disturbances are weak. Hence, let

$$\frac{C}{c_0} = 1 + \varepsilon c_s^* + \cdots, \tag{5.2.54}$$

so that the wave-speed formula is

$$(1 + 2\varepsilon c^* + \cdots) - \frac{\gamma + 1}{2}(1 + \cdots)(\varepsilon u_s^* + \cdots) - 1 = 0$$

or

$$c_s^* = \frac{\gamma + 1}{4} u_s^*. \tag{5.2.55}$$

Equation (5.2.55) shows the difference in shock speed from the acoustic value in relation to the shock strength. The fact that the shock always moves slightly faster than the corresponding sound wave implies a non-uniformity in a small region $x > t$ in the inner expansion, but becomes a large difference which must be accounted for in the far field. The local sound speed behind the shock is also easily calculated from Equations (5.2.51) and (5.2.52):

$$\frac{p_s}{p_0} = 1 + \gamma\varepsilon u_s^* + \cdots, \qquad \frac{\rho_0}{\rho_s} = 1 - \varepsilon u_s^* + \cdots$$

or

$$(1 + \varepsilon a_s^* + \cdots)^2 = \frac{p_s}{p_0}\frac{\rho_0}{\rho_s} = 1 + \varepsilon(\gamma - 1)u_s^* + \cdots. \tag{5.2.56}$$

Thus

$$\frac{a_s^*}{\gamma - 1} - \frac{u_s^*}{2} = 0. \tag{5.2.57}$$

To this order, the Riemann invariant is unchanged by the shock. Equation (5.2.57) applies at all points of the shock path, so that $R(x^*) = 0$ in Equation (5.2.50). Thus, everywhere we have

$$\frac{a^*}{\gamma - 1} - \frac{u^*}{2} = 0, \tag{5.2.58}$$

and the basic nonlinear equation to be studied is first-order:

$$\frac{\partial u^*}{\partial x^*} - \frac{\gamma + 1}{2}u^*\frac{\partial u^*}{\partial \tau^*} = 0. \tag{5.2.59}$$

The initial conditions for Equation (5.2.59) come from matching the expansions, Equations (5.2.43), (5.2.44) and (5.2.16), and (5.2.17). Since the solution (u_1, a_1) depends only on $\tau = t - x$, matching can be expressed very simply by using

$$\tau^* \equiv \tau = t - x, \qquad \delta(\varepsilon) = 1, \qquad x^* = \varepsilon x, \qquad \nu \equiv \varepsilon. \tag{5.2.60}$$

The limit intermediate to those used in the inner and outer expansions has

$$(x_\xi = \xi(\varepsilon)x, \tau) \text{ fixed}, \tag{5.2.61}$$

where $\xi(\varepsilon)$ is such that

$$\lim_{\varepsilon\to 0} \xi(\varepsilon) \to 0, \qquad \lim_{\varepsilon\to 0} \frac{\xi}{\varepsilon} \to \infty.$$

In this limit, we have $x = x_\xi/\xi \to \infty$, $x^* = (\varepsilon/\xi)x_\xi \to 0$, $\tau = t - x$ fixed.

The inner expansion under this limit is, thus,

$$u(x, t; \varepsilon) = \varepsilon\left\{f'(\tau) + \frac{\gamma + 1}{2}\frac{\varepsilon}{\xi(\varepsilon)}x_\xi f'(\tau)f''(\tau) + \cdots\right\}. \tag{5.2.62}$$

Hence, we have

$$u^*(x^*, \tau) \to f'(\tau) \qquad \text{as} \quad x^* = \frac{\varepsilon}{\xi}x \to 0. \tag{5.2.63}$$

The boundary condition for the far field is thus the same in this case as that of the near field. The near field generates disturbances which propagate unchanged along $\tau = \text{const}$, and these appear near $x^* = 0$ as the boundary condition for the outer solution. The far field is thus uniquely determined, except that the shock wave has to be fitted in. The shock path can be represented in the coordinates of the far field as

$$x = t + \phi(x^*) \qquad \text{or} \qquad \tau = -\phi(x^*). \tag{5.2.64}$$

Note that the shock speed is

$$\frac{1}{1 + \varepsilon c_s^*} = \frac{c_0}{C} = \left(\frac{dt}{dx}\right)_s = 1 - \varepsilon\phi'(x^*),$$

so that

$$c_s^* = \phi'(x^*) = \frac{\gamma + 1}{4}u_s^* :$$

on the shock $\tau = -\phi(x^*)$. The solution to Equation (5.2.59) can be represented parametrically by the integrals of the characteristic differential equations with parameters λ, η (see Figure 5.4):

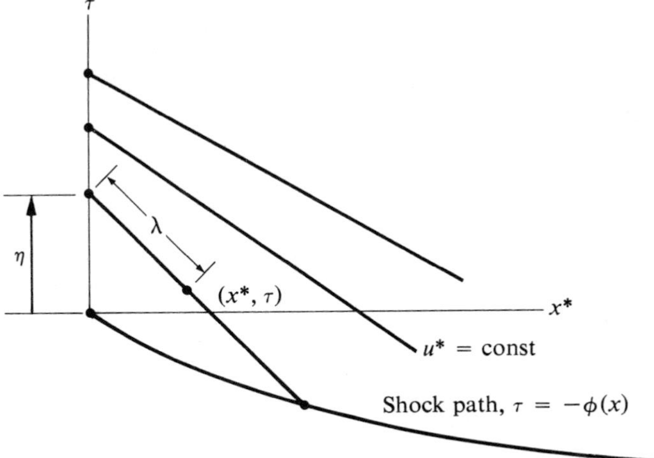

FIGURE 5.4 Far field.

$$\frac{dx^*}{d\lambda} = 1, \qquad \frac{d\tau^*}{d\lambda} = -\frac{\gamma + 1}{2}u^*, \qquad \frac{du^*}{d\lambda} = 0. \tag{5.2.65}$$

Thus, we have

$$u^*(\lambda, \eta) = u^*(\eta), \qquad x^*(\lambda, \eta) = \lambda, \qquad \tau(\lambda, \eta) = \eta - \frac{\gamma + 1}{2}\lambda u^*(\eta). \tag{5.2.66}$$

Taking account of the initial condition (Equation 5.2.63), we have a one-parameter representation of the far field, where the parameter η identifies the characteristic which is along $\tau = t - x$ in the near field:

$$u^*(x^*, \eta) = f'(\eta), \qquad \tau(x^*, \eta) = \eta - \frac{\gamma + 1}{2}x^* f'(\eta). \tag{5.2.67}$$

From this relation, the shock path of Equation (5.2.64) can be found. It can be noted from Equations (5.2.67) and (5.2.64) that the shock path bisects the characteristic directions of the outgoing waves since in the ambient state the characteristics are

$$\tau = 0,$$

while behind the shock on $\eta = \text{const}$, we have

$$\frac{d\tau}{dx^*} = -\frac{\gamma + 1}{2} f'(\eta) \qquad \text{and} \qquad \left(\frac{d\tau}{dx^*}\right)_{\text{shock}} = -\phi'(x^*) = -\frac{\gamma + 1}{4} f'(\eta).$$

The picture in Figure 5.3 is drawn for the typical case of a decelerating piston in which the leading shock is followed by an expansion fan; acceleration or stoppage of the piston can produce following shocks, and the analysis has to include these. Explicit results are easily obtained for a uniformly decelerated piston motion, where

$$f(t) = \begin{cases} t - \frac{1}{2}t^2, & 0 < t < 1, \\ \frac{1}{2} & t > 1, \end{cases} \tag{5.2.68}$$

$$f' = 1 - t, \qquad f'' = -1.$$

Elimination of the parameter η in Equation (5.2.67) enables the far-field solution to be written

$$u^* = \frac{1 - \tau}{1 + [(\gamma + 1)/2]x^*}. \tag{5.2.69}$$

Thus, Equation (5.2.64) evaluated on the shock gives the differential equation for the shock shape:

$$\frac{d\phi}{dx^*} = \frac{\gamma + 1}{4} \frac{1 + \phi(x^*)}{1 + [(\gamma + 1)/2]x^*}. \tag{5.2.70}$$

With the initial condition $\phi(0) = 0$, the integral of Equation (5.2.70) gives a parabolic shock shape

$$\phi(x^*) = \sqrt{1 + [(\gamma + 1)/2]x^*} - 1. \tag{5.2.71}$$

In physical coordinates,

$$x_s = t + \sqrt{1 + [(\gamma + 1)/2]\varepsilon x_s} - 1.$$

The asymptotic slope of the shock (τ, x^*) is zero, so that all the characteristics up to that originating at $t = 1$ or $\eta = 1$ overtake the shock (see Figure 5.5). If the piston continues to decelerate after $t = 1$, these characteristics do not interact with the shock.

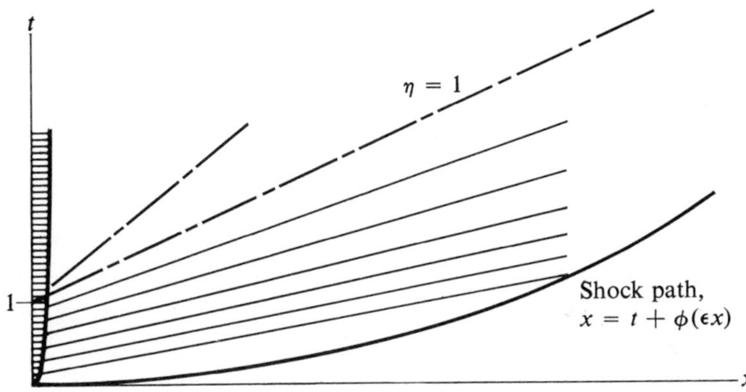

FIGURE 5.5 Asymptotic field.

In the example of this Section the "far" field equations contain the first approximation of the near field and, hence, provide the uniformly valid first approximation. However, if information on the piston surface only is required, the linear near-field theory can be used.

REFERENCES

5.2.1 W. LICK, "Wave Propagation in Real Gases," *Advances in Applied Mechanics*, Vol. XII, New York: Academic Press, in print.

5.2.2 *Small-amplitude waves on shallow water*

The problem considered in this Section is very similar to that in the last, Small-amplitude waves are generated near $x = 0$ either by some initial conditions or by a wave maker acting as a piston, and these waves propagate one-dimensionally to large distances. However, two small parameters enter, namely the ratio of wavelength to depth and the ratio of wave height to wave length. Different expansions lead to different approximate equations, several of which are indicated below. As before, one interesting case has linear near-field equations which match to nonlinear far-field equations.

Consider a channel of undisturbed depth h (see Figure 5.6) with the origin of $\bar{y}$ in the undisturbed free surface. Let the free surface be given by

$$\bar{y} = \bar{\eta}(\bar{x}, \bar{t}). \tag{5.2.72}$$

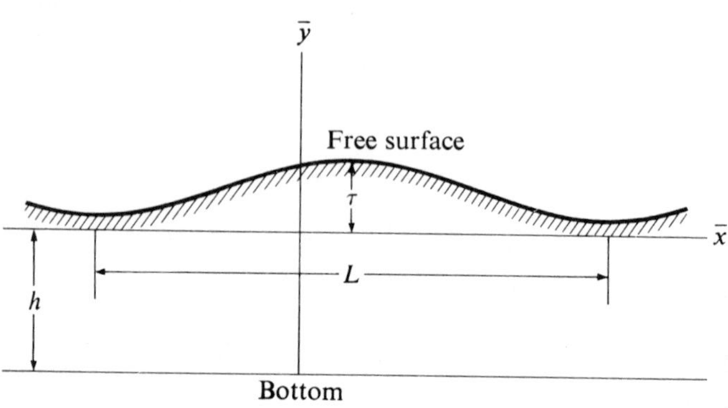

FIGURE 5.6 Geometry of water waves.

The fluid is considered to be incompressible and the flow irrotational, so that the whole problem is one of solving Laplace's equation for the velocity potential with boundary conditions on the bottom $\bar{y} = -h$ and on the free surface, initial conditions, and possibly boundary conditions on a wave maker. Thus, we have

$$\mathbf{q} = \text{grad } \bar{\Phi}(\bar{x}, \bar{y}, \bar{t}), \tag{5.2.73}$$

$$\frac{\partial^2 \bar{\Phi}}{\partial \bar{x}^2} + \frac{\partial^2 \bar{\Phi}}{\partial \bar{y}^2} = 0. \tag{5.2.74}$$

A Bernoulli equation, obtained by integrating the momentum equations, holds throughout:

$$\frac{\partial \bar{\Phi}}{\partial \bar{t}} + \frac{q^2}{2} + \frac{p}{\rho} + g\bar{y} = \frac{p_\infty}{\rho}, \tag{5.2.75}$$

where g = gravitational acceleration.

This provides one boundary condition on the free surface, where $p = p_\infty$,

$$\frac{\partial \bar{\Phi}}{\partial \bar{t}} + \frac{q^2}{2} + g\bar{\eta} = 0 \qquad \text{on} \quad \bar{y} = \bar{\eta}(\bar{x}, \bar{t}). \tag{5.2.76}$$

The other condition on the free surface is kinematic; a particle in the surface remains in the surface:

$$\frac{\partial \bar{\Phi}}{\partial \bar{y}} = \left[\frac{\partial \bar{\eta}}{\partial \bar{t}} + \frac{\partial \bar{\Phi}}{\partial \bar{x}}\frac{\partial \bar{\eta}}{\partial \bar{x}}\right] \qquad \text{on} \quad \bar{y} = \bar{\eta}(\bar{x}, \bar{t}). \tag{5.2.77}$$

The bottom is flat, so that

$$\frac{\partial \bar{\Phi}}{\partial \bar{y}}(\bar{x}, -h, \bar{t}) = 0. \tag{5.2.78}$$

For initial conditions, $\bar{\eta}(\bar{x}, 0)$ is prescribed, and a wave maker can be represented, for example, by a piston curve or an approximation like

$$\frac{\partial \bar{\Phi}}{\partial \bar{x}}(0, \bar{y}, \bar{t}) = F(\bar{t}). \tag{5.2.79}$$

Now, a characteristic velocity c exists in the fluid,

$$c = \sqrt{gh}.$$

Hence, suitable dimensionless coordinates can be introduced. Let L be a length scale characteristic of variations in the x-direction; for example, a wave length imposed by initial conditions. If a wave-maker problem is considered, a period T can be characteristic for the motion, and $L = cT$. Thus, we choose the following dimensionless coordinates:

$$x = \frac{\bar{x}}{L}, \qquad y = \frac{\bar{y}}{h}, \qquad t = \frac{c}{L}\bar{t}, \qquad \Phi = \frac{\bar{\Phi}}{cL}, \qquad \eta = \frac{\bar{\eta}}{h}. \tag{5.2.80}$$

The following dimensionless problem is obtained:

$$\delta^2\Phi_{xx} + \Phi_{yy} = 0; \tag{5.2.81}$$

bottom:

$$\Phi_y(x, -1, t) = 0; \tag{5.2.82}$$

free surface:

$$\Phi_t(x, \eta, t) + \frac{1}{2}\left(\Phi_x^2 + \frac{1}{\delta^2}\Phi_y^2\right)_{y=\eta} + \eta = 0; \tag{5.2.83}$$

free surface:

$$\Phi_y(x, \eta, t) = \delta^2[\eta_t + \Phi_x(x, \eta, t)\eta_x]; \tag{5.2.84}$$

initial condition:

$$\eta(x, 0) = \varepsilon F(x), \qquad F = O(1); \tag{5.2.85}$$

idealized boundary condition (if a wave maker):

$$\Phi_x(x, 0, t) = \varepsilon G(t) + O(\varepsilon^2). \tag{5.2.86}$$

The basic parameters that enter the problem are

$$\delta = \frac{h}{L} = \frac{\text{depth}}{\text{wave length}} \quad \text{and} \quad \varepsilon = \frac{\tau}{h} = \frac{\text{wave height}}{\text{depth}}.$$

The problem is elliptic but depends on the parameter t which enters the boundary conditions in a nonlinear and differential way. An exact solution is certainly very difficult and even numerical calculations for unsteady wave motion do not seem to have been carried out. However, a variety of approximate theories have been constructed. The first approximation to be discussed is that of long waves. This is later combined with the idea that the waves have also a small amplitude. The form of the expansion is

$$\Phi(x, y, t) = \alpha(\delta)\{\Phi_0(x, y, t) + \delta^2\Phi_1(x, y, t) + \delta^4\Phi_2(x, y, t) + \cdots\}. \tag{5.2.87}$$

The limit process has $\delta \to 0$, x, y, t fixed, corresponding to the fact that the characteristic wave length is much greater than the depth. The bottom condition (Equation 5.2.82) dominates the resultant form of the expansion. The Laplace equation (Equation 5.2.81) is satisfied in a simple way equivalent to a power-series expression in $(y + 1)$. The following successive-approximation equations and solutions are found:

$$\Phi_{0_{yy}} = 0, \qquad \Phi_0(x, y, t) = \phi_0(x, t), \tag{5.2.88}$$

$$\Phi_{1_{yy}} = -\Phi_{0_{xx}}, \qquad \Phi_1(x, y, t) = \phi_1(x, t) - \frac{(y+1)^2}{2}\phi_{0_{xx}}(x, t), \tag{5.2.89}$$

$$\Phi_{2_{yy}} = -\Phi_{1_{xx}}, \qquad \Phi_2(x, y, t) = \phi_2(x, t) - \frac{(y+1)^2}{2}\phi_{1_{xx}}(x, t) + \frac{(y+1)^4}{24}\phi_{0_{xxxx}}(x, t). \tag{5.2.90}$$

In summary, the long-wave expansion satisfying the bottom boundary condition is

$$\Phi(x, y, t) = \alpha\left\{\phi_0(x, t) + \delta^2\left[\phi_1(x, t) - \frac{(y+1)^2}{2}\phi_{0_{xx}}\right] + \delta^4\left[\phi_2(x, t) - \frac{(y+1)^2}{2}\phi_{1_{xx}} + \frac{(y+1)^4}{24}\phi_{0_{xxxx}}\right] + \cdots\right\}. \tag{5.2.91}$$

The corresponding expansions of the velocity components in the x- and y-directions, respectively, are

$$\frac{\partial \Phi}{\partial x} = \alpha\left\{\phi_{0_x} + \delta^2\left(\phi_{1_x} - \frac{(y+1)^2}{2}\phi_{0_{xxx}}\right)\right.$$
$$\left. + \delta^4\left(\phi_{2_x} - \frac{(y+1)^2}{2}\phi_{1_{xxx}} + \frac{(y+1)^4}{24}\phi_{0_{xxxxx}}\right) + \cdots\right\}, \tag{5.2.92}$$

$$\frac{\partial \Phi}{\partial y} = \alpha\left\{-\delta^2(y+1)\phi_{0_{xx}} + \delta^4\left[-(y+1)\phi_{1_{xx}} + \frac{(y+1)^3}{6}\phi_{0_{xxxx}}\right] + \cdots\right\}. \tag{5.2.93}$$

It is seen that due to the geometry of the domain, the main velocity component is parallel to the bottom, while the vertical component is an order of magnitude smaller.

NONLINEAR LONG-WAVE EQUATIONS

The nonlinear long-wave equations are the first-approximation equations derived from this expansion under the assumption that the dominant term in the shape of the free surface is independent of δ and, correspondingly, that $\alpha = 1$. Thus, on the free surface, we have

$$y = \eta(x, t) = \eta_0(x, t) + \delta^2\eta_1(x, t) + \cdots. \tag{5.2.94}$$

Now the expansion expressed by Equations (5.2.91), (5.2.92), and (5.2.93) holds in the boundary conditions (Equations 5.2.83 and 5.2.84), and the following dominant terms are obtained:

$$\phi_{0_t}(x, t) + \tfrac{1}{2}\phi_{0_x}^2 + \eta_0(x, t) = 0, \tag{5.2.95}$$

$$-(\eta_0 + 1)\phi_{0_{xx}} = \eta_{0_t} + \phi_{0_x}\eta_{0_x}. \tag{5.2.96}$$

Rewriting these equations in (u_0, η) shows that they are exactly analogous to the equations of one-dimensional unsteady gas dynamics with $\gamma = 2$,

$$\begin{aligned} &\eta_{0_t} + [u_0(\eta_0 + 1)]_x = 0, \qquad \text{continuity;} \\ &u_{0_t} + u_0 u_{0_x} = -\eta_{0_x}, \qquad \text{momentum.} \end{aligned} \tag{5.2.97}$$

Hydraulic jumps which are analogous to the shock waves of gas dynamics can be expected to appear in this theory. The second-approximation equations of this expansion are, of course, linear.

LINEAR LONG-WAVE EXPANSION

Now if the further approximation is made that the waves have small amplitude, a linear theory which corresponds to the equations above, as acoustics does to gas dynamics, can be obtained. Furthermore, second-approximation equations can also be obtained and studied. A second limit process ($\varepsilon \to 0$, x, y, t fixed) is considered, but later the connection of (δ, ε) is fixed. Thus, for the free surface we have

$$y = \eta(x, t) = \varepsilon\xi_0(x, t) + \beta(\varepsilon)\xi_1(x, t) + \cdots. \tag{5.2.98}$$

The expansions (Equations 5.2.98, 5.2.91, 5.2.92, and 5.2.93) are assumed valid on the free surface, and the free-surface boundary conditions (Equations 5.2.83, 5.2.84) become

$$\alpha\{\phi_{0_t} + \delta^2[\phi_{1_t} - \tfrac{1}{2}\phi_{0_{xxt}}]\} + \tfrac{1}{2}\alpha^2\phi_{0_x}^2 + \varepsilon\xi_0 + \beta(\varepsilon)\xi_1(x, t) + \cdots = 0, \tag{5.2.99}$$

$$-\alpha\{\delta^2\phi_{0_{xx}} + \delta^4[\phi_{1_{xx}} - \tfrac{1}{6}\phi_{0_{xxxx}}] + \delta^2\varepsilon\xi_0\phi_{0_{xx}}\} + \cdots = \delta^2\{\varepsilon\xi_{0_t} + \beta(\varepsilon)\xi_{1_t} + \varepsilon\alpha\xi_{0_x}\phi_{0_x} + \cdots\}. \tag{5.2.100}$$

Sensible first-approximation equations result only in the case where

$$\alpha = \varepsilon;$$

then the next largest terms are of order $\alpha\delta^2$, α^2, $\beta(\varepsilon)$ in Equation (5.2.99) and $\alpha\delta^2$, $\alpha\varepsilon$, $\beta(\varepsilon)$ in Equation (5.2.100).

It is clear that the most general case results when $\beta = \varepsilon^2$ and $\delta = O(\sqrt{\varepsilon})$, so that all the terms above are of exactly the same order. Thus, we introduce a similarity parameter K (independent of ε, δ), such that

$$\delta = K\sqrt{\varepsilon} \qquad \text{as} \quad \varepsilon \to 0,$$

and obtain, from Equations (5.2.99) and (5.2.100), the first- and second-approximation equations

$$\phi_{0_t} + \xi_0(x, t) = 0, \tag{5.2.101}$$

$$-\phi_{0_{xx}} = \xi_{0_t}, \tag{5.2.102}$$

$$K^2\phi_{1_t} + \xi_1(x, t) = \tfrac{1}{2}K^2\phi_{0_{xxt}} - \tfrac{1}{2}\phi_{0_x}^2, \tag{5.2.103}$$

$$-K^2\phi_{1_{xx}} = \xi_{1_t} + \xi_{0_x}\phi_{0_x} - \tfrac{1}{6}K^2\phi_{0_{xxxx}} + \xi_0\phi_{0_{xx}}. \tag{5.2.104}$$

This expansion can be expected to be valid for $K \leq O(1)$ but not for K large. The first system (Equations 5.2.101, 5.2.102) is a simple linear wave equation, while the second system (Equations 5.2.103, 5.2.104) is a non-homogeneous wave equation. The equations for the first- and second-order potentials can be written

$$\phi_{0_{tt}} - \phi_{0_{xx}} = 0, \tag{5.2.105}$$

$$\phi_{1_{tt}} - \phi_{1_{xx}} = \frac{1}{3}\phi_{0_{xxtt}} - \frac{2}{K^2}\phi_{0_x}\phi_{0_{xt}} - \frac{1}{K^2}\phi_{0_t}\phi_{0_{tt}}. \tag{5.2.106}$$

There are corresponding equations for ξ_0, ξ_1. This system has properties similar to the linear system of the previous Section. The results come out simply if we consider a problem corresponding to an idealized wave maker. The initial conditions are zero, and the boundary condition, from Equation (5.2.86), is

$$\phi_{0_x}(0, t) = G(t) = f'(t), \quad \text{say}, \tag{5.2.107}$$

$$\phi_{1_x}(0, t) = 0. \tag{5.2.108}$$

The general form of the expansion determined by this solution is

$$\Phi(x, y, t) = \varepsilon\phi_0(x, t) + K^2\varepsilon^2\left[\phi_1(x, t) - \frac{(y+1)^2}{2}\phi_{0_{xx}}(x, t)\right] + O(\varepsilon^4). \tag{5.2.109}$$

The solution for ϕ_0 is

$$\phi_0(x, t) = \begin{cases} -f(t - x), & t > x, \\ 0, & t < x, \end{cases} \tag{5.2.110}$$

and the equation for the corrections (Equation 5.2.106) becomes

$$\phi_{1_{tt}} - \phi_{1_{xx}} = -\frac{1}{3}f^{\mathrm{iv}}(t - x) - \frac{3}{K^2}f'(t - x)f''(t - x). \tag{5.2.111}$$

The particular integral corresponding to the right-hand side of Equation (5.2.111) contain terms like

$$xf'''(t - x) \qquad \text{and} \qquad xf'^2(t - x).$$

Thus, the expansion (Equation 5.2.109) is not uniformly valid when $x \sim O(1/\varepsilon)$, that is, at large distances from the origin. Similar results are obtained for more general boundary or initial conditions which confine a disturbance to the neighborhood of the origin.

The cumulative nonlinear effects demand a different far-field expansion. Just as we showed in the last Section, an expansion is sought in a coordinate frame moving with the speed of the linear waves. Since in the first approximation the near field is a function only of $x - t$, this can be used for one of the coordinates, and then a study of various possibilities shows that εt can be chosen as the other. Thus, consider a limit process with the fixed coordinates

$$\tilde{x} = x - t, \qquad \tilde{t} = \varepsilon t. \tag{5.2.112}$$

In these coordinates, the long-wave expansion, Equation (5.2.91), which involves only y is still valid and, furthermore, the orders of the dominant terms are fixed by considerations of matching. Thus, we assume a far-field expansion of the form

$$\Phi(x, y, t) = \varepsilon\varphi_0(\tilde{x}, \tilde{t}) + K^2\varepsilon^2\left\{\varphi_1(\tilde{x}, \tilde{t}) - \frac{(y+1)^2}{2}\varphi_{0\tilde{x}\tilde{x}}\right\}$$

$$+ K^4\varepsilon^3\left\{\varphi_2(\tilde{x}, \tilde{t}) - \frac{(y+1)^2}{2}\varphi_{\tilde{x}\tilde{x}} + \frac{(y+1)^4}{24}\varphi_{0\tilde{x}\tilde{x}\tilde{x}\tilde{x}}\right\}. \quad (5.2.113)$$

The derivatives of Φ are now, by Equation (5.2.112),

$$\Phi_t = -\varepsilon\varphi_{0\tilde{x}} + \varepsilon^2\left\{\varphi_{0\tilde{t}} - K^2\varphi_{1\tilde{x}} + \frac{(y+1)^2}{2}K^2\varphi_{0\tilde{x}\tilde{x}\tilde{x}}\right\} + \cdots, \quad (5.2.114)$$

$$\Phi_x = \varepsilon\varphi_{0\tilde{x}} + K^2\varepsilon^2\left\{\varphi_{1\tilde{x}} - \frac{(y+1)^2}{2}\phi_{0\tilde{x}\tilde{x}\tilde{x}}\right\} + \cdots, \quad (5.2.115)$$

$$\Phi_y = K^2\varepsilon^2\{-(y+1)\phi_{0\tilde{x}\tilde{x}}\} + K^4\varepsilon^3\{-(y+1)\varphi_{1\tilde{x}\tilde{x}} + \tfrac{1}{6}(y+1)^3\varphi_{0\tilde{x}\tilde{x}\tilde{x}\tilde{x}}\}. \quad (5.2.116)$$

The free surface has a corresponding representation

$$\eta(x, t; \varepsilon) = \varepsilon\tilde{\eta}_0(\tilde{x}, \tilde{t}) + \varepsilon^2\tilde{\eta}_1(\tilde{x}, \tilde{t}) + \cdots, \qquad \eta_t = -\varepsilon\tilde{\eta}_{0\tilde{x}} + \varepsilon^2(\tilde{\eta}_{0\tilde{t}} - \tilde{\eta}_{1\tilde{x}}) + \cdots. \quad (5.2.117)$$

Thus, again equations of motion result from a study of the form of the expansions in the free-surface conditions (Equations 5.2.83, 5.2.84). These take the form

$$-\varepsilon\varphi_{0\tilde{x}} + \varepsilon^2\{\varphi_{0\tilde{t}} - K^2\varphi_{1\tilde{x}} + \tfrac{1}{2}K^2\varphi_{0\tilde{x}\tilde{x}\tilde{x}}\} + \tfrac{1}{2}\varepsilon^2\varphi_{0\tilde{x}}^2 + \cdots$$
$$+\varepsilon\tilde{\eta}_0 + \varepsilon^2\tilde{\eta}_1 + \cdots = 0,$$

$$K^2\varepsilon[-(\varepsilon\tilde{\eta}_0 + 1)\varepsilon\varphi_{0\tilde{x}\tilde{x}} + K^2\varepsilon^2(-\varphi_{1\tilde{x}\tilde{x}} + \tfrac{1}{6}\varphi_{0\tilde{x}\tilde{x}\tilde{x}\tilde{x}}) + \cdots]$$
$$= K^2\varepsilon[-\varepsilon\tilde{\eta}_{0\tilde{x}} + \varepsilon^2(\tilde{\eta}_{0\tilde{t}} - \tilde{\eta}_{1\tilde{x}}) + \varepsilon^2\tilde{\eta}_{0\tilde{x}}\varphi_{0\tilde{x}}]. \quad (5.2.118)$$

The dominant terms of both these conditions produce, perhaps surprisingly, practically the same equations:

$$-\varphi_{0\tilde{x}} + \tilde{\eta}_0 = 0, \qquad -\varphi_{0\tilde{x}\tilde{x}} + \tilde{\eta}_{0\tilde{x}} = 0. \quad (5.2.119)$$

The integration function of $\tilde{t}$, which might distinguish the two forms of Equation (5.2.119), is zero from the conditions as $\tilde{x} \to \infty$. In these coordinates the first-approximation equation is not obtained until the second-order terms in Equation (5.2.118) are studied. Again, both of these relations are the same as far as (φ_1, η_1) are concerned:

$$-K^2\varphi_{1\tilde{x}} + \tilde{\eta}_1 = -\varphi_{0\tilde{t}} - \tfrac{1}{2}K^2\varphi_{0\tilde{x}\tilde{x}\tilde{x}} - \tfrac{1}{2}\varphi_{0\tilde{x}}^2, \quad (5.2.120)$$

$$-K^2\varphi_{1_{\tilde{x}\tilde{x}}} + \tilde{\eta}_{1_{\tilde{x}}} = \tilde{\eta}_{0_{\tilde{x}}}\varphi_{0_{\tilde{x}}} + \tilde{\eta}_0\varphi_{0_{\tilde{x}\tilde{x}}} - \frac{K^2}{6}\varphi_{0_{\tilde{x}\tilde{x}\tilde{x}\tilde{x}}}. \tag{5.2.121}$$

Integration of the last relation gives

$$-K^2\varphi_{1_{\tilde{x}}} + \tilde{\eta}_1 = \tilde{\eta}_0\varphi_{0_{\tilde{x}}} - \frac{K^2}{6}\varphi_{0_{\tilde{x}\tilde{x}\tilde{x}}}. \tag{5.2.122}$$

Now, the right-hand sides of Equations (5.2.120) and (5.2.122) must be the same, and this fact provides the second relation between $(\varphi_0, \tilde{\eta}_0)$. Thus, we have

$$-\varphi_{0_{\tilde{t}}} - \frac{1}{2}K^2\varphi_{0_{\tilde{x}\tilde{x}\tilde{x}}} - \frac{1}{2}\varphi_{0_{\tilde{x}}}^2 = \tilde{\eta}_0\varphi_{0_{\tilde{x}}} - \frac{K^2}{6}\varphi_{0_{\tilde{x}\tilde{x}\tilde{x}}}. \tag{5.2.123}$$

Using Equation (5.2.119) to replace η_0, we obtain the basic equation for the perturbation potential:

$$\varphi_{0_{\tilde{t}}} + \frac{3}{2}\varphi_{0_{\tilde{x}}}^2 = -\frac{K^2}{3}\varphi_{0_{\tilde{x}\tilde{x}\tilde{x}}}. \tag{5.2.124}$$

This equation is an approximate version of the equations associated with the names of Boussinesq, Korteweg, and DeVries discussed in Stoker's book (Reference 5.2.1). The equation is essentially dispersive in character. Steady solutions representing periodic wave trains and a solitary wave exist.† Current research, based to a large extent on numerical integrations, has the goal of elucidating the behavior of the solutions to Equation (5.2.124) and, in particular, of answering the question whether breaking of the waves occurs. Preliminary results give no indication of breaking. Similar dispersive equations occur in the theory of plasma waves. Since the left-hand side is of the form of a transport operator for $u_0 = \varphi_{0_x}$, the equation has a translation property. The equation is

$$u_{0_{\tilde{t}}} + 3u_0u_{0_{\tilde{x}}} = -(K^2/3)u_{0_{\tilde{x}\tilde{x}\tilde{x}}}, \tag{5.2.125}$$

so that

$$u_0(x, t) = w + f[(\tilde{x}/3) - w\tilde{t}] \tag{5.2.126}$$

is a solution for all $w =$ const, where $f(z)$ is a corresponding steady solution of

$$ff' = -\frac{K^2}{3^4}f'''. \tag{5.2.127}$$

† Recent work, not yet published, by Kruskal, Zabusky, and Lax has shown how the state at $\tilde{t} \to \infty$ can be represented as the interaction of solitary waves.

Boundary conditions for the far-field equation (Equation 5.2.124) here come from matching the expansions Equations (5.2.113) and (5.2.109). Since the near field depends mainly on $\tilde{x} = x - t$, an intermediate limit has $\tilde{x}, t_\xi$ fixed, where

$$t_\xi = \xi(\varepsilon)t, \qquad \varepsilon \ll \xi \ll 1,$$

so that

$$t = \frac{t_\xi}{\xi(\varepsilon)} \to \infty, \qquad \tilde{x} \text{ fixed}; \qquad t = \frac{\varepsilon}{\xi} t_\xi \to 0, \qquad \tilde{x} \text{ fixed}.$$

According to the previous discussion, for a typical case the near-field expansion can be written as

$$\Phi = -\varepsilon f(-\tilde{x}) + O(\varepsilon^2 x f n(\tilde{x})) = -\varepsilon f(\tilde{x}) + O\left(\varepsilon^2 \frac{t_\xi}{\xi(\varepsilon)}\right) \tag{5.2.128}$$

since

$$x = \tilde{x} + t = \tilde{x} + \frac{t_\xi}{\xi} \to \frac{t_\xi}{\xi} \to \infty.$$

In the far field, $\tilde{t} \to 0$ so that Equation (5.2.128) provides the initial condition for φ_0:

$$\varphi_0(\tilde{x}, 0) = \begin{cases} -f(-\tilde{x}), & \tilde{x} < 0; \\ 0, & \tilde{x} > 0. \end{cases} \tag{5.2.129}$$

Thus, matching to the first-order provides a well posed initial-value problem for the domain $(-\infty < \tilde{x} < \infty, \tilde{t} > 0)$. If a problem with an initial wave profile is considered instead of the idealized wave maker or radiation problem, the situation remains unchanged.

REFERENCES

5.2.1 J. J. Stoker, *Water Waves*, New York: Interscience Publishers, 1957.

Index

A B C D E F G H I J 5 4 3 2 1 7 0 6 9 8